Black Market Medicine

Also by Margaret Kreig
Green Medicine: The Search for Plants That Heal

BLACK MARKET MEDICINE

BY MARGARET KREIG

PRENTICE-HALL, Inc.
Englewood Cliffs, N.J.

To The Memory Of My Father

Contents

FDA Documentation

This is a factual book based on the author's firsthand observations of undercover investigations conducted by U.S. Food and Drug Administration (FDA) inspectors. Dialogue is abstracted from tape recordings made on the scenes. Details of cases, as well as general descriptions of criminal and law-enforcement activities are supported by investigational reports, records of hearings, statements made on oath, court transcripts, and other legal procedures. This documentation is corroborated by files made available to the author by FDA and, we understand, by other Federal agencies, Congressional investigators, local police departments, private detectives, and pharmaceutical manufacturers.

Margaret Kreig is the first writer not employed by FDA to participate in our undercover operations and to have access to many of these records.

The idea for this book originated with the author. Her viewpoint and conclusions are her own. As a condition of FDA's cooperation, we placed only two restrictions on her completed manuscript:

—that it be technically accurate, and,

—that it be written, insofar as possible, so that lives and pending cases would not be jeopardized.

While working undercover, the author's life and the lives of

several FDA inspectors were threatened by ex-convicts known to
have close affiliation with Mafia leaders. These men are still at
large, as are most of the individuals whose illicit practices are
described.

The events in this book are so contemporary that we could not
permit the use of actual names, locations, and other identifying
characteristics.

GEORGE P. LARRICK
COMMISSIONER (1954–1965)
U.S. FOOD AND DRUG ADMINISTRATION

Black Market Medicine

Briefing

Counterfeiting of new and potent drugs is on the increase. If permitted to go unchecked, it could lead to chaos. . . . The Federal Food, Drug and Cosmetic Act is intended to assure that all manufacturers have adequate facilities, control and personnel. Counterfeiting, done clandestinely and worked through bootleg channels, circumvents all safety provisions set up to protect the public.

ROBERT F. KENNEDY
(ATTORNEY GENERAL, 1961)

This is a report on the mushrooming, hoodlum-infiltrated illicit prescription drug industry that few people outside the Food and Drug Administration know exists.

Black-market medicine-makers and -distributors operate beyond all laws designed to protect people from dangerous medications. Their broad spectrum of activity ranges from the sale of out-dated and contaminated medications to the theft of formulas and the hijacking of legitimately produced drugs. They smuggle substandard products from abroad to market with false labels. Dangerous restricted drugs like LSD and the stimulant, amphetamine, are manufactured specifically for illicit distribution. A wide variety of other drugs used to fill prescriptions for sick people are produced in totally unregulated plants operated in the manner of bootleg stills. There is a complex intermingling of legal and black-market medicines all along the distribution chain from the

1

synthesizer of active ingredients to the medicine cabinet of the ultimate consumer. (Distribution Chart, Appendix A.)

While covering many aspects of illicit drug production and distribution, I have focused upon the particularly vicious crime of prescription drug counterfeiting, which began to grow enormously in 1960 according to the FDA.

Industry sources and the FDA report that every major drug company has, at one time or another, had to cope with the problem of imitations or counterfeits of its products.* Preparations of underworld origin have been found intermixed in almost every type of commonly prescribed medication: tranquilizers, sedatives, stimulants, hormones, heart drugs, diuretics, antibiotics, appetite depressants, blood-pressure–lowerers, asthma remedies, arthritis compounds, and so on. Dosage forms range from liquid injectables, such as vitamin B_{12}, to tiny round tablets of thyroid extract. One of the most complicated drugs to produce, the hard-gelatin capsule filled with medicated pellets for timed release, has been a favorite with drug counterfeiters.

Counterfeit tablets and capsules are usually so nearly perfect in their resemblance to genuine products that physicians, pharmacists, and patients cannot on sight distinguish any differences. It is necessary to compare them with the authentic product, both microscopically and chemically, in special laboratories staffed by "pillistics" experts (See "Pillistics" Appendix B).

The trade names and monograms of leading companies are printed on individual phony pills by means of stolen or forged punches, dies, and engraved rollers for tableting and imprinting machines. Recently, there has been a trend toward packaging bogus drugs in bottles and shipping cartons that are exact reproductions of those used by legitimate companies. Labels, package inserts, wax-paper sanitary sealers, even special metal bottle caps, are duplicated.

To old hands at forging checks and mass-producing fake government stamps, stock certificates, licenses, and, of course, money, the "paper work" required for illicit drug marketing poses no technical problems.

---

*The mention in this book of specific brands being counterfeited should not be taken to mean that all others are "safe." Patients should never discontinue prescribed medication without first consulting their doctors.

Most disturbing is the fact that hoodlums could not produce pharmaceuticals and distribute them through legal outlets such as pharmacies without the collaboration of professionally trained people who are willing to trade their ethics and know-how for cash on underworld deals. The familiar Syndicate gambit of using a legitimate front has taken a new twist: a scientifically oriented breed of criminal consultant has been spawned.

My objective in writing this book is to reveal these people and their methods through first-hand observation and, wherever possible, their own tape-recorded conversations. My concern about criminal infiltration of legitimate business began with my first assignment as a Chicago crime reporter, when I covered the Senate Judiciary Committee's investigation of interstate racketeering. At that time, I wrote:

> Racketeers own, operate, or control soft drink companies, night-clubs, taverns, liquor and beer distributorships, vacation resorts, grocery and meat concerns, laundries, dry cleaning plants, hotels, apartment buildings and many other legal enterprises. If left alone, it would be only a matter of time before they imposed their hoodlum tactics on small businessmen everywhere. Such a reign of terror *could* happen *here*. . . . The Syndicate seems so powerful, so well-organized . . . while We, the People, are comparatively weak through indifference. Will we all sink back into our usual complacency after the "heat" is turned off in our various communities? If so, the Senate investigation might just as well *be* a roadshow.*

If Senator Estes Kefauver were alive today he could hold hearings combining a cast of colorful underworld characters (like those who appeared on his televised crime investigations of 1950–51) with the subject matter of his inquiries into pharmaceutical production and pricing (*circa* 1960).

Imagine, if you can, underlings of a "Greasy Thumb" mixing up counterfeit Serpasil, and Equanil. Henchmen of a latter-day "Machine Gun" Jack tableting it. "Legs" supervising, through channels, the divvying-up of the lucrative wholesale distribution pie. "Dandy" Phil's counterparts acting as fronts whenever contacts with legitimate businessmen, or legislators are required.

---

*"Will We Follow Through on the Kefauver Investigation?", *Kiwanis Magazine*, April, 1951.

And, the likes of a "Buggsy" Siegel supplying muscle to keep everything running smoothly. Meanwhile "Lucky" Luciano's loot-laden ghost laughs all the way to the Swiss banks, for "Lucky" was very interested in pharmaceutical manufacturing.

This is no LSD-induced hallucination.

From many reliable sources—FDA, FBI, IRS, Customs, the Federal Bureau of Narcotics, state and local policemen, prosecutors, Congressional investigators, experts on labor racketeering, private detectives working for ethical drug companies, attorneys and other specialists in pharmaceutical law—I have compiled sufficient evidence to state that organized crime already has a good start in the infiltration of yet another major industry. This time the muscling-in constitutes a life or death matter for millions. We have been content to let gamblers worry about green-felt jungles and tax collectors fret over black money skimmed off the take in gambling casinos—but now our apathy could be the death of us. The "black hand" that cuts the deck in Las Vegas is reaching out to tip the apothecary scales.

Before going into detail on the who, what, where, and how, we should first consider the *why* of all this. The connection between heroin and the international crime Syndicate has been spelled out many times; everyone knows about the tremendous mark-ups along the trail of the opium poppy. Few realize that hard-to-obtain nonnarcotic prescription drugs sell illicitly for 100 times their cost. Even in normal trade channels, some active ingredients are, by weight, far more precious than gold. Crystalline B_{12}, for instance, costs over $8,000 an ounce, or 229 times the cost of an ounce of gold. Vitamin B_{12}, a life-saver in pernicious anemia, has been smuggled, adulterated, counterfeited, and sold to unsuspecting ethical manufacturers by criminals.

A small amount of white powder—representing a breakthrough drug about to be marketed—or a tiny vial containing a new antibiotic strain can bring fantastic sums; yet couriers run few risks when transporting such minute, deceptively innocent contraband. The international crime syndicate moves in where there is money—and the United States legitimate drug industry has a $4.1-billion-dollar-a-year global business. Publicity about profits in prescriptions has not escaped criminally inclined opportunists who talk about "what's hot, what's moving, and [above all] what's a fast buck." The *Drug Topics* "Red Book" is a kind of buyer's guide for pharmacists, listing thousands of manufacturers and distributors of drugs along with the prices for all sizes of products. It is a thick book—over 700 pages. I heard a burly ex-con refer to the *Red Book* as his "bible," and I am sure that a good many of these characters are as familiar with the drug trade press as they are with the *Racing Form*.

Hoodlums with narcotic records have discovered there is not only a "faster buck" but also a "safer buck" to be made in medicine for the ailing than in dope for the addicted. Even when stimulants and sedatives are peddled to drug-abusers, the penalties are nowhere as severe as for trafficking in hard-core narcotics. In many courts punishment is virtually nonexistent. A hip character summed up the situation while persuading a petty crook, who had taken many "falls," that he would be better off counterfeiting prescription drugs than continuing in the numbers racket:

"You won't believe me, but there are *no* problems! It's not like junk [narcotics]. FDA has a helluva time makin' any kinda case. And when they get you—*if* they get you—it's only a misdemeanor for misbranding, or some such. So you hafta pay a couple hundred dollar fine. You can make it back in a couple of hours."

The nonnarcotic prescription market is far greater than that of illicit narcotics. The Federal Bureau of Narcotics estimates a total of about 60,000 opiate addicts, 95 percent of them concentrated in our five major cities. Some insist that this is a conservative figure. But even doubled or tripled, it can't compare with the fact that at some time or other almost every one of the 196,226,000 people in the United States alone must take prescribed drugs. On our pill-happy planet there is an enormous, steady demand for mood-elevators, tranquilizers, and sleep-inducers. Millions of patients suffer from chronic diseases that require continuous medication every day of their lives.

Last year, slightly over 1 billion prescriptions were filled in this country. No one knows how many were filled with black-market medicine.

We do know, however, that the following clear-cut examples of the crime Syndicate's *modus operandi* exist on the fringes of the ethical drug industry. Counterfeiting and other forms of black-market medicine overlap.

Experienced bootleggers are utilized in ferreting out manufacturing equipment from shady salvage-dealers and fences. Raw materials are stolen; half-million dollar trailer loads of finished drugs are hijacked. Finger men, using walkie-talkies to communicate with bribed drug-handlers inside legitimate plants, lay in wait for big shipments. After holding-up tractor-trailer drivers at gunpoint, the hijackers transfer cartons of drugs to other waiting vehicles. The loot moves swiftly through the hands of fences, some of whom are drug wholesalers and pharmacy-owners. All of this is done with professional dispatch and split-second timing.

The standard way of doing business in these circles is strictly cash or barter. If any records are maintained, they invariably involve two sets of books. Because new laws require that production records be kept on drugs subject to abuse, shady manufacturers keep a "clean" set of production figures for FDA inspection, and do their illicit unrecorded drug-making after hours; or they subcontract this type of work to unregistered, wholly clandestine operators. Single drug companies may have a dozen different corporate names within several years. When they are caught violating the law, they go out of business to avoid prosecution. For fly-by-nights, setting up new companies across state lines or in different Federal court jurisdictions is standing operating procedure. Often such companies are managed through legitimate fronts, as are pharmacies owned by persons with criminal records.

The bankruptcy-for-profit racket, setting of fires to collect insurance, loss of business as a result of loan-sharking, and the use of "muscle" to force honest men to stock underworld drugs have been documented. It has been almost impossible for FDA to learn the origin of contraband drugs by questioning retailers, who profess fear of bodily harm should they reveal such information. Hoodlums have staked out ruthlessly defended pill territories, which may extend over three or more states. These are protected through typical gangland threats of violence. Slayings have occurred; one involved a renegade dispensing physician who diverted millions of dangerous drugs to brothels, truckstops, and other illicit outlets. The pill traffic is definitely tied in with traditional mob enterprises like prostitution, pornography, pinball machines, bootleg whisky, and policy or, the numbers. Fees of $10,000 for top criminal lawyers are considered a normal business overhead, as are bribery payments for corrupt policemen and local officials.

As with narcotics there is evidence of an international network involved in the movement of illicit pharmaceuticals. For instance, high-profit items such as breakthrough drugs in the process of development by ethical companies have been stolen from under the noses of researchers, only to turn up in countries where the Mafia is especially active. At least one Italian manufacturer of drugs other than narcotics has been caught shipping heroin out the back door. In this country, international dope peddlers took over a small drug company in order to facilitate the cutting of heroin with quinine and other nonnarcotic adulterants. The counterfeiting of synthetic pain-killers for sale to hospitals was one of the first ventures into "ethical drug production" by known Mafia members in the New York area.

The smuggling of raw materials and finished products across national borders follows the pattern and techniques used with opium, marihuana, and cocaine. Criminal masterminds have now diversified their product line: Federal and local law enforcers report increasing numbers of peddlers who handle all kinds of tablets and capsules, as well as "hard stuff." As one goes up the pill distribution pyramid, one seldom finds a "pill head," or drug-dependent peddler above the street-level pusher-user, exactly as in the case with narcotics. Several big pill dealers have told me they wouldn't take pills because, in the words of one, "I know what *that* stuff can do to you" However, knowing didn't stop him from selling "goof balls" by the millions.

In his March 8, 1965, health message to Congress, President Lyndon B. Johnson recommended legislation to correct the "serious gaps in our ability to protect the consumer under the Food, Drug, and Cosmetic Act." He called attention to the widespread traffic resulting from inadequate controls on barbiturates, amphetamines, and other drugs. He specifically urged Congress to give FDA the power needed to seize counterfeit drugs and manufacturing equipment used in producing these fakes, which he pointed out may be contaminated and deadly. He noted that FDA was powerless to act against counterfeit drugs unless they could prove that such drugs had entered interstate commerce.

On July 15, 1965, the President made the following remarks on signing the Drug Abuse Control Amendments to the FD&C Act (Public Law 89–74, 89th Congress, H.R.2):

> The Drug Abuse Control Act of 1965 is designed to prevent both the misuse and the illicit traffic of potentially dangerous drugs, especially the sedatives and stimulants, which are so important in the medicines which we use today. Unlike narcotics, some of these drugs are very easily and very cheaply manufactured. Production has been rapidly increasing. Some of that production has been counterfeit. But more important, the Food and Drug Administration estimates that at least one-half the annual production of certain useful drugs is being diverted to criminal traffic. Enough goof balls and pep pills, for instance, are being manufactured this year to provide two dozen pills to every man, woman and child in the United States. We know all too well that racketeers in this field are making victims of many of our finest young people. The Congress hopes, and I hope, that this Act will put a stop to such vicious business. I cannot express too strongly my determination that this good and decent and law-abiding society shall not be corrupted, undermined, or mocked by any criminal elements, whether they are organized or not. . . .

The Drug Abuse Control Amendments (DACA), which went into effect February 1, 1966, state "that there is a substantial traffic in counterfeit drugs simulating the brand or other identifying mark or device of the manufacturer of the genuine article; that such traffic poses a serious hazard to the health of innocent consumers of such drugs because of the lack of proper qualifications, facilities, and manufacturing controls on the part of the counterfeiter, whose operations are clandestine. . . ."

Counterfeit drugs are produced under the worst possible conditions. Sewer pipes have been found dripping into drug mixing machines. Oral medications have been tableted on machinery immediately after it was used to make poisonous pellets, with no cleaning whatsoever in between. Filthy incrustations on the floor of one drug plant had to be removed with jackhammers. In their most recent seizing of counterfeits, FDA reported the following: none of the active ingredient was used to make up the tablets; the color was sprayed on with a flit-gun; finished drugs were stored in containers that previously held rat poison.

As Ralph Nader, the writer on auto safety, has pointed out, before we become aroused over a health threat in this country, we demand "proof of corpses." Succeeding attorneys general and countless crime commissions have despaired of ever motivating the public to act against organized crime because the activities of underworld kingpins are shrouded in mystery and are far removed from our daily lives. A farm family in Bee Branch, Illinois, is unlikely to be seriously inconvenienced by the existence of either bookies or dope-peddlers in East St. Louis. But a counterfeit-pill–pushing ring, operating through dishonest drug wholesalers who supply their local pharmacist, rural dispensing physician, or county hospital *could* hit home. There still would be no "proof of corpses" directly attributable to counterfeits or other black-market medicine. A desperately ill member of the family is given medication and fails to respond; if the drugs are brands known to be reliable, no attempt would be made to have them analyzed, or to trace them back to their source. (Black-market drugs *cannot* be traced.)

In interviewing physicians, I found that few knew exactly what is meant by "a counterfeit prescription drug." They had the term confused with one or more of the following:

Generic drugs: Every drug has a generic and a chemical name, but the term "generic" is generally taken to mean a drug that is unbranded. Some of these are produced by reliable companies, others are of unspecified origin.

Look-alikes, imitations: These are drugs manufactured to resemble in size, shape, and color the products of other companies.

Pirated compounds: Stolen formulas and antibiotic cultures are used to produce drugs (usually abroad), which are then sold in competition with the patent-owner's own product in this country.

Substitutes: These may be generics, imitations, counterfeits, look-alikes, or branded drugs. The important thing is, you are not getting the drug specified on your doctor's prescription.

Adulterated drugs: Drugs may include a substance that is not part of the professed ingredients. Usually a cheaper material is added.

Contaminated drugs: These may contain impurities, filth, or traces of other drugs.

Misbranded drugs: FDA considers a drug misbranded if its labeling is false or misleading in any particular.

Counterfeit drugs: Drugs which are exact physical copies of trade-marked drugs, including brand names or monograms on tablets or capsules and containers, are true counterfeit drugs. Ingredients may or may not be the same. They may be adulterated or contaminated. Pirated compounds may have been used in their manufacture. They are always considered misbranded when officially detected.

In this book the reader will encounter other terms.

Amphetamines are stimulants, also known as pep pills, Bennies, crossroads, hearts and footballs. These terms come from trade names like Benzedrine or from the double-scoring (crossroads) on the tablets, or the tablet's shape.

Barbiturates are sedatives commonly called sleeping pills. Some descriptions refer to capsule colors: yellow jackets, red birds, and blue heavens. Pills, meaning a solid, usually round form of medication have been largely replaced in medicine by tablets and capsules, but "pills" lingers on as an all inclusive term for many oral dosage forms.

According to FDA, the first counterfeit prescription drug in commerce was officially detected in 1950. It was a hormone and only 50 percent potent. But Dr. Chauncey Leake, the eminent medical historian, told me that drug counterfeiters of one sort or another are ancient in the trade. They may well have provoked the warning, "*Caveat emptor*—Let the buyer beware!" When frankincense and myrrh were considered therapeutic, they were imitated. The Egyptian Queen Hatshepsut commissioned the first plant-hunting expedition (to Punt in 1500 B.C.) to obtain genuine healing herbs, because the bazaars were flooded with bogus botanicals. Nero's surgeon Dioscorides wrote *De Materia Medica* to thwart peddlers of spurious drugs. Illustrated herbals were introduced in the Middle Ages primarily to help physicians and patients differentiate between plants with proven medicinal value and look-alike species of no worth.

Discovery of the New World introduced the valuable malaria remedy Cinchona bark, containing the still-useful alkaloids quinine and quinidine. Immediately, crude counterfeits were concocted by coating ordinary barks with bitter aloes so they could be palmed off as the costly new cure for the number one scourge. In the sixteenth century Andreas Vesalius wrote a treatise on China Root, a syphilis treatment, in which he emphasized the need for standards by which drug frauds could be detected.*

During the Civil War in this country, opium, chloroform, and paregoric destined for surgeons' field kits were adulterated. It is no wonder that whisky became the drug of choice for many soldiers wounded in battle.

With the development of synthetic drugs around the turn of the century, the makers of spurious medicines had a difficult time of it for awhile because they needed the cooperation of chemists and technicians. During the Depression, bootleggers and rum-runners secured such help in operating their stills, and after Repeal they turned to making medicinals.

Professor Leake, who is author of *The Amphetamines*, explained:

> The expansion of black market drugs is not merely a commercial push, it is meeting an extraordinary demand. As Al Capone said of his activities, "I am only in the business of supplying a demand." The strict control of such drugs as the amphetamines is necessary to protect individuals and society, but the very regulations that make the drug difficult to get, also create an area of demand for which there is no legal supply, exactly as in Prohibition. The same mob elements that pander to any legally or socially inhibited activity, whether gambling, prostitution, or dope peddling, are now counterfeiting and diverting huge quantities of dangerous prescription drugs. Black-market medicine-makers can offer a better price to wholesalers and retailers because they eliminate overhead costs for research, quality controls, advertising, and so forth. The underworld provides restricted drugs without any trace of the transaction. The profits are enormous.

*FDA's Frances O. Kelsey, M.D., told me that the first United States Federal law directed toward drug regulation was passed after the Mexican War of 1848 largely because troops suffered unnecessarily after being given bogus antimalarials. The law prohibited importation of adulterated or deteriorated drugs. The first four years after enactment 300,000 pounds of spurious Peruvian bark were rejected at the New York Port of Entry.

For years, Congress, the press, and the public ignored the warnings of former FDA Commissioner George P. Larrick:

> Racketeers are taking over this lucrative business. The criminals with whom our inspectors deal are armed and would not hesitate to kill. Our agents have been informed repeatedly by drug boot-leggers that they would be killed if they turned out to be government men. . . . The illegal sale of prescription drugs constitutes the largest block of serious and deliberate criminal violations we un-cover each year. . . . Our District Offices receive many times more leads to illegal drug sales than we can pursue.

When I began my research on this book in 1964, I had just completed a five-year close inspection of the ethical drug industry for a book on pharmaceutical research. Legislation designed to strengthen FDA and to curb the illicit traffic in dangerous drugs had "died" in the 88th Congress, the fortieth bill in 14 years to suffer this fate. I asked Mr. Larrick to allow me to become, for a time, "an insider" working on criminal cases. He directed me to the New York District where a ring of drug counterfeiters was operating.

During the next two years while I worked closely with under-cover inspectors in the field, there were many changes in FDA. Mr. Larrick retired, Mr. Winton B. Rankin served as Acting Commissioner and then Deputy Commissioner, after Dr. James L. Goddard, a physician, took office early in 1966. Stricter controls over illicit drugs, DACA, for which old FDA hands had fought long and hard, shortly thereafter became legally enforceable. A Bureau of Drug Abuse Control (BDAC)* was established to administer the law through nine field offices throughout the country. (Appendix C, and Appendix E.)

What follows is a largely chronological account of what I saw, felt, and heard while exploring the unregulated drug industry during the year before and the year after DACA was enacted. The average reader will start out as I did knowing little about FDA, its men and its methods, still less about the complexities of enforcing the Federal Food, Drug, and Cosmetic Act. Through the discovery and development of the counterfeiting case in the New York District, a pattern of national and even international

*Pronounced "BE'-DAC".

pharmaceutical gray- and black-marketeering emerged. These aspects were explored during several trips I made to Latin America, Europe, and some Communist countries.

I am greatly indebted to many people the world over for their cooperation, suggestions, and encouragement. Particularly, I want to thank the FDA Commissioners for permitting me to work with their men on current cases. I am especially grateful to the FDA inspectors and BDAC agents who helped me to keep the manuscript updated and technically accurate while new laws were discussed, passed, and continued in debate.

For their very important contributions on racketeers and organized crime, I wish to thank Sgts. Ralph Salerno and Ben Gregor of the New York City Police Department, and Deputy Commissioner George H. Gaffney of the Federal Bureau of Narcotics, as well as a number of former special agents of the Federal Bureau of Investigation.

The passage of DACA marked a period of transition in our drug laws. The only unchanging reality in this story is the ingenuity of confirmed criminals in circumventing *all* laws. From the black-market medicine-makers themselves came the answers to my questions about the nature and extent of the counterfeit drug racket and related activities.

MARGARET KREIG
JANUARY, 1967.

PART ONE

In the Black Marketplace

When FDA held its first conference on the new Drug Abuse Control Amendments in March 1966, some 450 drug trade and professional representatives were invited to hear John H. Finlator, Director of the just-established Bureau of Drug Abuse Control, explain its purpose. Mr. Finlator, who had transferred to FDA from the General Services Administration only four days before, commented:

> To find out where we are going, we must first find out what our problems are. At this point we have only a dim outline of what has always been an illusive, shadowy picture. . . . The man who will do the leg work is classified under the Civil Service System as a criminal investigator. In our terminology he is an agent, a significantly different position from that of the Food and Drug inspector with whom many of you are acquainted. Up to now, however, FDA inspectors have been doing some of this—in fact, their work was, in large part, responsible for the passage of these Amendments. It involved dealing with willful criminals, some of whom are quite dangerous.

A year earlier, while Congressmen were still listening to arguments against stronger drug controls and the establishment of the Bureau, there were in the entire country fewer than a dozen FDA inspectors with even a minimal amount of training and experience

in coping with organized crime. One such man was Wallace
Jackson, working under the direction of Chief Inspector Clemens
Westerly.

Chapter One

The Chase

From FDA Undercover Inspector Wallace Jackson's Daily Log:

Met [Tom] to finalize sale and distribution of counterfeit drugs. He said The Group could duplicate
any drug on the market and asked me to suggest drugs
that moved good in my area. I said tranquilizers
did. He asked if Librium was a tablet or a capsule.
I told him it was a capsule. He asked if it was
monogrammed, and I replied that it was monogrammed
"Roche." He stated it was easier for them to produce
tablets, but if I could bring them about 3 dozen
samples of authentics, they could duplicate it. We
then discussed other drugs, including Miltown,
which he said they produced. He asked if I could take
up to 200,000 Orinase and Diuril per week. I said
possibly 300,000 each per week. . . .

Monday afternoon, Manhattan:

I met Chief Inspector Clemens Westerly of FDA's New York
District to observe firsthand these counterfeit drug dealings between Inspector Jackson and Tom, the salesman. My instructions
were to dress comfortably and to bring along enough cigarettes
to last. There would be no stopping for anything, once we got
moving.

The District had been trying since the late 1950's to complete a case against a man I'll call "Chameleon." Although he had been hiding under the protective coloring of several legitimate businesses, FDA was now closing in on him for the kill. Tablets sold by Tom had been traced, through punch marks, to machinery from one of Chameleon's defunct drug companies. While the tablets bore monograms of leading ethical manufacturers and were visually indistinguishable from the authentic trademarked medications, laboratory analysis proved they were fakes.

The intensive sleuthing of the past few months was aimed at locating a clandestine drug manufacturing plant believed to be part of a counterfeiting network remotely controlled by Chameleon. Inspector Jackson, posing as a Denver go-between with legal —as well as illegal—drug distribution connections out West, had made a dozen buys. Today he was carrying $4,000 in "front money on a string" for one million Dexedrine Spansule capsules, plus some Diuril and Orinase—all counterfeit. As the Chief Inspector explained: "The money's 'on a string' because the buy will be predicated on seeing the manufacturing equipment and samples of raw materials. Wally Jackson supposedly distributes the drugs through wholesalers, as well as to some truck stops. That's his cover story. One customer has ordered a million amphetamines a week and wants to be certain of a continuing supply. So, no plant tour, no deal."

Before we started, I signed a statement saying that I would not hold the U.S. Government responsible for any harm that might befall me. I wouldn't have blamed the Chief Inspector for resenting the FDA Commissioner's order to include me in on the chase. I imagine he thought they had taken leave of their senses in Washington, for he told me: "FDA has never before had anyone from the outside along on these cases and we don't have women inspectors, yet." Later he admitted that he had never known any writers.

That made two of us not knowing what to expect. All I knew about FDA undercover inspectors—the front-line fighters charged with putting down prescription drug racketeering—was that they were required to be college graduates with a background in biology or chemistry. This man, one of FDA's 18 District Chief Inspectors, had been a medical student. Unlike some "Feds" I had met, who were hip to the underworld argot and seemed to revel in their own derring-do, Clemens Westerly was quiet, soft-spoken, almost courtly in his manner. He hailed from the old Mark Twain country, and I was not surprised to learn that he read American history for relaxation. Appropriate adversaries for such a lawman might have been rascals or bounders. But he was an authentic twentieth century sleuth and his quarry was hardly in the cad category:

Tom belonged to a vicious ring of armed criminals I'll call "The Group." That they would do anything to make a dishonest dollar was borne out by the arrest records of just six men, which I later collected from a number of sources. There were 156 entries dating back to the 1920's. It was by no means a complete dossier, but it included: Arson, manufacturing explosives, extortion, coercion, malicious mischief. Terrorizing small businessmen for protection money was one of their specialties from the old days. During the war, they had been engaged in fraudulent activities involving meat stamps, gas ration coupons, war surplus, and so on. All had connections with shady salvage dealers. There were violations of the Securities' Act, Mann Act, Federal Narcotics Laws, and charges of pickpocketing, forgery, safebreaking, conspiring to deliver sugar to illicit distilleries, passing worthless checks, sale and possession of lottery slips, assault and battery, threatening to kill and maim—even kidnapping.

Tom's first arrest resulted from putting a slug in a turnstile some 30 years ago. He was fined $25, but The Group's cost of doing business was minimal—small fines and few convictions with jail sentences. One member had told Inspector Jackson that the only time he was sent to a Federal penitentiary, he came out with his ulcers cured. The crooks have everything going for them —drug counterfeiting, despite its threat to the nation's health, is not even against the law in most states. Under Federal law, it is still considered a form of "misbranding," and as such, only a misdemeanor. FDA inspectors could not carry guns, make arrests, search premises, seize goods, or subpoena witnesses.

As the Chief Inspector and I walked down the block toward an unmarked government car, he explained about FDA's most valuable aid in criminal investigations. A handful of specially trained undercover men were permitted to wear tiny microphones and transmitters to record conversations during underworld deals.

Our car would be electronically equipped to enable Mr. Westerly to monitor the transaction between Wally and Tom.

Waiting in our car was a muscular young man in a black T-shirt and tight black chinos, introduced as: "Inspector Kermit Shore. Kerry's one of our best wheelmen." With curly brown hair lengthening into sideburns, a definite five-o'clock shadow, and a grin like Belmondo, he could have been an East Village poet, painter, or pothead. It turned out that he was a registered pharmacist who spent most of his time now on LSD cases.

As we drove downtown on Broadway, I learned that a policeman, friendly with The Group, had warned them they were under surveillance. He had given them full descriptions of almost all the local FDA inspectors and their vehicles. This brought the counterfeiting investigation to a full stop, until Inspector Jackson was "imported" from a Western District to infiltrate the mob. This car had been brought in from the Philadelphia District for today's use. Chief Inspectors rarely went into the field as undercover agents, but in this case, there were only two trained men available who had not been "burned."

"We're glad you're along," Mr. Shore said. "Having a woman riding with us looks less suspicious."

I wanted to know when the trap was going to be set for Tom.

"Any minute now," Mr. Westerly replied. "The bait is in that black Impala just behind us—don't turn around—I mean the $4,000 in Wally Jackson's pocket."

When the Impala drew alongside us at a stop light, the sole occupant was a man of indeterminable age, who sat hunched over the wheel nervously dragging on a cigarette cupped inside his hand. With his prominent Adam's apple and with blond hair brushed into an oily duck's tail, he resembled a certain raw-boned type one sees hanging around rural gas stations. He had, in fact, used this to good advantage in breaking up rings of truckstop "Bennie" peddlers. His background as a chemistry major and salesman for a West Coast drug company was especially useful in his current assignment, which required inside knowledge of drug distribution systems, contacts with wholesalers, and the ability to size up a production plant.

About a stone's throw from Macy's, we parked and turned on

our recording equipment. The black Impala continued on, then disappeared around the next corner. That was the moment I should have been memorizing the car's license number, but I was thinking how strange it was to be in hot pursuit of a criminal band while surrounded by shoppers intent only upon their purchases. Suddenly, two men's voices filled the car. As Kerry turned the volume down, he identified Wally, who said: "I left the Barracuda at the airport, and rented this Impala. Those Colorado plates might attract fuzz, y'know?"

The other man, Tom, had a proposition: "We could put a new block in this, change the title, get a thirty-forty-dollar paint job and ship it West in a covered van. Gotta watch for hidden numbers on the body, though. Well, listen—" A waitress asked if that would be all. Dishes clattered. Tom spoke softly: "Uh, Wally, this is just between us, understand? The others don't know too much about my sideline. But don't you want to have a look? These are high class broads."

Wally told him, "O.K., but make it fast." We heard a rhythmic, swooshing sound—his jacket brushing against the concealed microphone as he walked—then street noises. They were probably going into a building with electrical interference; there was a lot of static and we couldn't pick up their voices. It could be a trap for Wally and his $4,000 cash, but we were boxed in by a huge truck from which racks of cocktail dresses were being unloaded. The Chief Inspector told us that he was going to walk around the block and look for them. After putting a Handie-Talkie inside his jacket, and holding a folded *Wall Street Journal* over the bulge, he got out and disappeared into the crowd. I was startled to hear his voice coming from the glove compartment:

"Kerry, can you read me?"

Inspector Short picked up a microphone from the tangle of wires on the floor, held it at seat level, and without bending his head toward it, replied: "I read you loud and clear, Clem. Over."

Clem Westerly radioed us that Wally and Tom were probably in a small hotel on the other side of the block-square building containing their restaurant rendezvous. We were to get into a position to move fast! Before getting out to check traffic in Herald Square less than a block below us, Kerry quickly explained how to operate the various buttons, knobs, and switches that controlled the whirling tapes in the attache case and the box with the red and green "eyes" in the glove compartment. I double-checked the toggle under the dash to be sure it was flipped to RECEIVING.

4:40, according to Macy's corner clock:

We were stuck in the rush-hour jam. As soon as the garment truck pulled away, another driver double-parked. When I signaled him to move on, he jumped out and peered into our car, wanting to know how soon I'd be leaving. (I'd kicked the wires under the seat, and draped a scarf over the other equipment, but the latch on the glove compartment wasn't working and the door flopped open.) Tom's voice broke in just then: "Take Thirty-ninth to the tunnel." *They were headed uptown!* Kerry rapped on the window —I'd locked all the doors in my panic. The other driver now moved up to let us out.

We were on a downtown street choked with traffic. While the lights held cars at the intersection behind us, Kerry eased out of the tight parking space, shot backward half a block between push-carts and pedestrians, then nosed into the left-turn lane going east. It was the only way to get on an uptown street fast. As we slowed for that turn, the Chief Inspector stepped from the curb and slid into the back seat.

The FDA men speculated on where Tom and Wally were headed. It wasn't necessarily the tunnel to New Jersey, for The Group usually followed devious routes. Possibilities were: a butcher shop in lower Manhattan run by Tom's son, Buggsy; a novelty factory up in the Bronx operated by Mannie, who also owned a disreputable bar near the docks; a new supper club in the east 50's in which a leading mobster contact of The Group had an interest; an egg-mix company; and Mauser's truck stop and diner. Their multiple covers involve many occupations. One might say they ranged from butchers and bakers to novelty makers. As these places were discussed, I gathered that they could be fronts for clandestine drug plants, but there was no chance for explanations now. Kerry asked me to keep my eye peeled for that Impala. Many seemingly identical black vehicles were all around us.

We turned toward the Lincoln Tunnel and then, up ahead I

saw Wally driving. The man sitting in the front seat beside him was wearing a Homburg and gesturing freely.

Tom's voice suddenly came in all too clear, for he was saying: "It's not *easy* to get really *young* girls with such *big* boobies. But that girl with the two guys, she's only sixteen."

"The one with the dark glasses," Wally asked. "How did you get her to—"

"—Like I told you, a coupla drinks with a coupla pills, and for a coupla hunnerd dollars, you're in business!"

"It's the pills that make 'em do it, huh? I mean, they *did* look like straight girls."

"Oh, these *are* straight girls from, you know, college and secretaries and like that. The one you said—with the dark glasses —she's a college girl. We gave her the pills in a drink and she went crazy. She wanted to take on *every* man in the bar!"

Tom's sideline was pornographic or "blue" movies. He was enthusiastically trying to sell his wares: *Four for Fun, Sadist, TV Casting Director, The Psychiatrist, Male Prostitute,* and so forth. "Films," he said, "that respectable people go for, so it's safe."

Wally turned the conversation back to counterfeit drugs, demanding to know what was holding up the Miltown that had been promised but never delivered. Tom said they were having second thoughts on continuing with Miltown because the patent on it had run out and several generic products were on the market in competition. The price had been declining steadily. Wally said Miltown was still selling at a pretty fair price and that a trade had built up on the brand-name that should hold out against generic meprobamate for at least another couple of years. Tom gave it only another year. But so what—they could duplicate *any* drug on the market. He asked Wally just to glance at the drug illustrations in PDR [*Physicians' Desk Reference*]—"Look here, all the good movers!"

Tom said The Group, in addition to counterfeits, could supply drugs made in Italy with formulas stolen from American laboratories. These would be imported pharmaceuticals. It was a two-way deal. "They just bought a lot of amphetamine powder and counterfeit Dexedrine from us." He explained that the contacts had been made "through a VIP." Tom also offered drugs to Wally that were part of recently hijacked tractor-trailer loads.

References were made to an earlier talk about developing and expanding the counterfeit drug business by setting up clandestine plants in the Northwest. In fact, because of the FDA "heat," The Group was seriously thinking about moving their headquarters to the West Coast. Tom pointed out:

"I got this *Drug Topics* 'Red Book' here. Almost all your big drug companies are right in this area, see? But way out there, there's very little chance of the FDA people coming in, if you're smart. I figure to work, say, four months, then rest two months, then back four more months. Then I'll say, 'Gentlemen, let's forget this for a while.' You get in for a year, then get out and lay low. Doesn't pay to rip and tear.

"During prohibition we learned a lot of tricks. You get a farmhouse way out in the country. You put a family in it with kids, so she puts out a clothesline, hangs out clothes. Then at night they go away and you come in. You put in the special phones. . . . I had some guinea partners, most of them dead now. 'Squeaky' and 'Louie' used to cook near New Brunswick. Cooked 30 cans a day and the gas man could come in there, or anybody during the day, and they wouldn't see anything. Everything done after five o'clock at night. And where do you think the still was? In the closets! When the house was built, all the closets were put one over the other in the corners. The column was 16 inches in diameter, inside them, see? Get this now, they built the house with enough sand around it so the overflow of the shit [mash] and stuff never went into the creek, it ran right into the sand.

"Now, the thing to do is put up our drug plants on the West Coast. What the hell is there to moving merchandise? Put it on a plane, it's only $35 a hundred pounds. Overnight you got merchandise. Those Spansules don't weigh much. You call it something else . . . get a shipping company . . . next day you got the stuff, air freight. Moving the stuff, getting the equipment and raw materials are no problem. Money is no problem. Selling is no problem—I can get cash for 250,000 HydroDiuril right now in 20 minutes. There's a dozen people I could get it off to, and not from this part of the country, either, which is nice."

Inspector Jackson steered the conversation to chemicals, and Tom said they were easy to buy except for Orinase. "You gotta have a chemist for that." But he parried questions about exactly where The Group got their active ingredients for pharmaceuticals.

When the undercover man asked Tom what he thought about the current congressional hearings on stricter drug controls, the criminal reassured him that any new laws passed wouldn't bother *their* setup:

"That's for the legitimate producers to worry about. We're not subject to rules and regulations!"

After we followed the Impala into the tunnel, our electronic equipment failed to pick up conversation in the car ahead. During this period, Clem Westerly gave me more background on the case against The Group.

Mannie, the novelty manufacturer, and tavern-keeper, had been under investigation for more than a year. It seemed that a West Coast pharmacist, while trying to extricate himself from trouble with narcotics agents, had offered information that counterfeit SK&F (Smith Kline & French) Dexedrine was available through one of Mannie's contacts. The agents passed this along to Smith Kline & French Laboratories, which hired a private detective agency—FDR Associates, run by former FBI agent Franklin D. Rooney—to collect evidence for a civil suit. After intensive surveillance, a $6,000 drug buy was arranged, with armed cover to be supplied by state police. But at the last minute, the police protection was withdrawn, the excuse being that all men were needed at a political convention. Frank Rooney refused to send his detectives in without police protection because they did not carry firearms, and he considered Mannie, an ex-convict, dangerous. Mannie was known to possess a Smith and Wesson and a Luger, ostensibly for "payroll protection." (Actually, his bar was a policy or numbers "bank.") No further action was taken on the buy, except that the information collected was passed on to the New York Chief Inspector by the drug company's legal counsel, for whatever use FDA could make of it.

As it happened, those clues were invaluable. They came at a time when FDA was stymied. Mr. Westerly had asked several Midwest Districts to investigate local counterfeit drug sales and make sample buys in drugstores. Suspicion was growing that the source was somewhere in the New York area. One large buy of counterfeits was monitored: the drugs were delivered to a Midwest wholesaler's warehouse by Rocco, a known St. Louis hoodlum with a record of more than two dozen arrests. But he proved to be just a go-between. Payment was made through him to another man waiting in a motel outside the city. There the trail had ended, until the New York District received a description of Mannie from SK&F, and found it matched that of the mysterious "man in the motel." A second buy was arranged in the Midwest, with the wholesaler agreeing to cooperate to the extent of placing another telephone order. The man he called turned out to be none other than Chameleon, who said that "his man" would transport the counterfeits in his private automobile. (This is a common method for eliminating shipping records, and thus foiling FDA's attempt to prove interstate traffic—a requirement for successful prosecution at that time.) FDA wanted to record at least two illicit buys for cases to stand up better in court.

The New York Chief Inspector mapped out an intricate reporting system utilizing toll booths along various routes. Mannie's black Lincoln Continental was clocked from the moment it was loaded with cartons of drugs (by Mauser, the trucker) until it arrived at the Midwestern motel rendezvous. The go-between delivered the drugs to the warehouse, but said that he would come back the next day to pick up the money. FDA was all set for a big "bust."* The St. Louis hoodlum never returned. Despite the fact that he was on Federal probation, he disappeared. Mr. Westerly was certain that he was being well paid by Mannie to keep out of reach. The FBI was still looking for him.

Without the go-between, the government's case against Chameleon, Mannie, et al., was weak, indeed. A way had to be found to make direct buys, or, even better, to infiltrate The Group, itself. The Chief Inspector had a lot of ideas, but no money. There was the usual District budgetary problem, plus the fact that many thousands of extra dollars were needed, with no guarantees that the investment would pay off. To support the cover story he was concocting, drug purchases would have to be in wholesale amounts for fairly extended periods.

---

*Bust: In FDA parlance, before the passage of DACA, a "bust" took place when undercover inspectors revealed themselves and asked suspects to talk things over. It was not usually an arrest, as police use the term.

Then, SK&F came forward with an offer to put up most of the money, with some being contributed by Merck & Co., *if* FDA would supply an undercover man willing to take the personal risks. Enter: Inspector Wallace Jackson, to be transformed into a shady drugs and sundries dealer known as "Wally-from-Denver," with connections in Omaha, Kansas City, Cincinnati, Philadelphia, and Baltimore. Along this trade route to New Jersey, the nation's medicine chest, Wally had "legit" customers for wholesale drugs. It was his job to supply them with the extra-special deals that only black-marketeers can offer. But these outlets were never to have any direct contact with his illicit sources. His criminal suppliers understood that he had to keep "his people" clean.

After several FDA Districts helped build Wally's fictitious background, he left his family behind and began running with pep-pill racketeers, who peddled Bennies and "hearts." He also was offered amphetamine dosage forms he could sell to drugstores as SK&F's monogrammed Dexedrine Spansule capsules.

Wally's most useful contact was in the East where an ex-convict known only as "Red" controlled a pill distribution territory extending into the Carolinas. Red promised Wally a good buy on bulk amphetamine and on sleeping pills called "blue heavens" to be picked up at a later date. Red did not handle monogrammed SK&F Dexedrine, himself, but referred Wally to "one of his partners," Mauser, who operated a truckstop and diner outside of New York City.

Mauser, a member of The Group, had been arrested in the early 1960's as the mastermind of a million-dollar narcotics ring with international connections. His trucking operations had been used to distribute heroin. From hard-core narcotics for addicts, he had branched out into the distribution of morphine derivatives and substitutes used in hospitals to treat patients suffering severe pain from surgery and cancer. The products he handled *appeared* to be legitimate, but their labels bearing such names as Wyeth, Squibb, and Merck, were counterfeited, as were the government tax stamps on them. The drugs could have been adulterated or contaminated—Mauser was interested in fast profits, not pain relief. Chameleon, Mannie, and others organized a "Hospital Supply Company" about this time.

In the course of arranging the deal on Dexedrine, Wally bought a large quantity of blue heavens from a pill peddler he met at Mauser's. Then, because he was interested in other prescription items, he was introduced to a close friend of Mauser, a renegade pharmacist I'll call "Doc." Doc proved to be Wally's entré to The Group's inner circle. Wally and Doc found they had several friends in common operating on the fringes of the legitimate drug trade. (FDA quickly arranged to shore up these mutual contacts, so that proper references would be given if Doc checked back.) The pharmacist was satisfied with Wally's credentials, but the more hardened criminals, especially Mannie and Mauser, were still suspicious. Yet they saw the possibilities Wally presented for opening up the Northwest territory—something they had long discussed, but never acted upon.

Tom, as the corporate vice-president in charge of plant expansion and market development, was the most eager to go West, but even he had asked Doc many questions about Wally's reliability. Their conversation, Doc later reported to Wally, went something like this: "How long do you know this guy Wally?" Doc had told him not to worry, that Wally was "legitimate." (Legitimate by their standards; that is, not a double-crosser.) Doc stated that he'd been sending Wally merchandise for years, through mutual contacts in the trade. (As, indeed, he now believed was true.) Tom kept pressing: had Doc ever been under the ax with Wally? Had he ever been to Wally's place out West? "How does he stack up with Our People out there?" Doc said, "Look, he's a mover!" Tom was skeptical: "You'd never think in a million years—a mover *this* guy is! Those clothes he runs around in. . . ." But Doc reminded Tom of "the guy in Jersey City, the one with the tattered rags who used to hide $3,000,000 in the trunk of his old car. Nobody knew he had it, or what he was doing. . . . Wally's smart like that," Doc said.

I had wondered myself whether Wally was properly dressed for infiltration into the mob. He was wearing a pink sport shirt with the collar spread open over the lapels of a sleazy blue business suit. Shouldn't he be sporting a white-on-white custom-made shirt, pale satin tie, and a diamond on his pinky? The Chief Inspector said no, that he was not posing as a successful gangster but as a fast-buck operator, a wheeler-dealer. Not being from the

East, he was looked upon as something of a yokel; not expected to be sartorially splendid. What put him in with Doc was his knowledge of the prescription drug distribution system and his hot customers, wholesalers and pharmacists looking for monogrammed best-seller drugs. Wally had immediately been offered the oral antidiabetic Orinase, supposedly manufactured only by Upjohn, and Diuril and HydroDiuril, two leading diuretics produced by Merck.

We had finally reached the New Jersey end of the Lincoln Tunnel, and our receiving equipment began to pick up the voices of Tom and Inspector Jackson again:

TOM: Orinase is a fantastic item. Fantastic! It's the hottest thing in the drug industry right now. You know that. Six million worth a month is what they [Upjohn] get rid of.

INSPECTOR JACKSON: I don't care what 'they' get rid of, what do *you* consider profitable?

TOM: Me, personally? To me, profitable means at least 200,000 tablets or capsules a week per order over a 60 week period.

We followed their car south on the New Jersey Turnpike. As we neared Newark Airport, the Chief Inspector explained that if they went into the terminal, we would have to split up and follow on foot. Since we were strangers to Tom and other Group members, we might be able to get close enough to overhear what they were saying. The Impala circled Lot Number One slowly in the outside lane, picked up a short, swarthy-looking man—Tom's son, Buggsy—and sped off.

"I'll bet they're going to Doc's!" Clem Westerly said, as we trailed them to a congested, downtown business district. We parked half a block from a modern, prosperous-looking Prescription Center, identified as one of Doc's pharmacies. Wally, Tom, and Buggsy went inside and came out with a tall, suntanned, handsome man in a white jacket—Doc. The four men entered a large hotel next door, where Doc lived with his sister in a penthouse apartment. "She is terrified that he'll be killed, and is always pleading with him to get out of the rackets," Clem said.

When I asked how Doc became involved with the underworld, I was told that he had ingratiated himself with a leading mobster by administering first aid when the man received a painful injury. Doc had been in solid with "the big boys" ever since. But his sister doesn't trust them, she keeps buying more and more insurance on his life.

After the men entered the hotel, we moved to a better location for radio reception. The conversation was bantering. Buggsy, a "dese-dem'n'dose" type, who bore little resemblance to his tall, elegantly dressed father, was describing a $1,000 talking bird he had bought one of his girlfriends. It could only say five words, but, as Tom pointed out, the girl was a bird-brain, herself, so it didn't make much difference. "At $200 a word, I'd expect some hot tips from that bird, or else!" They then discussed getting rid of Cuban cigars at $25 a box. Apparently an entire shipment was involved. Mr. Westerly explained that Doc obtained from Mauser a considerable amount of hijacked loot—cigars, cigarettes, razor blades, cosmetics, drugs, and so on. "His principal practice is larceny, not pharmacy. He's a fence."

Referring to the trucker, Tom said, "When he goes up, he'll go for a long time, maybe 25–30 years. The government says he owes on anywheres from two to ten million, maybe it's six million. That don't mean he's guilty of it." Doc asked, "Income tax evasion on *that* much?" And Tom summed up: "Ahhh, taxes! Nobody can save, what the hell!" Doc began to complain, "*I* was the one that got hurt. *I* never saw any of that, cost me a small bundle ——" At this point, Wally Jackson irritably told them he didn't have all day and wanted to get down to business on the Orinase and HydroDiuril. Tom excused himself to make the first of a series of phone calls.

Returning, he explained that the man they were dealing with was "a hard man. Went through a lot of money and so forth. Not an easy man to get along with. They were operating pretty big and got stopped—him and that loud-mouth. Had quite a drug plant. Used to work 'til 5 o'clock in the afternoon, legitimately, and after 5 o'clock, they'd go until 3 o'clock in the morning. Day crew knew nothing about it. The machines were all washed up and dried up and so forth, see? They brought in all the raw materials and took out all the finished drugs. The legitimate help never knew what was going on."

WALLY: Yeah, so.

TOM: Reason I mention it, [Mauser] had two of his trucks in it. Made a lot of money moving those Spansules— and he said the other day they're trying to be careful. They've got another plant. A place where nobody goes near. They're very careful not to lead people to it, after [Mannie] saw that station wagon and took the number down and had it checked inside, inside the department. It belonged to a private detective agency.

DOC: Christ! They could do away with all this if they'd just move all the operations out West. There's such a thing as being too careful, you know!

This caused Tom to criticize Doc's lack of telephone security. (Tom never gave his name when making long-distance calls; in fact, he used a stolen telephone credit card.) He described an elaborate method for contacting members of The Group:

> Go to a place like Newark Airport, sit on the bench and read the paper. I'll find my place next to you— I've already got the number in a phone booth across the way. I write it down and slip it to you. In five minutes, I go to my booth and you go to another booth on the other side and you tell me where you're going to put the key to, say, a locker. If something doesn't look just right around there, forget it. You can't be *too* careful!

WALLY: You said you'd have the Orinase and Hydro when you delivered the one million amphets—

TOM: They're going into full production on Orinase and Hydro—right now there's a little trouble with the chemist on account of the "heat" at [Mannie's].

Tom said he was waiting for a call, if it didn't come, he'd try again in ten minutes. There was another general discussion about hiring chemists and setting up other plants. It became evident that The Group was not a corporate entity, but a loose organization of various subsidiaries.

Doc: What does the chemist want for that Orinase, did he say?

Tom: $35.

Doc: Not a bad price. An item as hard as that is worth buying at that price.

Tom: Between you and I, that chemist's another hard man to talk to. He's arrogant.

Doc: Your biggest problem is getting him away from—

Tom: No, I can't get him away from him—I can't go over his head. It's his man. I'll have to go along with them, see, or get another man. Uh, could that doctor do it? Is he available?

Doc: He's over in his office at the research institute testing new products for a company.

Tom: Could we take him away for a month or two, just to set up a plant, uh, you know, give him a piece of it. Would he be interested?

Doc: I'd have to see. I think he would. But don't forget, Orinase is not something you buy, it has to be made. The man that's making the Orinase now, he's a real chemist. If you have the perfect man, there's a fortune in this set-up.

Buggsy: Is it just one chemical? Or is it a little of this and a little of that and you put them all together? 'Cause I have to look up in this book—it's all in the book here.

Doc: Orinase is tolbutamide.

Buggsy: How many component parts does it got?

Tom: (*Laughing*) *You* don't know. I'm talkin to Doc, here.

Boy, is he tired after last night! Now, can anybody make that for anybody?

Doc: Anybody that knows *how* to make it. Takes a lot of knowledge to make this sort of thing. These are the most important people in the set-up. You can't make it without these chemists. I'm very anxious for Orinase. Take a million—that's a $35,000 order right there. With a thousand accounts, it takes a million every couple of weeks. That's 70,000 bucks a month on that item alone! For a distributor, it's easy to move a million tablets of anything. But you have to watch, when you're buying like me. You should keep on buying from your regular suppliers the same amount. Like, I'm using over 8,000 Orinase a week here. I'd never stop buying that much from them. If I did, they'd want to know where the hell I'm getting it. Right away I'd be suspect. There's an awful lot of merchandise being sold as one thing and billed as something else. Sell Drug A, and bill for Drug B, so there's actually no way to, uh, be caught on this type of operation. No trace whatever.

Buggsy: Uh—is there any dope in that Orinase?

Doc: It's not a narcotic. These are not abuse drugs, like amphetamine—that's nothing but trouble and not worth bothering with because it's too cheap.

Tom: Yeah, that's right. From now on we ought to stick to drugs like Orinase. But what about chemists? Say, [Mannie] had another one—

Doc: He's no kid anymore, he wouldn't want to go out West. Besides, he's mainly in plastics. Different field altogether.

Tom: Well, Doc, I'm talkin now, open, you understand? It means we just might have to put that [Ph.D.] fink out there. . . . You know how it is with raw ingredients, you take a portion of this, and a portion of that, and a portion of the other and keep adding and mixing it up. You got to get all the right proportions before it goes into the hopper. I just don't know—I never handled the powder it's made from. I always just handled the tablets.

BUGGSY: Well, tablet men you ain't got either for out West.

DOC: Anybody can be a tablet man. *You* can be one—

BUGGSY: What, *me* run a Spooks machine!

DOC: Stokes, Stokes machine. You can turn out 5,000 tablets an hour with one pin—they already have the dies up there. You can run that machine 24 hours a day and you still won't have enough. Wally, here, gets the first million, I could use half-a-million—

TOM: I told them that, I said some of this has got to go to Doc—The only thing is, you kept us waiting on that HydroDiuril powder and you know how [Mannie] flies off the handle.

DOC: You mean he won't sell me any Hydro? Is *that* what he said?

TOM: Don't worry, when I get the Hydro, I'll tell him it's for 'John Jones,' see? By the way, what was *wrong* with that Hydro powder, what do they mean by 'recrystallizing?'

DOC: Something went wrong with the chemical itself, so they reworked it.

TOM: Drums and drums of it's been laying there. Enough for millions of tablets. But it's got specks in it. It was peach color, but it got white specks—

DOC: It was moldy.

TOM: Well, he threw something in there, to make it so he could have good samples.

DOC: You could never tell the difference between the sample tablets and the real thing. The edge of the tablet, the lip, everything was perfect. When I was

>   over at [Mannie's] house, he was telling me how
>   much we were all going to make in this thing to-
>   gether.

Tom: But, he's been tipped off, they're sittin on his door-
              step watchin' him, a private detective agency.

Doc: You think the FDA—

Buggsy: The FBI don't come out 'less a crime's been com-
              mitted.

Doc: The *FDA*, not the FBI. The Food and Drug Ad-
              ministration. FDA's got their own inspectors.

Tom: There's no crime committed. You know that chemist
              stole all the formulas and everything from Lederle?
              He's out on a $50,000 bail and I hear they're gonna
              leave him go.

Tom explained how he handled his most recent brush with the
law: "I got the bail down from $25,000 to $15,000 through that
lawyer with the connections with 'the people.' You never know
when you need a lawyer. I send them over $100, $50, then another
$100, and so on, all for nothin' special. I say, 'I'll see you in time
to come.' They know what I mean. [A mobster] paid *his* lawyer
$196,000; had to pay it before they took him in. Now he's out
waitin on the appeal."

Someone asked Tom what happened when Federal agents last
came to his house. (They were not from FDA.) He replied, "Well,
for five hours they went through my mattresses, books, everything.
I said 'Look, I ain't no hoodlum.' Numbers. They were also
lookin for numbers. Now, I never *mark* no numbers *down*. As a
rule of certainty, I try to memorize numbers. There was nothin
there. Pretty smart, see?"

Doc: Yeah, yeah.

Tom: I dunno . . . God was in my corner. Luckily, the U.S.
              Commissioner happened to notice my [lodge] button,
              see? I told him I just had this ear operation and
              everything was very hard for me. I told him I'd sign
              anything.

At this point, Wally interrupted and stated that he was tired of waiting around and was going to call all deals off. He told them that his money man was not putting out any front money until someone showed him dies, punches, and other manufacturing equipment, as well as samples of drug powder to be *sure* they could really deliver. He said that he had to go back West where he had these large orders and give his customers firm delivery dates. If Tom's people couldn't deliver, he'd be out on a limb.

Tom said they'd leave in a minute. The man he wanted to talk to was out. Doc commented on the fact that Buggsy had fallen asleep. Tom said, "He draws a good living outta the butcher-shop, but he's gonna keel over and die—those hours—4 o'clock in the morning and at 11, 12 o'clock at night, he's still up yet. Then he's got these other people he runs around with."

DOC: Like [supper-club owner]. He's doing the same thing with those East Side restaurants. Terrific business. What a clientele. The first night I was in his new one, Sinatra was there. Leonard Bernstein was there —lot of society people. You start getting that kind—

TOM: I'm thinkin of going in with him on one of them. You wanta go in with me? Take a piece of it and run it. . . . First, you gotta pay off, like, $10,000 right away for [bribes]. People are pressing, you gotta pay em all.

DOC: He's doing a very dumb thing in that new place. He's now letting in an awful lot of, uh, hard-looking people. Looked like the entire [Mafia "family"] was in there the last night I was there. That's no good. . . .

WALLY: I didn't come here to discuss this guy's new joint.

TOM: We're going to see my man, only he can't make it right away. In about fifteen minutes we'll leave.

Doc mentioned that one of the supper-club owner's associates, an accountant, had just come out of prison and had been calling him for the past few days. Tom wondered if he wanted to make a touch somewhere along the line, but Doc told him that the

accountant owned a Junior-Miss—something or other—Beauty
Contest and wanted to give him a piece.

TOM: Why, for your looks, or what? Who knows? He might
          have a good piece there.

BUGGSY: Hey!

DOC: Well, let's get back to drugs.

TOM: Yeah, Doc, why dontcha' just stick to the *one* line
          you're in!

When Wally, Tom, and Buggsy left the hotel, they got into
the Impala and drove back to Newark Airport. We followed.
But when they left the airport we lost them, and even more
discouraging, we no longer heard anything from the radio. Chief
Inspector Clem Westerly asked Inspector Kerry Shore to pull over
at the first telephone, so he could tell Frank Rooney at the FDR
Detective Agency what had happened.

"The FDR men don't have any information," Mr. Westerly
said after telephoning. "Let's get up on the Pulaski Skyway. I
think we might get better radio reception with that height."

Now began an itinerary that was to be repeated many times in
the hours to come. Through the dreary slums of Jersey, where
Negro children played with broken toys and every other doorway
was a tavern. ("There's the bar owned by Mannie . . . I wouldn't
even drink bottled beer in there!") Into the Hackensack salt
marshes on a narrow road, with tall Phragmites grass waving on
either side, coal heaps, garbage dumps, asphalt plants, carcasses
of old cars piled in a rusty funeral pyre. ("A lot of gangsters took
their last ride out this way.") Fish House Road to Kearney, Pennsylvania Railroad's truck-train terminal, Hudson County Police,
oil refineries, chemical plants, storage tanks, and more storage
tanks, oil slick, stench. ("Smells worse than an egg–cracking
barn.") Now under the highway on a truck route. Shadows, con-
crete pillars. ("Might as well take a swing around Mauser's truck-
stop and diner and have a look.") Acres of trucks parked behind
high, metal fences. A sign on a barnlike building, TRUCKS STEAM
CLEANED. Another long frame structure, a trucker's dormitory?

Rat-faced man, greasy black cap on the back of his head, staring at us suspiciously from the diner's steps, thumbs hooked in a wide leather belt, thin arms tattooed from wrist to elbow. A huge tractor-trailer being backed into a corner with obvious finesse. ("I used to drive a rig from Detroit to Atlanta. Hard life that." "You weren't with Food and Drug?" "I *was* with Food and Drug, my partner and I were the first undercover men to sign on as regular drivers." "Benzedrine, wasn't it?" "Yep, that's part of your story, they're *still* 'ridin with Benny. ' . . .") Last look at the truck stop. A sign behind the gas pumps: DRUGS & SUNDRIES—UNIFORMS—WESTERN UNION MONEY ORDERS. ("That place, somehow gives me the creeps. . . ." "It should, the State Police think Mauser had something to do with the killing of two of their men, but they can't prove it.")

"That man on the diner's steps, that wasn't Mauser, was it?"

"No, it would take three or four little runts like that to make one of him—he's a giant of a man, with a temper to match. Even the gang fears him. All except Mannie. He's afraid of nothing and no one."

Up now, to the long sweep of the General Pulaski Skyway, arching over the Hackensack and Passaic Rivers, with the old, decrepit freighters moored below.

"Hush a minute! Was that a bleep?"

We hardly dared to breathe. From the attaché case came a medley of sounds: an order for a hamburger "well done," Sinatra singing "I've Got A Crush On You," many voices, a telephone ringing, and a little bell's tinkle.

"That's the bell that rings when the front door opens! They're having their dinner in that restaurant ahead. We'll just go on down the road and sit this one out. Park over there behind the gas station, Kerry, so we can keep an eye on the lot. I see that Buggsy has joined them—his Satellite's beside the Impala."

I learned that The Group liked isolated places surrounded by parking lots and frequented by transient customers; one of their favorite hangouts was a certain chain restaurant near Trenton. "This one is particularly hard to keep under surveillance because you can't cruise around it," Clem said. "Notice the barrier between the two lanes going over the Skyway? Once you start in either direction, you have to cross the entire span before you can turn around. We should have half-a-dozen radio cars controlled from a base station tonight."

As we sat watching one of the parking lot exits, I learned that FDR's detectives were staked out at Buggsy's butcher-shop, Mannie's factory, and Mauser's truck stop. They were periodically reporting back to Frank Rooney's office, which then served as a message relay center for the Chief Inspector. He, of course, had to use public telephones. It seemed a roundabout way for Federal agents to have to work, especially when one considered the fact that Mauser used radio communication in fingering tractor-trailer leads to be hijacked. Still, we had Wally's "bug," and a fine thing it was—when it was working. Just now Kerry explained that the mike cord seemed to be partially disconnected; whenever Wally made a certain move, his words were cut off. We caught only a few phrases:

"Coconut pie, please. . . . The dog tracks out there. . . . Down in Miami, a million and a half a day. . . . Oh, to Cuba, or where? . . ." Then came swishing sounds that told us he was walking. The bell's tinkle. "C'mon, ride with us. . . . Going back tomorrow, Wally? . . . Hell, if this comes out all right. . . ."

They did not leave through the exit nearest us, so we tore across the Skyway. There was little traffic in that direction and we made good time. But when we reached the far end, there were several possible outlets, and they were nowhere in sight. Acting on a hunch, the Chief Inspector told Kerry to turn right.

"We may as well make a pass at the egg company while we're over here," he said. "The other places are covered."

I learned that FDA literally got its first whiff of the drug counterfeiting racket while tracking down the illicit sale of rotten eggs, "inkies" or incubator rejects, that were salvaged and sold to various shops. Curiously, FDS's men had photographed a Ph.D. researcher going into Buggsy's butcher-shop many times, but they had yet to document a single instance in which he came out loaded down with any cartons, or even carrying a parcel. The Ph.D. spent a lot of time in the building owned by the egg company, too. He was supposed to be engaged in research on exotic compounds, fine chemicals that did not come under FDA's jurisdiction. I wondered if he might be putting some of these into the egg mix to cover up the smell.

"You don't need a Ph.D. to make a go of the 'inky' egg racket," the Chief Inspector said. "All you need is a washing machine to spin the eggs and a deep freeze."

I was to learn more about this later. After driving up and down hills on lonely back roads, we entered an isolated industrial area. It had grown quite dark and the only sign of life was flickering neon that signaled first BAR, then EATS, off in the distance. As if he could read my mind, Clem said, "No matter how hungry you are, you wouldn't want to go in there." I said I'd give anything for a cup of coffee, but I was told they never drink coffee on surveillance because of its well-known diuretic action.

We rounded a block of seemingly deserted warehouses, slowly, with our car lights off, then pulled into an alley. The second floor rear of a loft-type building was dimly lighted. Through the window we could see two shadowy figures, one much taller than the other, struggling with a heavy object between them—I thought it looked like a man, limply doubled over. But the inspectors said it was probably a piece of lab equipment covered by a dust cloth. If this was a laboratory, I couldn't understand why, under the circumstances they didn't go in and raid it. The Chief Inspector told me: "We have no authority to 'raid' drug laboratories or manufacturing plants; we are supposed to inspect them."

But what if this Ph.D. researcher was making counterfeit drugs, or LSD? He seemed a more likely suspect than Buggsy-the-butcher, or Mannie-the-novelty-manufacturer!

"That may be, but we have no evidence of illegal activity to support a search warrant. We have inspected his laboratory. There was nothing there on which we can charge him, even though he may be violating the law. We need a sample of an illegal drug that he has delivered into interstate commerce. That we don't have. There are a number of so-called research chemists like this man on the fringes of The Group, but we can't touch them. If he's a drug counterfeiter, face it, he doesn't comply with anything."

The light in the window went off. A few moments later, a tall man came out with a carton under his arm and got into a station wagon. (He was the Ph.D.; the shorter man was a technician who stayed in the building.)

"It's easy to tail him," Kerry said. "His right rear light is out."

Now it was pitch-dark and raining. The windshield wiper wasn't working and the glove compartment kept flying open, spilling flashlights and electronic gadgets every time we came to an abrupt stop. As we sped through narrow, twisting streets and brazened our way across lightless intersections, I wondered what shape the brakes were in on this G.I. vehicle. It was the wildest ride I've ever had. The Ph.D. zigzagged in and out of every back alley for miles around before entering Manhattan. To keep him in sight, yet not follow too closely, required driving in spurts and sudden stops that had me finally riding with both hands holding the glove compartment shut. In New York City, he took a circuitous route to the corner of 58th Street and Sixth Avenue, where he parked. We dropped Clem Westerly off down the block and began cruising in the neighborhood of the Plaza.

Ten minutes later we picked up Clem, standing beside one of the horse-drawn carriages at the entrance to Central Park. He told us that the Ph.D. had taken the carton into an apartment house on Central Park South. His elevator had stopped on the seventeenth floor. Several physicians happened to have apartments on that floor, but it was impossible to determine which one he entered. The names of all occupants were noted and would be checked out.

"He might be here all night!" the Chief Inspector said. The Ph.D. had three or four bases of operations; this could be just another one. The FDA men wondered if he had counterfeit punches and dies in his package.

"If it's true that they paid $4,000 to have that last set made, they'd be worth taking home for safekeeping," Clem said. He explained that these were parts for a tableting machine that would have cost a legitimate manufacturer only $40. They were used to make the "W" on Wallace Laboratories' Miltown, for instance.

The radio was still dead. It was time to call FDR Associates again.

When Chief Inspector Westerly came out of the phone booth, there was a very serious expression on his face, as he told us: "FDR's men have lost all contact with Wally Jackson. Their man at the butcher-shop says Wally's Impala was just parked in front by Buggsy. The man watching Mauser's diner and truck stop reported earlier that Wally, Tom, and Buggsy drove up in the Impala. A few minutes later, Mannie arrived in his black Continental. The Continental is still there. My bet is, so is Wally, and that's not good."

It was the Skyway again, this time at 90 miles an hour.

"Could be a heist," Inspector Shore said. "He's always worried about that. With $4,000 on him. . . ."

"Is it possible that The Group might have set up a mobile lab in one of those big trailers at Mauser's, and they're now looking at it?" I asked, hoping for the best.

"Anything's possible. But if the plant is 'parked' there, why did Buggsy leave in Wally's car? I find it hard to believe that they turned him over to Mannie, after friendly introductions. Mannie has always taken care to remain in the background. They save Mauser to apply 'muscle'."

I had a vision of the torture possibilities in a steam-cleaning at the truck stop. We were passing through those desolate salt marshes again, and I recalled what a Mafia expert had told me about underworld methods for disposing of bodies. They put victims in an old car, which is run through a metal crusher and compressed into a slab of steel. This was almost as popular as tossing the body into a newly poured cement foundation, or into the river with a slot machine around his neck.

We passed an auto graveyard, where smouldering fires silhouetted towering monuments against the sky. "They wouldn't *dare* hurt Inspector Jackson, would they? Isn't there a law to protect Federal agents?"

Inspector Shore took his eyes off the road long enough to glance at me: "All but Food and Drug inspectors. We aren't covered by that law."

"Is he really not armed?" I asked.

"We're not *permitted* to carry weapons," Clem Westerly said. "And we don't. We may issue a Notice of Inspection. Then, we inspect. If we find violations of the Food, Drug, and Cosmetic Act, we send a Notice of a Hearing, a written invitation to come to our District Office—with their lawyers, if they wish—to discuss their views as to why they should not be prosecuted."

The present laws were designed with negligent businessmen in mind, he explained. "Gentlemen who failed to do something, possibly for compelling reasons that we should know about. That is why this section, 305, was put into the Act. We can't move capriciously against vital industries run by responsible citizens, and the big portion of our time *is* spent with people of this type. Now the counterfeiter is a different breed of critter, a *willful* law-breaker. We're trying our best to cope with him."

As we sped through the night, Mr. Westerly continued trying to get a response from the electronic equipment. There were occasional hopeful bursts of static, but no true signal from Wallace Jackson. The realization struck me, fully, now: A tiny microphone was the only weapon that man had; a bit of plastic and wire.

"I hope his nerves are steady."

"Steady as any, though he's been through a lot. His wife recently received a call threatening the lives of their youngsters. She was mighty shook up, since the caller gave the full names and exact ages of all four. Wally is away so much that she's the one who has to have steady nerves."

"Do you think he might have ditched the mike, Clem?" Kerry asked. "He's dead if they frisked him."

"I don't think so. He could use it to bluff them. Say something like: 'There are a dozen men out there listening to your every word.' It could work for or against him, depending on the situation."

If only that "bug" of Wally's were working. We were well within range if he was at Mauser's. Those were the diner's lights ahead. Before we went charging in, Clem wanted to call FDR again for the latest report. Frank Rooney, at least, was in contact with his men.

There was a roadside telephone booth coming up, and Kerry was already pulling over for it. The Chief Inspector returned with the news: Before he disappeared, Inspector Jackson passed on the word—we didn't know how or to whom—that Mannie had agreed to show him the manufacturing plant. The question still was: Is it a trap? We were to rendezvous with FDR's men, now.

We roared down the six-lane highway, "Hell bent for Lexington," as Clem would have put it. Next thing I knew, we had accomplished a sort of musical chairs maneuver whereby Kerry and I were dispatched to Newark Airport's parking lot to keep Wally's Barracuda under surveillance. Clem Westerly and FDR's men drove off in the other direction.

The explanation: "Wally is supposed to bring the drugs to the Barracuda after he sees the plant and makes the purchase. If there is any slip-up, we want to be sure it isn't at that end. We can keep in touch by using the Handie-Talkies."

Inspector Jackson was waiting at the airport, chain-smoking Camels. Up close, the network of fatigue lines around his eyes underscored the strain he had been under. After the others arrived a short time later, we heard his story over coffee in a secluded spot. When Buggsy drove back from Mauser's, he dropped Wally and Tom off a block away from the butcher-shop. Tom wanted to sell Wally a Malibu for $400. (He had rented it six months earlier with a credit card stolen from the president of the state bar association!) But he claimed that it was no longer "hot." Tom insisted that Wally take it for a trial spin, during which time he offered several other cars, including a '64 Chrysler, for aproximately the same price.

"When I drove around the block," Wally recalled, "I saw Buggsy transferring a carton from the butcher-shop truck to my Impala. When he drove my car back to where Tom and I were parked, he began to give me some more double-talk about seeing the plant."

"Did you see it?"

"*No.*"

Evidently, Mannie had queered the deal at Mauser's. But they had definitely promised to show him the manufacturing equipment "tomorrow," when they delivered the balance of the buy, the one million "amphets."

"*Equipment?* You mean *just* the punches and dies?" the Chief Inspector said, disgustedly.

Inspector Jackson agreed that this was no good. He had to see the plant itself, preferably in operation. They then decided to try to "turn" one of The Group, get him to inform on the others. Tom seemed the best bet. He was wanted by the Treasury Department—maybe something could be worked out between the two Federal agencies. The call to arrange the "amphet" pickup was supposed to be made at noon the next day, Tuesday. By that time, the Chief Inspector would have talked with Treasury.

The plan took form: Clem Westerly and I would pose as Wally Jackson's big customers, a fictitious "Mr. & Mrs. Price of Price-Rite Wholesale Drug Company." We would pretend that we had just arrived at La Guardia Airport early Wednesday morning. Wally would ask Tom to meet us there for a conference called by Mr. Price. Mrs. Price would be on a shopping trip, a good cover.

"That would be the story to lay on them," Wally said, "because my excuse—when I got away from them long enough to call the FDR agency tonight—was that I had to pacify my big customer, who wanted to know what the hell was going on. Why all the delays?"

Disappointment and exhaustion seemed to evaporate as the new angles were explored. The men were oblivious of the coffee standing cold in their cups, the tired waitress wanting to go home. "What if . . . What if. . . ." The debate continued while most of the lights were turned out and it did not break up until an exasperated counterman began turning chairs upside down on nearby tables.

Outside, Inspector Jackson said that he had the partial order of counterfeits in the carton in the Impala. Tonight it would be sealed, given a sample number, put under lock and key, and a report written about the events leading up to its purchase before Wally's day was officially over. "I was $200 short," he told the Chief Inspector. "The price was $4,200. Tom made up the difference out of his own pocket. For a while there, I was sure it was going to be a heist down at the truck stop."

The Chief Inspector said that he had considered having Wally bonded, because if he had lost the money along with his life, his family technically would have been liable for it. But he gave up the idea when he learned that bonding would only have insured the government's being repaid. Wally's family still would have had to repay the bonding company. It seemed incredible to me that these Federal agents had to risk their lives *and* their death benefits, as well. Clem Westerly recalled that when he was learning the ropes as a young undercover inspector, he had to keep pill-peddlers under surveillance in honky-tonks along truck routes. This naturally required his ordering at least a beer from time to time. In those days, starting salaries were around $3,100 a year, but Fiscal disallowed beer as an official expense. Eventually, he complained about his overhead. "Someone came up with the seriously meant suggestion that we carry a small hot water bottle under our jackets and pour the beer into it, then submit this as a so-called 'sample' to the FDA laboratory. They thought we then could be reimbursed."

Inspector Jackson, reflecting his worry over almost losing the $4,000, now looked his age, which I suspected was closer to 40, than 30. His pale blue eyes were red-rimmed and bloodshot and his skin had a prison-like pallor. The palm of his hand, from cupping the ever-present cigarette, was stained an orangey-yellow, his nails were broken. He explained that the toughest thing about his job was having to stay so "cruddy." If he had "Born Loser" or "I Hate Cops" tattooed on the back of his hand, the image would have been complete. Standing there in his black pointy-toed shoes, sleazy white socks, pin-striped suit, *and* pink sport shirt, he seemed just the type of ratty little crook one would suspect of wide dealings in bogus drugs, Bennies, and blue movies.

Tuesday, 8:30 A.M.

Chief Inspector Westerly received a call from another FDA chief in the Midwest, who had just heard from his local FBI contact that one of the biggest Bennie-peddlers in the East was "Wally-from-Denver," believed to have good connections with the Kansas City mob. Wally's "cover" was holding up.

Next, a call came in from Wally, who was in a New Jersey motel. Red had just sent word that he would be around with the blue heavens some time during the night. These had been ordered weeks earlier when Wally was working his way into The Group. As a matter of fact, there had been so many delays getting delivery from Red, Wally had bought blue heavens from a pill-peddler who seemed to be one of Mauser's suppliers and a prime source of bulk amphetamine, as well. It was inconvenient to have to deal with Red tonight—what with "Mr. and Mrs. Price" arriving at the airport early the next day—but Red insisted on the meeting.*

Wally hoped that Red wouldn't want to "party" all night—he'd had enough of running around with his gang, which included

---

*This happened frequently—several cases breaking at once for a single undercover man. Wally had gone five days without sleep in Texas the month before.

several 15- and 16-year-old girls with babies, whose apartments were used as hangouts. Red was a heavy pill-user, and had a violent temper. In fact, it seemed to Wally that he had become paranoid as a result of amphetamine abuse. It was unusual to find a major pill-distributor taking drugs himself, but Red did.

Tuesday, Midnight. Inspector Jackson's motel room:

Wally answered a knock on the door. In came Red, followed by—and this surprised him—the peddler who had sold him the blue heavens. Two strangers crowded in behind them. As soon as the door was shut, Red shoved a gun in Wally's face, pulling back the hammer.

RED:	I'm gonna blow your head off. You didn't think I'd find out. You tried to go right under me. You can't buy a pill here without my say so!
WALLY:	Listen! This man [pill-peddler] said he could lay 'em on me—
PILL-PEDDLER:	You're tryin to cut *my* throat now. It ain't done around here.
WALLY:	. . . Where I come from, if I say I've got the bread, the man brings the stuff. You know I really tried to do business with you. I laid around here and you still couldn't come up. I told you I would take what I said I'd take, regardless of what I got from others. . . .
RED:	When people works for me, they're *my* people. I carries the mail.

The two strangers searched Wally's room and car. (He learned he had been thoroughly investigated by Red's contacts out West; he was not suspected of being an FDA man, but rather of trying to "muscle in.")

After several hours of drinking, complaining, and gun-brandishing, Red evidently was satisfied that Wally-from-Denver would "tromp no more" on his toes.

It was clear enough from this and other cases that major sec-

tions of the country are divided up into pill territories, each
controlled by hardened criminals.*

*When Red was later arrested by the police, he had a gun in one hand, pills on his
person, another gun on a nearby table, and a third gun under the cushion of his
chair. He had beaten a man to death, but had gotten off with fourth degree manslaughter. Familiar with liquid oxygen, nitro putty, and picric acid—materials
used by professional safe-crackers—he was breaking in his younger brother as a
burglar. They were caught with two suitcases full of jewelry. He had started his
10-year-old son on a life of crime by sending him to walk the railroad tracks looking for stands of marihuana, and rewarding him with money when he found some.

CHAPTER TWO

The "Bust"

Wednesday, 10 A.M., La Guardia Airport.

From Inspector Wallace Jackson's memo to his District Director:

> I arranged to meet [Tom] at the American Airlines
> passenger terminal. The Chief Inspector and I felt
> there was a strong indication (from information
> received from other law enforcement agencies) that
> [Tom] would 'turn' and give us any information he
> had regarding the counterfeit drug manufacturing
> operation. . . . The Chief Inspector was introduced
> as my tight-fisted money man from out of town, [Mr.
> William Price]. Margaret Kreig, a writer authorized
> by the Food and Drug Administration to accompany us
> during the investigation, posed as his wife. . . .
> [Tom] was told that [Price] was engaged in a legiti-
> mate drug wholesale business and wanted nothing to
> do with this counterfeit business except to dis-
> tribute them. All contacts were supposed to be made
> through me in order to keep him clean.

The Chief Inspector and I, posing as Mr. and Mrs. Price, met
Wally and Tom in the airport bar. Tom was so well preserved
that he could afford to boast about his true age and soon did so.
In his mid-60's with silvery gray hair, he was deeply tanned and
looked years younger. He told me he'd been recuperating in

Florida from an operation on his inner ear. When I expressed interest in the operation, he began to go into detail. This gave the Chief Inspector the opportunity to assume his role of the "heavy" heartless member of the "turning" team; Wally, by asking friendly questions about Tom's convalescence, continued to play the "light" side.

"We're not here to discuss all that," "Price" interrupted, giving me an annoyed glance. "Let's get down to business."

Wally underscored "Price's" statements that he was an ethical drug wholesaler with a good reputation in his community and a great deal at stake. He was a high-volume dealer who was interested only in a continuing supply of specified drugs, not sporadic shipments. As a hard-headed businessman, "Price" dismissed Tom's frequent assurances that he had well-established laboratories in full production. "If that's true, why haven't you shown my man your plants, then?" Tom kept saying that for various reasons this had, so far, been impossible. When challenged, he insisted that, *of course*, he knew the locations—with uptown traffic the way it was this time of day, they were less than an hour away. The Bronx? Westchester? Across the bridge in New Jersey? He would have to make telephone calls before saying anything more. Price's parting shot was that since he would be investing upwards of $25,000 per week on a drug order, if his man couldn't see the main plant *today*, forget it!

Wally went with Tom to make the call. We didn't learn until later that "The Boss said 'nothing doing!' " Tom asked Wally to go along with the pretense that there would be a plant inspection, for the sake of hanging on to Price's business. He'd make it worth Wally's while. Wally agreed, and they lied to us when they returned.

"Price" decided to stay in town, in that case, to confer with Wally after he had inspected the plant. Tom offered to drop us off at a hotel, since his son, Buggsy, was waiting outside in a car. As we were walking out of the terminal, I chatted with Tom, giving Wally and the Chief Inspector a few moments to confer. They agreed to try to separate Tom from Buggsy in order to "turn" him. With some difficulty they persuaded Tom to ride with us in Wally's Barracuda. Buggsy went on to get the pills ready for delivery. Inspector Kerry Shore, in a car electronically equipped to pick up our conversation, drove behind us at a discreet distance.

The Chief Inspector had to stop and call FDA in Washington to check out the action he was about to take. We pulled over in front of a pharmacy. Showing his identification card to Tom, he said: "We are stopping here because my name is Clemens Westerly and I am an inspector from the Food and Drug Administration. I think you have a lot of things to tell us, and we have a lot of things to tell you. Now is the best time to talk about them."

Tom appeared to be stunned. He looked ill. The inspectors urged him to see a doctor, but he refused, and insisted that he knew the name of the drug he usually carried and the dosage. We all went into the drugstore where the pharmacist gave Tom a single dose of medication. Ironically, this drug counterfeiter had no more control over the source or quality of his medicine in an emergency than any other sick person.

In a few minutes Tom began to look much better, and insisted we go to a bar down the street for our talk.

I could see that neither FDA man relished the job he had to do, but Tom seemed to feel that Inspector Westerly had been conducting a personal vendetta against him, while Wally, forced to go along with it in order to hold his job, was, nevertheless, "on his side." Tom confided to Wally that the one thing he feared most was publicity about his sex-pills-pornography racket. He repeated several times that the women in his family must not be embarrassed because they were innocent bystanders. Wally reminded Tom that he was not under arrest, therefore crime reporters wouldn't know anything about the bust.

At the word "reporters," Tom became very agitated. While drinking his third straight Scotch, he charged that a newspaperwoman had "killed" his mother by "blowing things up all out of proportion" a few years earlier when family members were implicated in a crime. (I later learned that this crime had been a brutal kidnapping related to a murder that had made world headlines.) He complained that a crime reporter had destroyed his home, cost him over $50,000 in fees, and had caused his mother to die of a broken heart. "Law enforcers got a job to do, but there's no excuse for writers," he said. "I hate all writers."

Tom responded to the Chief Inspector's direct question on

what he knew about the drug-counterfeiting operation by saying he was just a salesman who bought and sold hard to move goods in the garment district. Why then had he pretended to know the location of the drug manufacturing plant? Just to build his image with Wally. He responded to questions about Mannie, Mauser, Chameleon, the Ph.D. chemist, and the doctor mentioned at Doc's by saying they were all engaged in legitimate businesses and professions: "He owns some kind of novelty factory. . . . He's a trucker, you know that. . . . Last I heard he's in machines, a distributor, I think. . . . He's doing research. . . . He's a physician, takes care of the sick. . . ."

The Chief Inspector excused himself to make a telephone call and Inspector Jackson got up saying he needed a pack of cigarettes from the machine. Tom leaned forward and warned me: "You better not be a writer!" I said nothing. But from that day to this I've experienced many moments of panic, when I thought I recognized Tom in faraway places—the lobby of the Principe e Savoia Hotel in Milan, for instance. Unlikely—or was it? During one period I could not write a word for weeks after being told by a Mafia expert: "These people bide their time, but they always get their revenge—even decades later." When Mr. Westerly said something about being lied to by experts, Tom retorted: "Look, Whiskers, you don't bother me. Your kind is a dime a dozen." Thrusting out his foot so we could see his custom-made shoes, he said, "What I got on my feet cost more than what you got on your back."

When the inspectors returned, Wally suggested that they go down to the FDA office first because talking there would be in Tom's best interest. The inspector made it clear that he couldn't promise any kind of immunity to Tom from prosecution of the crimes in which he had been involved. "The sentencing," he said, "is completely out of our hands. I don't want to build false hopes. But you ought to try to help yourself, Tom. I'll do all I can by explaining how you cooperated."

Tom whispered nervously: "Listen, I'm in with a lot of the Big Boys—I'm in a very ticklish spot here. But from you at least I get time. From them I get no time at all. . . . I won't sign an affidavit, understand. And I'll never take the stand. I won't say a word for the record. If I do they'll dump me in the river with my feet in cement or a slot machine around my neck." He repeated this during the hours to come. Each time he was told that he would not be forced to testify against himself, that he was *not* under arrest, and that he was free to leave. In fact, he was offered transportation home.

The Chief Inspector asked Tom about the last time he was at Mannie's house.

"I can't remember—maybe I was never there. These people you are always bringing up mean nothing to me."

Next question: Why does the chemist always go to the butcher-shop?

Tom jumped to his feet, angrily demanding that Buggsy be left out of this. He worked hard for a living. He had no record. It was a shame to drag honest businessmen into this and ruin them. Turning to Inspector Jackson, he said, "I'm gonna call him now." He was invited to make his call from the FDA office, if he wished. This caused him to explode into a declaration of his constitutional rights: he could call anyone he pleased, at any time or place.

The telephone happened to be next to the ladies' room. In passing, I heard him say, "Listen, it's all over. *Burn* the papers!"

The inspectors thought this warning could mean anything from taking back the "rented" cars to dismantling clandestine drug plants. They quickly discussed whether Tom was as "squeezable" as they had been told, for he seemed on the verge of taking off and they had no hold on him. Inspector Jackson said bitterly, "At *least* I'd like to get my hands on those millions of amphets—keep them off the street!" But the Chief Inspector pointed out that even if they could swing more buys through informants, the New York District's annual budget for illegal drug cases was already shot and there was virtually a whole year still to go. Washington might authorize a little more money to break up the counterfeiting ring, but for just another amphet buy, probably not. "We've got them on amphets now, anyway. Two buys of two tablets are as good as two million," he pointed out. (The large buys had been necessary to support Wally's cover story of supplying wholesalers with counterfeits.)

Inspector Jackson said wearily, "Any way you look at it, they are 'way ahead with that $12,000. Big profits and enough left over for lawyers' fees and bail bonds."

Returning to the table, Tom said he was ready to get it over with. Mr. Westerly called for the check, drew out enough money to pay for our coffee and a generous tip, then handed the check to Tom, who had consumed five Scotches by this time. "How *cheap* can you get, Westerly?" Tom said.

"You can afford to buy your own whisky," Clem Westerly replied.

We all drove to Manhattan. Tom insisted upon stopping at the mobster-owned supper club mentioned at Doc's, although it looked deserted at this hour. After a few minutes he emerged saying he wanted to eat lunch at a place in Chinatown. As we passed a well-known Hungarian restaurant on the Lower East Side, he observed, "That's for peasants!" He had told Wally of his childhood in this slum area—hardworking immigrant parents, a dozen mouths to feed, hand-me-down shoes with cardboard innersoles.

As Tom dined, the inspectors continued to question him. Wally asked about the "cut" Tom got. He said it was only $100 on each 100,000 tablets sold. When he learned that FDA had his arrest records, he said: "Last time I done time was over 20 years ago, a misdemeanor. Two-to-three. The union stepped in. I appealed the case. Let the record speak for itself. Some people used my name and office, I never knew what was going on." Tom said he was only a "leg man" and didn't even know who the real boss was. Mauser was only a go-between. As for the chemist who doctored up the moldy HydroDiuril, he said, "I don't know what that was all about, fact is, I wouldn't recognize that chemist again if I saw him." Wally wanted to know why the price on some tablets went from $1.65 per 1,000 to $7.00. Tom explained that the chemicals cost more. Who was making the chemicals for The Group? "Chemists who want the money, who else!" he said, laughing.

Whenever the Chief Inspector asked a question such as: "What's your connection with [Mafia member]?" Tom would clutch his chest and say, "What are you trying to do—you're gonna kill me with all this!"

Wednesday Afternoon, New York District Office:

After we entered FDA's office on the fringe of Greenwich Village, I was given some files to read while Inspector Jackson talked privately with Tom, and Mr. Westerly conferred with Supervisory Inspector Will Edmonds and a new informant on a fast-breaking facet of the counterfeiting case. Inspector Edmonds, in direct command of all undercover agents in the District, was, I knew, a much-decorated war hero with the nickname, "Wild Bill." He turned out a fantastic amount of work.

I read in an FDA brochure that inspectors must be able to perform arduous chores such as lifting cases or sacks weighing approximately 100 pounds, or climbing grain elevators 100 feet high. I had also seen disclaimers following FDA's annual statistics on drug violations and seizures: "This adds up to coverage of only a fraction of the foods and drugs bought by the American public and enforcement must therefore be selective." Just how selective —though back-breaking and nerve-shredding—was illustrated by the Chief Inspector's daily log of telephone calls. Here is a sampling:

Indiana drug salesman reported suspicious-looking drugs in store, could be counterfeit. Cancer specialist complained woman patient discontinued treatment to seek Krebiozen, fears she will die. Child hospitalized after chewing yard-long Jaquariti beans. A poison ant cup found in large jar of mustard. The U.S. Attorney advised that case against [prominent nutritionist] was ready for pre-trial hearings. Cheese labeled "whole milk" proved partly skim milk. Carload of tainted pork bellies—what to do? Query from drug company scientist on New Drug Application. Complaint from drug company officer who said: "An inspector is out here taking pictures of my equipment and procedures, how do I know he isn't a spy who will carry trade secrets to my competitors?" [Cameras are standard equipment, inspectors must support reports with photographs when indicated.] Order from Washington to seize a certain lot of wrinkle-remover immediately. Tip that a bartender had just received 250,000 pep pills. Collect all mailing pieces on [leading tranquilizer] immediately because contraindications are not adequate in medical journal ads. Call from angry physician—wanted to use drug he discovered on patients without prior testing since he is a Doctor of

Medicine. Threatened to write Dr. Frances O. Kelsey of the FDA Bureau of Medicine, his congressman, and others, because: "You sent your goon inspectors in here to harass me!" Note: send inspectors to monitor weekly forums on LSD in Greenwich Village nightclub and Town Hall lectures by ex-Harvard professors. Follow-up on information from Pharmaceutical Manufacturers Association that member-firm has received a series of amphetamine orders totaling millions from general practitioner in very small town. Query from *New York Times* reporter on student drug abuse. Texas hospital reported high incidence of chemical conjunctivitis in newborn from silver nitrate solution manufactured in this district. Consumer demanded that something be done about poisoned milk being delivered to her, claims police won't listen. Advertising agency wanted to know whether "grandfather clause" [pertaining to older drugs on market before new laws became effective] still stands if labeling has been changed recently. Recall [widely used drug] down to retail level immediately, dangerous to health. Smoked fish: botulism source.

San Marcos University, Lima, Peru, complained about ineffective test kits made here. Advise Marine Corps that contaminated tuna from Cherry Point, N.C., killed lab mice in test. Omaha Hospital detected wrong label on intravenous solution. Another shipment of aspirin contaminated with penicillin. [Still another Congressman] has scheduled full-scale hearings on FDA, submit reports immediately. Major drug company demanded to know why they are being asked to cite *all* adverse reactions to a drug while competitors only report on kidney and liver damage. FDA's resident inspector in Puerto Rico called about love potions imported from Honduras. Unsterile hypodermic needles, sample all lots. Seize misbranded Zen macrobiotic foods, cultist died of starvation. Counterfeit Arpege case ready. Water repellant [X] highly flammable, lacks consumer protection information required by Act. Prophylactics manufactured by [X] Company defective, contained holes. Vibrating chairs, sold with inadequate directions for use in treatment of arthritis. Explosive cracker balls from Taiwan caused serious facial injuries—children thought they were bubble gum. Plastic ice balls for cooling drinks made in Orient contained polluted water. Men's magazine urged readers to put page in four ounces of *methyl* alcohol and drink it to get the hallucinogenic effect of an additive used in the printing ink. [Ingestion of methyl (wood) alcohol can lead to blindness and death.] Salmonella in powdered milk.

For each of these, and hundreds of calls like them, some action had to be taken by the Chief Inspector picking up the phone. Mr. Westerly had five telephone lines, but no private secretary.

Consumer protection by FDA costs American taxpayers annually about 19 cents per person. I glanced around that dreary government office: chunks of plaster had fallen from the walls, paint was scaling off in ugly patches, and there were toe-tripping potholes in the cracked floor. At the end of a long corridor men and women in white coats worked in a cluttered laboratory; I hoped that the stringent economizing on office decor did not mean that they were obliged "to make do" with worn out scientific equipment.

Every day FDA makes hundreds of critical decisions, many a matter of life or death for American consumers. Yet working conditions in this busiest of all districts were intolerable: 67 inspectors' desks were jammed together in two rooms with scarcely enough space to walk between them. There was not a single empty place. Off and on for 18 months I was to work at the cleared-off end of the Chief Inspector's desk, surrounded by stacks of file folders, reference manuals, typewriter, collected drug samples in bags, bottles, and cans. Inspectors on all sides were dictating reports into machines. A quarter-inch layer of black grit sifted in around the loose window frames every night. The view of the Hudson River was obscured by a layer of grime on the window panes.

Still somehow, there was great *esprit de corps*. Despite the fact that a confidential personnel survey had recently shown that half of all FDA employees (a force of 4,000) had contemplated leaving the agency during the past year, this small band of men reminded me of a poor but cheerful family unit. Chief Inspector Clemens Westerly would say, "So we've got a lemon, let's make lemonade!" On his personal bookshelf I saw an illustrated volume, *The Confederate Navy*, and Russell's *Frontier Rifles*. In many ways, it was that kind of an outfit. The odds were tremendous . . . the spirits courageous.

The workload was heavy: in my first four days in the District I observed that Mr. Westerly put in 35 hours of overtime on the drug-counterfeiting case, alone. The FDA Commissioner had

pointed out that illegal prescription-drug work accounted for
only a small part of FDA's duties. In the previous fiscal year, in
the entire country only 56 inspector man-years out of a total
inspector force of 687 man-years had been devoted to the investigation of drug counterfeiting and mass diversion of dangerous
drugs.

In the New York District, about 61 percent of the time was
devoted to drugs, 34 to foods, and 5 to hazardous substances like
inflammables. About 7 percent of the drug time was allocated to
counterfeiting, illegal distribution, and investigating New Drug
Applications from legitimate manufacturers. Most major pharmaceutical manufacturers are located in New York, New Jersey,
and Pennsylvania, and here, too, is the heaviest concentration of
smaller drug plants. The Chief Inspector told me: "Out of our
available inspector 'man-years' about 3 are devoted to 'over-the-
counter' illegal sales of prescription drugs and counterfeiting. We
call this 'OTC' work."

When I protested that the equivalent of three inspectors seemed
woefully inadequate, I was shown a tabulating machine card
listing code numbers for 39 projects including: beverages, grains,
eggs, meats, pesticides, food storage, radioactivity in foods, medical lecturers, medicated feeds, and so on, in addition to "Code 40
—Improper Sale of Rx Legend Drugs," the OTC category. That
month the District was ordered to concentrate on cheese factories,
food warehouse inspections, and also to corroborate the number
of peanuts in peanut butter because of a big "to-do" in Washington. Most of the Administration's time in the past had been
devoted to foods because many more foods are processed than
drugs. But the 1962 Drug Amendments caused the ratio to
change. Now, more time is spent on new and experimental drugs
and on pesticide residues on foods.

While I was in the office, the annual tea-tasting session was
going on, as required by the Import Tea Act of 1897. Inspectors
were also supposed to check butter pats in restaurants to make
sure they weren't margarine. Washington, however, did not deem
the LSD threat sufficiently important to require a formal investigation. In the entire country's FDA inspector force, there were
fewer than a dozen experienced, well-trained undercover agents
like Wally Jackson. (I was to see one resign in disgust after spend-

ing all of his evenings and weekends for most of a year following-up on cases of severe bad reactions after LSD use. He felt the problem was getting out of control, but despaired of anything being done about it.) Lack of official backing for FDA in those days went right to Capitol Hill. The New York District could have used 100 additional undercover agents on illicit drug leads alone—yet Congress refused to increase FDA's entire force by even *one* inspector!

Instead, during Congressional hearings that session it was charged that FDA men are "Storm troopers, Gestapo agents, who violate the privacy* of *decent, upstanding citizens* with the use of their insidious electronic devices. . . ." A former governor told Senators:

> If these misguided, inept and incompetent FDA functionaries persist in their criminal conspiracy and loathsome vendetta against my clients [he represented producers of an infant food that proved low in protein] . . . I intend to file civil damage suits against each of the FDA conspirators from top to bottom. . . . Personal civil damage suits will force the FDA master spies to employ their own personal lawyers at their own expense. . . . If American citizens were supplied antibugging devices . . . when the FDA James Bond master spies set out to frame businessmen, the secret electronic equipment of the agents would be immunized and made ineffective.

From the files I learned about some of the "decent, upstanding citizens" under investigation. A New Jersey pharmacist bought counterfeits very cheaply from a seller who explained the low price was possible because the active ingredient came from "sweepings" in a larger drug plant. Counterfeit thyroid tested 50 percent subpotent. Illicit HydroDiuril was 27 percent below declared strength. Counterfeit Miltown took 2 hours, 52 minutes to dissolve when it should require less than 30 minutes. A scavenger was reworking and rebottling drugs salvaged from broken bottles. In addition to the peril from glass particles, his premises were filthy.

---

*FDA scrupulously observed the President's ban against wiretapping and used electronic equipment within the legal limits defined by the Supreme Court: "Only to obtain the most reliable evidence possible of a conversation in which the Government's own agent was participant and which that agent was fully entitled to disclose." (Lopez v. U.S., 373 U.S. 427 [1963], p. 439.)

Another cover story offered by counterfeiters to pharmacists: "These drugs are so popular that the patent-holders can't supply the demand, therefore they have asked us to help them out by manufacturing additional stocks." A pharmacist who became suspicious because a tablet had ragged edges, analyzed it and found that it contained no "tracer"—an inactive ingredient used by some drug producers to identify their own products. When he complained to the seller, who happened to be an "enforcer" for the mob working with Mauser, he was told: "Pay up or we'll throw you down the basement stairs!" A counterfeit drug plant, operating as a legitimate generic producer by day, had been inspected five times, but FDA could find no evidence to prove these drugs were being sold in interstate commerce, which is its jurisdiction. The plant, by the way, also had been inspected by a joint Army-Navy Medical Purchasing Service and the owner said they had given his company approval but that he had not yet entered bids. The company subsequently went out of business after state health inspectors declared the premises were filthy.

A former Congressman, serving as an attorney for one of the defendants in a drug counterfeiting case, called on FDA and made threatening references to a grand jury investigation. The crooks were indicted, but didn't go to jail. Interestingly enough, the grand jury handed down a presentment against the Chief Inspector, the District Director, and the Secretary of the State Board of Pharmacy because they "had for too long permitted drug counterfeiting to continue unfettered."

There was evidence of friction between local and federal agencies and between various federal law enforcement bureaus. For instance, this tape-recorded conversation between a pharmacist and a counterfeiter:

FDA and the state boys got sore at each other. FDA said, You ruined our case, we had these guys dead to rights. They said, What the hell were you holding back for, why didn't you give us all the information so we'd know what to do? You just gave us part of the story, you made us look stupid. They had a fight. In fact, things haven't been right ever since.

In his 15-minute testimony before the county grand jury, Mr.

Westerly had said: "It is axiomatic that the fewer number of individuals who know of a confidential investigation, the less likely the compromising of that investigation. . . ." I was interested to see that one of the lawyers defending a notorious counterfeiter had recently been an Assistant U.S. Attorney. Also, a letter from another government prosecutor then working on counterfeit cases contained the phrase: "I don't know how long I'll continue in this position." Shortly thereafter he left for private practice.

Before tackling a file of complaint letters, I went in search of a drinking fountain. On the desk of a very young-looking inspector I saw the hand-lettered sign, MY WORK IS SO SECRET EVEN I DON'T KNOW WHAT I'M DOING. I was beginning to feel like a CIA agent in Peking, as I was told to go *straight* down the hall and all eyes seemed to be following me to make sure I didn't open any Bluebeard's closets. Later I learned why they were afraid I might open the wrong door:

FDA is responsible for regulating "therapeutic devices." The wildest inventions of Rube Goldberg pale beside some of the contraptions FDA inspectors are required to collect, test, and store. They didn't want me to stumble upon their official samples of potency restorers, artificial male sex organs, and bosom developers that operate on the vacuum principle, à la "the plumber's friend."

There were letters from Congressmen demanding action on the counterfeit drug threat, but some of the most moving documents came from ordinary citizens. For instance, a mother wrote:

I have a neurologically disturbed youngster who needs tranquilizers for her illness and a younger child with a metabolic problem. I'm sure you realize I consider these medications of considerable importance. I'd appreciate knowing as soon as possible whether the following drugs are ever counterfeited: Thorazine, Stelazine, Cytamel, and Dexamyl?

A lawyer wrote:

Several members of my family have chronic ailments for which they take medication regularly and we have been sending prescriptions to this [catalog enclosed] mail order firm in order to cut costs. We use the following and are concerned that they may not be the standardized drugs our doctors have ordered: Coumadin, Benadryl, Seconal, Miltown.

In the same file was a memo on a telephone call received by FDA from a mail order distributor's lawyer:

What's the deal? Why are you singling out my client to the exclusion of all others with your libelous newspaper releases? [Clipping stated client distributed counterfeit drugs.] My client has been in business for over [quarter of a century]. Just because he's trying to give the public a break by lowering prices, you are hounding him. It's a conspiracy of the local, state, and Federal retail drug associations to make him raise his prices, that's what it is, and you are going along with them. I'll tell you what, we are going to get another injunction to force *you* to leave us alone. [This man was notoriously "injunction happy," having successfully prevented the State Board of Pharmacy from trying to keep him from advertising cut-rate prescription drugs.]

A marginal note on the typed memo stated: "He discounts prescriptions up to 50 percent lower than most retailers. . . . He says while prescriptions make up only 25 percent of sales in the average retail pharmacy, they account for over 50 percent of the profits." In addition to prescriptions, sundries, and physician's supplies, the same man advertised mail-order diamonds for up to $3,000. With pharmacies and jewelry stores in every neighborhood, some people apparently are still willing to buy life-saving drugs and expensive jewels sight unseen.

The tip-off on one counterfeiting case was an anonymous letter, sent to Smith Kline, & French Board Chairman Walter A. Munns, which said: "I think there are bogus labels for drugs being printed in this city by the thousands."

A *New York Times* clipping, captioned MILLIONS OF FAKE DEXEDRINE PILLS SOLD, said that these had been dispensed on doctors' prescriptions in good faith at pharmacies across the country.

A letter from an FDA official to the Secretary of the Department of Health, Education, and Welfare (HEW) outlined methods for handling complaints:

We informed inquirers that because we knew very little about the conditions under which the counterfeit tablets had been produced we could not give any assurances that every tablet was as pure and potent as it should be. We advised that the use of any tablets purchased on prescription from [named counterfeit retail outlets] was a matter for the purchaser to decide for himself on the basis of his own judgment. We suggested, too, that he consult his physician for advice. . . . We are planning to issue a press release on the general subject of counterfeit drugs after we have gathered sufficient information to give us a reliable picture of the nature and extent of the counterfeit problem.

The subsequent press release was no more helpful than the "use your own judgment—see your doctor" advice in the official letter. Clearly, consumer protection in this vital area was faulty. I was beginning to understand some of the reasons, but as for *excuses?* Chief Inspector Westerly summed up the situation when I asked whether he was guilty as charged* in the grand jury presentment:

"Yes, we must find a way to stop this thing—there's no *excuse* for it!"

That night after finishing with the files, I rode with Inspector Westerly and Jackson as they drove Tom to his suburban home. He complained that after all the questioning he would have trouble sleeping. Wally suggested that he might take one of the many pills he and his cohorts manufactured. Tom replied: "I wouldn't touch *any* of that stuff!"

Thursday, District Office:

The next day while the Chief Inspector was frantically calling Washington and the local U.S. Attorney's office, trying to obtain search and arrest warrants against members of The Group, I looked through clippings on crimes committed all over the United States by murderers, rapists, and other violent persons under the influence of amphetamines, barbiturates, or drug mixtures.

By day's end, Mr. Westerly had not been able to communicate the urgency of the situation to various government attorneys. Part of the problem: drug counterfeiting is only a misdemeanor. The local U.S. Attorney was involved in spy trials and other national security threats; and who could blame him for not putting a high priority on something called "misbranding"?

---

*In fairness, I think it should have been noted by the grand jury that he had recently transferred from the Midwest to the New York District and had become Chief Inspector only two months before the presentment.

Friday, FDA Resident Inspector's Office outside New York:

> No warrants shall issue but upon probable cause, supported by
> oath or affirmation, and particularly describing the place to be
> searched and the persons or things to be seized. . . . No person shall
> be held to answer for . . . an infamous crime unless on a present-
> ment or indictment of a grand jury. . . .—From *the Bill of Rights.*

During this day—that shall always be Black Friday—I tried to
keep in mind Constitutional civil liberties, and balance these
against the duty FDA inspectors had to enforce the public protection laws passed by Congress. For eight hours I witnessed a struggle
waged largely in a basement of a Federal building—the FDA
resident inspector's quarters in a nearby state. When I arrived
that morning, a darkly handsome young man—Food and Drug
Officer Tony Magnus, a law student by night—was on the phone
pleading with an attorney in the Department of Health, Education, and Welfare in Washington. FDA has no separate legal staff
to handle its complicated cases. It must use HEW's General
Counsel.

"Don't you understand," Tony was saying. "We want to file on
complaint, not information. And we don't want to leave it just a
misdemeanor. We can show conspiracy to defraud; it'll be a
felony, then. (*long pause*) But don't you see, we *must* arrest these
guys today—we have to search the premises. . . . I know, but informants tell us that they have already dumped some of the stuff.
. . . Look, this is *Friday.* Monday's a holiday. If we have to wait
'til Tuesday to get the papers, forget it, we've had it!"

The legality of the proposed arrests and searches was still being
questioned, although many buys of illicit drugs had been made,
and surveillants had seen drugs being carried from Mannie's home
and from the butcher-shop by various members of The Group.

The premises to be searched had to be described, the time of
the search specified, and so on. Yet these individuals habitually
ran their operations at odd hours. One discussion centered on
whether certain butcher-shop products were sold on Saturday and
Sunday. If not, would anyone be at the butcher-shop on Friday
night? A young Assistant U.S. Attorney had come down from his
office on the fifth floor to "walk the papers through." He com-

mented: "If these people are also selling rotten eggs, can you *really* expect them to observe the Sabbath!" But an inspector pointed out that some of The Group's "respectability cover" included going to temple and to church.

A search warrant for Mannie's house finally was typed by an extremely nervous secretary who feared a typo would invalidate the document. An hour was lost while the county line running across Mannie's property was verified. As the afternoon wore on, however, there was a feeling that despite the obstacles of working with an archaic drug law and no FDA police powers, The Group would be bagged before sundown.

Tom, brought in by Inspector Jackson, was not asked to make a sworn statement because they didn't want to "burn him." Tom insisted that he had not tipped off other Group members, but an informant phoned in word that one of the chemists said, "The Big Boy's driver was picked up for questioning Wednesday, then kicked loose."

Friday, 4 P.M.:

Inspectors Westerly, Jackson, a U.S. Marshal, Tom, and I drove to another building for Tom's arraignment before a U.S. Commissioner there. We were stunned when the Commissioner said that he could not be arrested, there were not sufficient grounds. Tom, perhaps, was most incredulous of all: "You mean I'm *not* under arrest? Are you sure? It's not some kind of trick, is it?" Tom remained suspicious and tagged along when we returned to the FDA residency office, where the 22 inspectors waiting to go out on the arrests were dumbfounded by the news. The secretary looked as if she were going to cry. The Chief Inspector told her "I want you to know that those papers you typed were perfect." He then picked up the phone and began trying to salvage the case. Inspector Jackson worked off his frustration by pacing up and down as he described the consequences of the illicit amphetamine traffic.

A man in the Midwest had been eating Bennies like peanuts at the racetrack and developed a paranoid-type psychosis. When he returned home, he flew into a rage, grabbed his two-month-old baby as a shield, and began firing a gun out the front window.

His wife, with their five-year-old clinging to her skirts, tried to take the baby from him, saying, "Use me, instead." The man stabbed her with a kitchen knife, puncturing her lung. He also cut the infant's neck in several places. When the police arrived, they found the man on top of the woman, repeatedly inserting the knife in the wound he had made in her chest. He told police he was very glad to see them because he needed protection from "Enemies who were trying to get him."

On another case, Inspector Jackson described meeting Eddie, a heist man, who usually carried no less than $20,000 on his person. While on a drug binge, he shot one man and stabbed another, but is still at large. He told Wally: "I'm nothin' and know it, but when I take a shot of chicken powder [amphetamine sulfate] I can stand alongside the best in the business and feel ten feet tall!"

Hoodlums get kicks from picking up "straight girls," who are not involved in crime. By shaking amphetamine in large doses into mixed drinks (the powder won't dissolve completely), they use the powerful stimulant to get the girls to "do anything." Researchers who have studied male amphetamine abusers—especially those who use "splash," the injectable form of the drug—have reported that the "jolt" produces weird orgasmic fantasies.

Chronic users become emaciated, as the continuous hyperstimulation, loss of sleep, and lack of appetite take their toll. Serious mental illness can follow. A successful commercial photographer deteriorated to the point where an agent found him sitting in his bed wrapped like a mummy in a cocoon of hundreds of women's stockings. He had inserted various tubes into his body's orifices. "The poor guy was completely flipped out," I was told. "He's still in a mental hospital under intensive therapy."

The threat inherent in The Group's continued illicit manufacture of amphetamine—as well as their counterfeiting of other drugs—was so obvious I could not understand why HEW's General Counsel and the Department of Justice had changed their minds about going ahead with the arrests.

Tom, obviously as bewildered as I, eventually drifted out of the office. No doubt he told The Group that opening up the Northwest territory's clandestine drug plants was "a cinch."

The following Wednesday:

Now, five days later, racketeers of "soldier" rank in one of the area's Mafia families called a "sit down." The purpose of the meeting: to arrange "a contract" on Inspector Wally Jackson's life.

Thursday:

This information was immediately conveyed to Washington by Chief Inspector Westerly. One of the very few warrants in the history of FDA was finally approved, but it had taken the planned assassination by hired killers of an unarmed inspector to convince officials that the New York District could not employ the customary civil action (the use of a libel)* to seize The Group's contraband drugs.

Inspector Jackson left for his Western District, collected his family, and departed for parts unknown. At his own expense, of course. A short time later, he began working undercover in another FDA District.

Narcotics agents, familiar with The Group's record for violence, urged me to assume a new identity. I moved to Greenwich Village and continued working with FDA undercover inspectors, whose first order of business was the rounding up of The Group and simultaneous "inspections" of Mannie's house and Buggsy's butcher-shop.

*See chart, Appendix D, FDA Legal Procedures.

CHAPTER THREE

The "Stash"

From Chief Inspector Westerly's Affidavit for a Search Warrant:

United States of America v. Brick Ranch House . . .
Confidential Informant A has informed me that in
this house he was given a bottle of counterfeit,
and, therefore, misbranded HydroDiuril tablets.
. . . Confidential Informant B, known in the past to
be reliable, telephoned [Mannie's house] and purchased a quantity of counterfeit drugs to be delivered at [Midwest warehouse]. Later, these drugs
were seized . . . an analysis reflected that they
were counterfeit Dexedrine. . . . Confidential Informant C, acting in an undercover capacity observed [Mannie] depart from his residence carrying
a container similar in appearance, shape, and size
to those cardboard containers sold to Agents, as
described aforesaid. . . . From my experience, from
the information supplied to me, and from my own personal knowledge and observations, I believe that
there is presently concealed and secreted at the
premises for which this Search Warrant is sought
. . . drugs, drug manufacturing and drug handling
equipment, and other paraphernalia relating to the
manufacturing, packaging and distribution of drugs,
in violation of the Federal Food, Drug and Cosmetic
Act, Title 21, United States Code, Sections 331 (a)

and 352. WHEREFORE, this Deponent prays that the
necessary Search Warrant be issued authorizing the
United States Marshal . . . or any of his deputies
. . . to enter and search for and seize the afore-
mentioned. . . .

It had taken one week for the Justice Department to issue the
search warrant on Mannie's residence in a Westchester suburb.
One entire morning was consumed in just trying to round up a
United States Marshal's "authorized deputy" to assist FDA in
serving the warrant.

Now it was Friday, high noon. A week earlier, I had thought I
would never again see such maddening delays, but once again, we
were stalemated. We *had* the papers: the search warrant and the
information to support the arrest warrants, signed by the U.S.
Attorney. But there was no U.S. Marshal free to serve them. Some
were ill, others had gone to lunch, and the few remaining were
tied up on another FDA case involving vitamins and a nutritionist.

The principal members of The Group had to be arrested before
Mannie's house was searched. The search must be made before
sundown, according to the warrant, which was now a matter of
public record. If the counterfeiters were not immediately apprehended, they would probably destroy all the remaining evidence.

The Chief Inspector was in contact with the FDR detective
agency, which was still serving as a message center. Their radio
transmitter, located in the mountains, could broadcast for many
miles. Inspectors, who were keeping Mannie and Buggsy under
surveillance, reported back frequently. (Tom had disappeared.)
We didn't know whether he had fled in fear of his life, or was
now at the bottom of the East River with a juke box around his
neck, for failing to observe *Omertà*, the humble silence.

An undercover man stationed in an attic next to Mannie's
reported that there were two children alone in the house; the
oldest had been kept home from school to care for the youngest
while Mannie and his wife went to the novelty factory. No one
had anticipated this development.

More and more clandestine drug operations were taking place
in private homes because the criminals know that it is much more
difficult to serve search and seizure papers on such premises. Aside
from constitutional rights to personal privacy, there is the un-

written law of sanctity of the home and protection of innocents.

Inspectors stood around glumly, clutching their cameras and other equipment, ready to go at a moment's notice. Time was running out; not just for today, but perhaps forever, on this case. One of these men, Inspector Oscar Cohen, must have been thinking of the years he had spent tracking the wily ringleader, Chameleon.

Then the Chief Inspector entered with a U.S. Deputy Marshal. He had a gun tucked in his belt, was swinging a pair of handcuffs, and very shortly set off on an extremely difficult assignment: arresting two men, first, one in Lower Manhattan; then, the other in the Bronx; bringing them before U.S. Commissioners; and finally executing the search warrant up in Westchester County— all to be accomplished consecutively and before sundown.

After the Marshal left, we all jumped into unmarked government cars and sped off toward our respective destinations. The car I was in went directly to the most centrally located Commissioner in the area. On the way, we heard over the radio that Buggsy had been arrested, and was being brought in from the butcher shop. After setting him free immediately on a $5,000 bond, the Commissioner turned to the Chief Inspector and me and suggested that we drive into the country for a late lunch at his club. It was now 2 P.M., and the U.S. Marshal was speeding to arrest Mannie at his factory.

After we begged off, I asked the Chief Inspector if the Commissioner was in league with them.

"No—no, he's just trying to be gracious. Search warrants are everyday routine to him. Not that he thinks this case is *unim*portant. He just doesn't comprehend the urgency of the situation —like the Commissioner last week who didn't want to issue the arrest warrant for Tom."

Meanwhile, Mannie was arrested.

A few days later, he described what happened to a friend:

"I got a call at the factory from [Buggsy], so I knew already they were comin' for me. Where am I gonna run? They were gonna put me on a $25,000 bail; I had to do a fuckin' lot of talkin' to get $5,000. A Deputy Marshal and a Food and Drug showed their credentials, 'You're under arrest.' The guy went for his handcuffs. I says, 'Just a minute—did I kill anybody? Why the handcuffs? I've got a business going here. People are gonna see all this!' He gives me a little push and says, 'Let's go.' So I told him, 'I don't want to be nasty with you guys, but you're supposed to be nice, too. I want to speak with my wife, is it too much to ask for two minutes?' So I told her to get a lawyer, quick. When I come out, here's Food and Drug takin' my picture, so I covered my face. They didn't even search the fuckin' factory, they had me so well tabbed. A week before I got busted, I had a plant there. I removed all the stuff, but the guy didn't take it all away, so I had to keep some in the house. I'm kickin' my ass all over. If they'd found nothin' in my house, they'd have been in plenty of trouble, brother. I'd slap a nice suit on them—the kids, the embarrassment, and everythin' else."

By the time Mannie's arrest was over, another U.S. Marshal accompanied us to a rendezvous point a block away from Mannie's house. While we waited there for Mannie and his arresting party to arrive from the factory, a neighbor became suspicious of us and called the police. (They arrived an hour later during the FDA inspection and permitted Mannie to keep all of his guns.)

When Mannie and the U.S. Marshal who had arrested him appeared, our car pulled up in front of Mannie's house, followed by several other cars belonging to FDA inspectors and to the State Department of Health. There were now a dozen people involved in the investigation. The inspectors went with Mannie, while I remained in the car with the recording equipment.

As soon as he reached the door, the Chief Inspector asked Mannie whether he wanted to send his family away. He did not. "Very well, then," Westerly said. "Let's get down to business. You've been through things like this in the past and you must know that you can make it easy on yourself or you can make it very difficult. We know you've got the stuff and we are going to find it."

"You gotta search warrant, so search!" said Mannie.

A few days later he told his friend: "I said to [Westerly]: 'You know what *you're* doin?' He says, 'Oh, we know what we're doing. The question is, do *you* know what *you're* doing?' Then he says, 'You better tell us where it is because we know you've got it.' I told them to go get it, then."

Although FDA had learned of the location of a secret room

from several sources, its existence had not been mentioned in the warrant because the Chief Inspector did not want to "burn" the informants. An "accidental" discovery was needed. Food and Drug Officer Tony Magnus pretended to stumble in the garage, falling heavily against a large pegboard holding tools. This actually was a door. Behind it, a room about 30-feet long and 15-feet wide had been dug out of the small hill backing up the far end of the garage.

Among the excited band of spectators gathered in the driveway was an irate, plump woman, who said she had asked Mannie a couple of years ago, "Where is all that dirt coming from?" He told her he was going to install a sauna bath to help with his weight-reduction program. When she later asked him to let her try the sauna, he told her that it wasn't ready yet. Another, more discreet neighbor was removing the organdy criss-cross curtains obscuring the view from her picture window across the street. She settled down with her knitting in a ringside seat. Dogs were being walked to the point of their owners' exhaustion up and down in front of Mannie's house. Two little girls set up a Monopoly game on his front steps. I would not have been surprised to see a lemonade stand go up next.

The Chief Inspector and his men must have been sweltering inside the secret room, because its only ventilation came through the tiny holes in the pegboard door. Finally, they left it open, and I saw a very strange scene: what appeared to be millions of capsules and tablets in bottles, plastic bags, and cardboard boxes. Drums of powdery chemicals. Parts of machinery for pharmaceutical manufacturing, including counterfeit punches and dies. It took over five hours to complete the inventory of about 60 separate items, and three trucks to haul it away for storage under lock and key.

An earlier "sanitary inspection" of Buggsy's butcher shop had turned up only one piece of evidence: a partially mutilated Dexedrine Spansule wedged in a floor crack. (Laboratory analysis later proved this to be a counterfeit.) If, as some believe, a drug manufacturing plant was operating in the butcher shop, Buggsy must have had the help of Mauser's men and trucks in a blitz evacuation. The question was, when? The butcher shop had been under almost continuous observation.

Mannie's place was obviously just a "stash." Although the dollar value of the materials confiscated was estimated to be around a million, this was secondary to the many vital clues unearthed. The men commented upon these as they called out their descriptions of specific items for the Chief Inspector, who was writing the inventory list. There were references to older, still-unsolved cases of counterfeiting, patent piracy, raw material smuggling, hijacking and other black-marketeering. In the year to come, the full implications of random items such as the following were made quite clear to me:

Item 1. "Green plastic pail half-full of brown and clear capsules, bearing marks 'SKF'," Inspector Oscar Cohen called out. While writing this down, Mr. Westerly said, "They just found an electronic capsule counter up in the attic. . . ."

Item 2. "Small wooden barrel. Hey, these are Lilly's Seconals. Their bullet-shaped capsules! Are they counterfeiting *these* now?" Someone else said, "Don't you remember, [Mannie] said he might be able to blunt the ends of regular capsules with heat and get the bullet-shape? . . ."

Item 7. "Cardboard Canadian Club Whiskey carton containing 17 empty, topless bottles labeled 'Dexedrine Spansule, 15 mg., 250 capsules; 2 bottles, control numbers scratched off; 3/1,000 tablet bottles labeled Hospital Supply Co. That's the fictitious firm [Mannie and Chameleon] set up. These empty bottles are filthy inside. Oh, look at this mess! . . ."

Item 32. "Cardboard carton containing 5 paper bags holding approximately 1,000 small yellow tablets engraved 'Ciba'; and numerous paper bags of soupy, water-logged unidentified tablets. . . ."

Item 38. "One fiber drum (50 kilos) labeled 'Made in Italy', bearing damaged air freight sticker. Full of white powder. . . . Better just list this as an 'unidentified powder 'til we can get it analyzed. . . ."

One of Mannie's younger children came to the doorway of the room and could be heard asking, "What is that, Mister?" An inspector answered, "I don't know. What do you think it is?" Later, the child said, "I was in there lots of times." The inspector remarked he'd hate to think of what would have happened had the children decided to play doctor in there!

Every scrap of waste paper was collected and cataloged; the floor was carefully swept, and the sweepings became *"Item 47."* The last entry in the inventory, *"Item 56,"* consisted of two small jars, each containing a live cockroach captured in the room.

MANNIE (*complaining later to a friend*): Can you imagine these jerk-offs selling to Food and Drug and bringing them down on my house, where they took pictures of me and my wife loading the stuff into the car? To top it off, they got the Board of Health up and took out two jars of live waterbugs. They said they were cock-a roaches! Cock *those* cock-a-roaches! They did everything they could . . . to make it look like a dirty plant with rats and roaches and stuff like that. . . . And now, because of all that, we've got trouble with the tavern, the ABC [Alcoholic Beverage Control] boys. That guy they picked up, [Tom] *he* saw the room where I had it.

FRIEND: I never heard that name before. Are you sure it wasn't Big Hamook [Chameleon]?

MANNIE: *He* couldn't afford to squeal. He's burying *himself* if he opens up, some of those were his punches from his old plant they took. They took $10,000 worth of tools out of here alone. Like the Food and Drug guy said, "Boy, you got to be good to get punches like these today!" Well, I get around. . . .

Mannie explained that he sat down and analyzed the whole thing and, while several others knew of the room, he is fairly sure [Tom] was the one who squealed:

This is the same little sucker I turned a deal down to a year ago—a $65,000 deal—a hundred cases each of Dexedrine and Dexamyl. I told him to his face I didn't like the way he did business. [Chameleon] brought in the guy, but, even so, I knew in my mind it was going to be a heist job. He was gonna hijack it. I've been around a long time. I decided only to bring $15,000 worth to hijack, but he didn't go for that deal—the $15,000 first.

FRIEND: Jesus! He can't be no piker, though, wanting 200 cases!

MANNIE: That was nothing. I've sold guys 200 cases and got the money in two days, half on delivery, half a day later. A guy gave me an order for half-a-million dollars—before all that shit broke with the Midwest case. He wanted a million of Miltown, a million of Serpasil, two million of HydroDiuril, half-a-million of Nembutal, and a few other items. Said it was going out of the country, Cuba, South America, I don't know where. This guy's a big dealer, been in more trouble with the law than I'll ever be. I seen him chase 'em [FDA] out of his place. "You can't look at my plant, you can't search," the guy said. Called his lawyer. I was sittin right there, heard everything. I'd just delivered him a hundred cases that week. He didn't keep it there, sent it to a wholesaler. This one guy alone, if this trouble wouldn't have come . . . who knows . . . five million dollars a year I could do with this *one* guy.

Mannie brooded for a few minutes, then explained:

When I saw [Tom] in on this deal, I said "What's that fuckin' monkey doin'?" They said, "Don't worry." *I* worry about *everybody*. He was in trouble [with the law]. They told him, "You give us this guy and we'll lift the weight off you." So he turned me over. If he thinks he's gonna walk out of this! I'll do my time, then when I come back in six months—I'm like an elephant, see? I'll never forget that I hadda do

time for this prick—after I come back, he ain't
gonna be 'round no more. *This* I can promise
you!

Revenge was a recurrent theme in Mannie's conversations during the next year. Six months after the raid, he was in financial
difficulty trying to collect several thousand dollars from the president of a small drug company—his deposit on some generic
capsules ordered, but never delivered.

Mannie let it be known that others who had let him take
various raps for them would "get their legs shot off and find
themselves walking on bloody stumps." As he told and retold the
story of his arrest, the number of men required to "take him"
grew.

> They were following me for months, hiding
> around my house and one guy even fell out of
> a tree. But [Chameleon] laughed and said *I* had
> hallucinations! Why the Hell do *I* have twenty-
> six guys, seven cars? The boss of Food and Drug,
> that [Westerly] was there from five o'clock to
> quarter to eleven. Took away that good electric
> counter, a $4,000 machine. I shoulda listened to
> my wife. She told me to put it in the attic, we
> got two attics. One they woulda never found.
> See, when you go in with a warrant to search
> a man's *home*, you've *got* to find what it says
> there. When you don't, you're in trouble! . . .
> There were a couple of guys I suspected of
> squealin'. One was a guy mixed up with those
> people stole that stuff from Lederle a coupla
> years ago. He was in my house. And a guy who's
> doin' time in the can, now. Got caught with
> junk and got five years. He had the contacts,
> imported stuff from Italy. Raw materials, stuff
> in the drums. They were all in my house, saw
> the room when they checked some powder for
> me. But I'll stake my life none of them squealed.
> It was that little rat bastard that sold—that *tried*
> to sell— Orinase to the Food and Drug from

out West. I shoulda stomped his fuckin head
open when I had him!

Mannie's recap of the background leading up to the raid shows
how hard some professional criminals work and worry:

> I was supposed to meet [Tom and Buggsy] down
> at the Diner. I knew Food and **Drug** were
> watchin the house—do I hafta tell you I couldn't
> get the stuff outta the secret room? I had other
> spots. So, I went there and got about 150 bottles.
> I hadda leave at four in the morning because I
> hadda be careful about people followin' me.
> Jeez! I got stuck for ten seconds and died a
> thousand deaths! I see two guys and I think,
> Oh! They got me in this fuckin' place and I
> can't get out! But they were just stoppin' to
> light a cigarette. Now it's five-thirty and my
> appointment is twelve noon, so I'm ridin
> around all this time with this shit in the car
> and can't stop. They weren't there. 12:30 they
> didn't show. Finally this [Buggsy] comes up and
> I'm so mad I say, "I don't wait this kind of time
> for nobody—you—the Pope—or the King of
> England! I'm loaded with a stick of dynamite.
> They're watchin my house. I bust my balls to
> make sure I don't get a tail, and *you* guys keep
> me waitin'!" At a quarter to two this [Tom]
> drives up in what turns out to be a Food and
> Drug station wagon. I load the stuff in, and all
> the time, Food and Drug is takin pictures of me
> in back. I tell you, the whole thing stinks!

Mannie explained that FDA didn't "nab" him then because
they were waiting for him to lead them to the manufacturing
plants. He said that he still has many other punches, as well as
manufacturing equipment, imprinting machines and rollers and
various powders. Some Orinase powder synthesized in a clandestine laboratory was disposed of:

> This [chemist] that was making it, soon as he

got a call, threw everything down the drain and
said to my friend, "Don't call me anymore,
Food and Drug is watching my place. Stay away
from here."

Mannie listed some things he still had left to work with:

> Let's see, two 110-pound drums of the Hydro-
> Diuril powder they took—we were going to bang
> it all up, shoot it out all over the country. But I
> still got a set of the HydroDiuril punches. Just
> had them made up—they cost $1,400; and I've
> got some more powder put away, you can't buy
> it today for what I paid. And I had that yellow
> stuff like cornmeal you mix with Raudixin. . . .
> I got no time to play around. I gotta reach out
> and get powder for my Miltown punches. I
> know a guy's got unidentified tools for the am-
> phetamine double-scores—he's fuckin' me with
> the price, this I know, I can't do nothin' about
> it. What am *I* gonna do, call a cop? They're on
> top of me and comin' at me from all sides. I
> lost a $45,000 home out of this. They've taken
> my factory. Our bar—some bar, that was! My
> wife—this is the worst I've ever seen *her*—I don't
> even get to bed nights. I'm up all night. I'm in
> so much hock, everybody down my neck. The
> publicity knocked my credit, so I can't get credit
> from anybody. People are suing me from all
> sides. Screwing me from all sides. Even the
> lawyers. *Especially* the lawyers!

Mannie told about having to pay his regular lawyer "ten G's
before he handles this current case." He had several other cases
pending, and had just received a letter demanding $500 for the
lawyer who has been arranging things while his Midwest go-
between is "on the lam." He said, "I have to keep giving him
money to run. He runs to the race track. But they can't bring
that case to a head 'til they nab him. The FBI's lookin'. . . . They
want to bring me into interstate; I hope they never find him. I

hope he's in Alaska, the West Indies—I gave him a load of stuff
worth $6,000, and he beat me for it, then says, 'Don't get mad.'
I give him $1,000 for each trip and *he* says he 'don't get paid
right.'

"I still owe one lawyer $7,000 for the last case and I already
paid him $10,000. If I didn't have kids, I wouldda grabbed the
pills and screwed outta the country altogether."

What does Mannie plan to do? "I'm comin' back. . . . If I can
just get in three or four good shots, I can start breathin' again.
This [drug counterfeiting] is the only thing now that'll pull me
up, because I can't get up no ways else. I can't get *out* no ways
else."

The panic was on. Black-marketeers were complaining, angry
with him for getting caught, making "waves." They accused him
of being tailed night and day. He took this as the ultimate in
insults. "I checked myself good," he'd retort. "I didn't get no
tail! They never tailed me yet!"

"Respectable" businessmen who had engaged in the drug trade
with him had a variety of interesting reactions:

A to his partner, B: How do such people get into the drug
                       business anyway? Imagine, one of them was a
                       butcher, yet they had all kinds of punches. . . .

B: The punches lead back to other cases. I *told*
                       you to stay away. There's millions of dollars in
                       this business. The big racketeers know it now.
                       They're going after it. They have a *regular
                       organization*. They make millions—when they
                       get caught—what's a $1,000 fine? They won't go
                       to jail. Don't you read the Food and Drug
                       Report anymore?

A: How big was [Mannie], do you think?

B: Ahh, he was small time. Just kind of a runner.
                       They've already set somebody up in his place.

A: I wouldn't want to cross those type of people. . . .

A production man complains to a friend in the business:

C: I had two or three good suppliers, but all of a
                 sudden they've pulled into the ground like
                 groundhogs. Everybody's afraid to move! Guys
                 promised me stuff, now they won't even talk to
                 me.

FRIEND: There was a little trouble. . . .

C: You don't mean that little guy connected with
                 butcher shops! What *is* this?

FRIEND: Well, you got to know who the Hell you're
                 dealing with, it could be Food and Drug. *You*
                 could be Food and Drug.

The next exchange was between D, E, and Dr. F., three officers
of a medium-sized drug company whose generic products had been
found by FDA among many others in Mannie's "stash."

D: So I saw him one afternoon. He's going to jail.
                 That's the end of him.

E: But he's got rough friends.

D: He's small time. He don't have no friends. I've
                 got news for you—if he had friends, the heat
                 wouldn't be on him, and the heat *is* on him!
                 He deserves it—he's such a big time operator,
                 after the heat was on him, he kept that shit over
                 there. He's no smart operator. I would've flushed
                 every damn bit of it down the toilet.

DR. F: Everything was going so good, then he got
                 greedy.

Mannie was never more desperate than on his last day in his
factory. (He was free on bail after his arrest.) The first of a number
of visitors was a "free-lance" pharmacist, who likes to keep moving,
supplying pep pills and goof balls to truck stops, bars, brothels,
and street peddlers. Their mutual contact is a renegade chemist
still employed by a leading pharmaceutical manufacturer, hence
the conversational opener about a similar case:

PHARMACIST: I see in *Drug Trade News* the chemist who

stole the ten million dollars' worth of tetracycline—his case has come up.

MANNIE: Yeah, I know.

PHARMACIST: Uh, whatever became of all your machinery?
               The rotary, the mixers—they're worth money.

Mannie agreed, but he was not interested in selling that type
of equipment, although he had just gotten rid of a single-punch
"E" tableting machine for $250. What he needed was raw ma-
terial. "Can you look around for powder for hearts?" he asked.

PHARMACIST: Yeah, but it'll cost an arm and a leg. Everything
               is so tight. They got new regulations coming
               up—

MANNIE: I'll pay $11 a pound, find out if he'll [drug
               company chemist] make it. Last night in Jersey
               City bulk hearts were selling for seven dollars
               [a thousand]. Seven for orange, nine for green.
               The whole market's gone crazy now. Every-
               body's jumping their prices. It's the government.
               Looks like I goofed it up for the truck drivers.

PHARMACIST: I never knew there were so many people con-
               nected in the field, though. Every time I turn
               around, I hear about somebody new who's set-
               ting up a plant.

MANNIE (impatient to get on with his work, terminates the
               conversation):   There's always plenty of big
               buyers around if you can get the merchandise.

Mannie's next visitor was a very old friend with an unbeatable
setup: he is a technician in a nearby drug company. In the past,
he has borrowed tools over the weekend; now Mannie wanted him
to "borrow" some materials, as well as to buy others at a good
price. The technician and Mannie worked out a code system for
discussing popular sedatives, stimulants, and tranquilizers over the
telephone:

TECHNICIAN: So, I'm to find stuff for the Seco, Amphet, Amo,
               and Miltown?

MANNIE: Yeah, now, I'll call your home from a drugstore
—no, from a phonebooth. I don't want Food and
Drug to see me hanging around a drugstore.
I'll ride around in my car, and if I don't have
a tail, I'll call you and give you a number where
to call me. We can't name drugs on the phone,
so I'll ask you about that guy, "M", for Miltown
[*other codes were planned*].

The technician explained that this was one of the best jobs he
ever had, so he didn't want to jeopardize it. Mannie told him,
"By all means, stay with it!" Mannie explained that he had lined
up some really big people, who wanted millions of tablets a week;
but the materials had to be top quality because these customers
chemically analyzed samples. (In order to land the initial order,
Mannie introduced a new trick to the trade: he palmed off *authentic* trademarked pills as examples of his superior counterfeiting ability! Now he had to have the cooperation of technical
experts in order to maintain high standards.)

The technician acted reluctant, "I'd like to help you, Mannie
but—" "Look, I'm not askin for *help*, I'm a dead duck, this is for
you. I'm lookin out for your ass." "Well, this is so tempting, it
isn't even funny. I do want to make a few bucks, Mannie. . . ."

Then they got down to such specifics as: "One big operator
might give me Miltown powder. I was going to charge him $32
for the Miltown tablets, but he says, 'I'll give you the powder,
buy the filler and you charge me $18 to run them.' Now, that's
a good deal."

TECHNICIAN: I stashed the machine and buried the punches
. . . till things cool down. Some stuff I took out
to my sister's in Pennsylvania. Listen, one thing
I have to know—I really got a good job right
now—

MANNIE: You've *got* to keep the job! Work nights, weekends, on your vacation for me, but *keep* the
job—

TECHNICIAN: OK, but I have to know how big these guys are.
Are they, really, well, you know. . . . I went
along with you all this time, taking risks—

MANNIE: I'll level with you. I have no money. I can't ask these guys for a D.P. [deposit] if I know I can't get the merchandise. After I make two or three deals and I know it's going to be steady, I'll say to you, take off from your job and come work for me steady. They are—believe me—big people. But big as they are, you find crumbs in every crowd. The last time I had you all set up, I know, the bust came and they all left me holding the bag. I take the powder for everybody. I'm gonna go to jail for half-a-dozen people. Not *one* would take it for me, but I'm not gonna try to drag them into jail *with* me. So, in the event I go away, you do business, just like me. . . . You don't want to meet nobody, 'cause why should anybody know who *you* are? I told these people, 'the minute you want to see my people, no more deals.' They don't care who. All they care is, 'Make the stuff right or it gets kicked back.' Now *we* gotta deliver!

Mannie had a brief conversation with one of his distributors.

MANNIE: Anybody you sold to with my old labels [fictitious hospital supply company] tell them to get rid of it because that's what they found in my room. Naturally, Food and Drug is going around in the stores and if they see it on the shelf, they're gonna snatch it.

DISTRIBUTOR: We have to be careful. [Another counterfeiter] had no active ingredient in his stuff. . . .

MANNIE: Well, I know up to the time they caught me, mine checked out all right. Don't forget, I had a couple of million Dexedrine and Dexamyl. It was laying there, you know, since the last bust, and I couldn't get rid of it because when it hit the market everybody was scared to buy mine. So naturally, this takes a year and the stuff starts to go bad already. Don't forget, I had it in a room where there was a lot of heat there. I knew it was going bad, the stuff. I still wouldn't give it away. Once you give it away, you break the market price. I'd rather dump it in the ocean. I wasn't getting fat on this, but still in all, if I sold it to you for $10 a thousand, you'd be looking to buy it for that all the time. I just had broken in for a contract from a guy out on the Coast—no Dexedrine or Dexamyls out there. He'll buy quite a bit off you. . . .

DISTRIBUTOR: How about the imprints? You still got a machine?

MANNIE: Yeah, I'll make the initials. And I got Orinase powder now, and the punches for that, and I still got a set of HydroDiuril punches. I got a place now where I can set up my own plant.

DISTRIBUTOR: I ran into [generic manufacturer] the other day. He's selling tetracycline. He isn't going no place, though.

MANNIE: He's got troubles? He's got nothin' but money!

DISTRIBUTOR: Well, some of these big people are makin money. With all your connections, is there no one big enough in the background in a position to do something to help you . . . ?

Mannie, it seemed, was abandoned by whatever mobster friends he had. Not only abandoned, but possibly held up by them. At least, there was evidence of something like this in what happened to a deposit in a complicated five-way deal. An upstate customer gave a dealer $4,000 to buy pills from Mannie. Mannie, in turn, gave the deposit to a middleman to purchase materials from his suppliers. The middleman's suppliers—whom he called The People —kept the deposit and refused to return it, *or* to produce the goods. Instead, they demanded $6,000 more, saying they were only interested in orders that add up to "10 G's." The dealer appeared at Mannie's factory demanding his deposit back:

DEALER: Got some money for me, Jake? [Even when serving as the president of a company, Mannie had a variety of aliases.]

MANNIE: Look, I knew you'd ask. I'm strapped like a horse's tail. I can't get any raw materials, the Food and Drug is all over. The constables are lookin' to close me up this afternoon—to auction off the place—and I've got to get some of this stuff loaded and out of here before they come. My wife just blew her top—and now, this: How much more trouble can I get?

DEALER: We've all got our headaches, Jake. Who's got the $4,000? I'm gonna get the money or I'm gonna get the goods. The next thing you know my customer is gonna be down here with an army lookin for all of us. I'll get somebody—

MANNIE: Listen, you might as well know who's behind it. I mean, Italianos got the money—

DEALER: Look, I don't care if they're Italians or Pollacks or what they are. I say, get the goods or the money. [*Refers to the fact that he carries a tire iron.*]

MANNIE: I don't want to be involved there again. I was dealing with one guy, like I told you. *He* was gonna bring *me* the stuff, right? Then he says, come on, they got anything you want over in Brooklyn. So, I went. I get there, they say, "Uh, uh, not til you get up the $6,000 more."

DEALER: God damn it! *I'll* go—

MANNIE: I don't know exactly where it is, myself. . . .

DEALER: Who *is* the guy?

MANNIE: (*Long pause*) Uh, Dino. That's all I know him by. Just Dino.

DEALER: I figger, when I give you money, you're good for it—

MANNIE: Let me explain somethin'. I done business with this Dino before and he's always before *delivered*. These suppliers are very big people. Very big. But when I tried to track 'em down, pin 'em down, ah, it's impossible! You know, even Dino has no address. The phone is different every day, a pay phone somewhere. But always before, he delivered.

DEALER: Then why the hell don't they give you the goods *this* time?

MANNIE: Am I supposed to fight with Italians in Brooklyn?

DEALER: My customer will blow Brooklyn apart. He's a little guy, but real nasty. If he doesn't get it tomorrow, he's comin down after it—and us. That means I've got to introduce him to you, and you've got to introduce him to this Dino so he can fight it out with them.

Mannie arranged for the dealer to talk with Dino.

DINO: Let me put it to you this way. I gave the money to The People. They won't do anything 'til they get $6,000 more. Mannie asked me to explain because he's more or less in a spot and he didn't have anything to do with it.

DEALER: Ah, that's beginning to sound a little—I don't *know* you—

DINO: I don't know *you*, either. That's all I can tell you.

DEALER: My customer's burned up. He thinks I'm kiddin him. He says to me, "What the hell, you've got the $4,000 in your pocket!"

DINO: Mmmmm.

DEALER: He's down for the elections. If his man gets into office, this guy will be a terrific customer. So to start in and piddle around and take $4,000 out of him in a hijack. . . . Uh, he knows someone here in New York and in two or three phone calls, he'll *get* the stuff!

DINO: Just let him do that, then. Look, Dad, I'm get-
                 ting a small P.C. [percentage] out of this whole
                 thing. To me, it's not worth the bother.

DEALER: This guy is not going to bother you, he's going
                 to bother Mannie.

DINO: Well, let him bother him. He's got so much
                 trouble, let him have a little more.

DEALER: Do you mean we *do* have to have this guy give
                 $6,000 more to get *any*thing?

DINO: That's right, Dad. It's gotta be ten G's or
                 nothin'.

Things began to look more and more suspicious as time went
on. Eventually, the Chief Inspector concluded, although he had
no proof, that the money was used by Mannie, with Dino's
cooperation, in getting reestablished again. The threat of The
People in Brooklyn may have been a red herring. About eight
months after the FDA inspection, Mannie was talking to an old
friend, and they agreed that it had been "one coo-coo of a year."

FRIEND: This trouble is not going to drive all these guys
                 out of the drug business, you know.
MANNIE: Drive 'em *out*? It's gonna make things better.
                 What are you talkin about, drive 'em out! Why,
                 I'd like to make up 26 million of each item
                 myself and flood the market. Then I'd pack up
                 the machines for awhile and lay low. Work a
                 coupla months, smack it out all over the coun-
                 try—Boom!

PART TWO

The Gray Marketplace

The naive belief that if the product was not good the FDA would prohibit its sales is just not realistic. FDA labors long and diligently to protect the public, but the fact of the matter is, it is completely impossible for FDA to check *every* batch of *every* product of *every* manufacturer that is marketed.

Dr. Albert H. Holland,
former FDA Medical Director

QUESTION: Don't you have to have a degree in pharmacy, or, at least, considerable technical training before you are permitted to manufacture prescription drugs?

ANSWER (*Production manager with experience in large and small firms—ethical and otherwise*): Are you kidding? The Kefauver Amendment said you have to send in for an FDA registration number, or you're supposed to, if you're making any pretense of being legit. But it may take FDA up to a year or more to get around to inspecting the premises. As for *who* is actually making the stuff . . . you could have a cage of ring-tailed monkeys doing it!

According to U.S. Treasury records there are 1,600 firms in the drug industry category, some with assets of up to $250 million; 300 with assets over a million. About half of their products are sold through 1,500 wholesale druggists and 900 jobbers. Drugs are legally sold, dispensed, or handled by 53,000 retail drugstores; 7,000 hospitals; 330,000 medical practitioners and researchers; 105,000 dentists; 20,000 veterinarians; and 550,000 professional nurses.

This is a vast distribution pattern. When one considers, in addition, the gray- and black-market variations, the regulatory task seems virtually impossible. As the FDA attempted to grapple with the immense and complicated problem of illegal manufacturing, illegal distributing, and illegal selling of prescription medications, the observations of informants, tape recordings, and undercover agents' reports flowed into the FDA from many directions. It became increasingly clear that there existed large, efficient groups of individuals—who had no apparent interest in the drug business—who were, in fact, cooperating to produce counterfeit medications. Their overall chain of supply was complete: from raw materials brokers and chemists to technicians, manufacturers, wholesalers, and retailers. To the FDA's shock, Mafia support and participation was beginning to be evident. FDA teams throughout the country now began what would be long, arduous, and risky investigations aimed at removing dangerous drugs from the market, and disbanding the rings of illicit producers and distributors. Conviction of such criminals is, as we shall see, another matter.

CHAPTER FOUR
Counterfeit Respectability

The on-going investigation of The Group in the New York District provided insights into the nature of the people involved in black-market medicine: special renegade breeds of drug company executives, registered pharmacists, researchers, technicians, salesmen. They may have no police records and appear to be respectable members of their communities. Some live in $50,000 houses, drive Chrysler Imperials and Cadillacs. Their children go to private schools and Ivy League colleges and become teachers, doctors, lawyers—or inherit the family business. One major diverter and dealer in counterfeit drugs has been given a commendation for his outstanding work with a national youth group; another is local president of a laymen's religious organization. An aura of respectability surrounds such people because they are involved in the health professions, supplying pharmacies, physicians, and hospitals with life-saving medications. Among themselves, their remarks sound as if they had just been released from Leavenworth. For example, this is from a tape of a pharmacist-production manager's discussion of "Good Manufacturing Practices":

"I tell you, we don't have anything to worry about. To this day, that section of the law [FD&C Act] is not well defined. You can stand and piss in the batch and turn around and shake the FDA inspector's hand. He's going to tell you that's not right, but when you go to court, they won't find you guilty. . . . They have not been able to make this law stick!"

Here is a vice-president of a fringe drug company talking to several employees, one of whom expressed concern about their latest product:

"So we are putting some oil in some capsules. I *label* it right. If somebody buys it from us and claims it cures cancer, that's their problem. Do you follow? I'm guaranteeing that the label is proper. That's all. I don't care if the people who buy it look like the Mafia when they come in, so long as they pay me cash. I don't care if they're Red Chinese. The fact that they're reputable or disreputable makes no difference. They can own Macy's or a push-cart on Delancy Street, so long as they are customers with money. . . . Their *money* is equal."

These are the people who fill capsules for The Group and other counterfeiters. Who make hearts for black-market distribution. Who are busily wheeling and dealing over the counter, under the counter, out the back door, in the front door. One of the men hot on their trail is:

INSPECTOR OSCAR COHEN

With his graying crew cut and patient smile, Oscar Cohen looks like the high school science teacher he formerly was. He still has an opportunity to teach as he conducts establishment inspections in legitimate drug plants where the goal goes beyond voluntary compliance with the FD&C Act, to the "zero defects" concept in production. One manufacturer told me, "Cohen is a genius for coming up with a suggestion, or simple little do-dad, that takes the kinks out of a problem. He would have made a helluva pharmaceutical engineer!"

Inspector Cohen was the New York District's first authority on radioisotope drugs, having been trained at Oak Ridge. As Clem Westerly explained, "The thing that makes Oscar a crack inspector is his creative imagination. He isn't the dedicated civil servant plodding along in a rut, never questioning procedures, just 'doing his job.' Not Oscar. He's plowing new furrows, digging in, and coming up way on the other side where he's least expected."

This is disconcerting to the gray-marketeers. One drug producer engaging in shady practices was heard to say of Cohen: "God, how I hate to see that guy—he's a bitch. Puts on overalls, crawls all over everything . . . when my customers see him around the place, they know it's a bad omen. Everybody knows him in the industry. If he comes here three days in a row, they figure you've had it." His colleague replied: "*Three* visits! Tell him to get off your ass or you'll see a lawyer because now it's becoming like *persecution* and *harassment.* . . ."

As Cohen tracked *schlock* shop (shoddy) drug producers through the swamps of New Jersey, he exhibited the endurance and determination of Inspector Javert pursuing Jean Valjean through the sewers of Paris.

The starting point for one counterfeit drug investigation by Inspector Cohen began in a ramshackle "inky" egg-cracking barn on a dirt road less than 50 miles from the New York District Office. I asked which came first in the minds of these fast-buck operatives, counterfeit drugs or "inky" eggs?

He answered: "These people were palming off fake Bayer aspirin in the 20's, but their kind has been dealing in 'inkies' and such since time began."

Mauser—that seemingly ubiquitous interstate trucker—and a loan shark he called "The Hunchback" roamed the countryside looking for potential "inky" egg-cracking barns. Their story was that they needed the buildings as factories for the production of dog food. Retired farmers were delighted to get whatever they could for the use of their empty and usually decrepit barns. There were never any business records—even light bills were paid in cash, and fictitious names were the order of the day.

Infertile eggs rejected by hatcheries after a certain period of incubation were purchased for about two dollars a crate. (Some hatcheries have poor quality controls in their candling operation, as evidenced by the peeping chicks frequently encountered in the crates.) Eggs and chicks were dumped into grinders; then, liquids separated from solids in spinner-type washing machines. Synthetic additives were poured into the material drained off, and this horrendous mess, loaded with Salmonella, the bacterial source of an acute intestinal complaint, was then tinned and stored in freezer rooms cleverly installed in the folksy-looking barns. Later, the gook was sold to noodle makers, egg-bagel bakers, and other commercial chefs wishing to buy 30-pound containers of so-called whole egg mix at a dandy discount.

Whenever FDA learns about egg-cracking barns of this type, inspectors are dispatched to make inspections and obtain egg samples for laboratory analysis so their charges will have a better chance of standing up in court—*after* the government proves the egg mix was shipped interstate, that is. Mauser's associate, the elderly loan shark "inky" entrepreneur, whom I shall call S, had become a familiar adversary to succeeding generations of FDA men. One of his successful courtroom gambits involved his eating one of the redolent eggs in order to prove the wholesomeness of his product. (Perhaps some judges are partial to that Philippine delicacy, *balut*—pin-feathered chicks on the verge of hatching, which are served upon ceremonial occasions.) At any rate, S frequently managed to have his Federal cases dismissed, while nauseated prosecutors no doubt reached for the Pepto-Bismol.

One day, however, Inspector Cohen discovered a powdery residue in an empty drum in one of the "inky" barns operated by S. It did not appear to be the type of chemical used for camouflaging rotten eggs. His educated guess was that this was the active ingredient in a drug currently popular with the counterfeiters. Labels on the drum indicated that the container, at least, came from Italy.

About this time, FDA learned that S owned, through a relative "fronting" for him, the egg company building where the Ph.D. researcher worked. S was put under surveillance, and government chemists began analyzing various powders collected in his wake.

Inspector Cohen, meanwhile, pursued other leads. Trudging up four flights to a print shop, he questioned a man on the ragged fringe between subsistence and destitution: Could the printer explain how he happened to be making Merck's HydroDiuril labels? The man said, "It was the first good order I'd received in God knows when. A sorta short, sorta dark, sorta average guy came in with a wrinkled label and told me to copy it—cash on the barrelhead." As for HydraDiuril, the bewildered printer asked: "What *is* that?"

Next stop, an engraver's where Inspector Cohen queried, "About those hobs—you say that *dozens* of dies of *each* engraving were made from the master hobs? Who got them?" The trail of the hot hobs had long since grown cold, but this much was known: a short, dark, average-looking man was involved in having the counterfeit tablet punches made up from these hobs engraved with trademarks belonging to Ciba, Schering, and other companies. He, or a man with the same general characteristics, had ordered the counterfeit labels printed. When would he turn up again?

Inspector Cohen waited for nightfall before making his last call of that day at a vitamin company, up another three flights in a loft-type building. He was not surprised to see a crack of light under the door or to hear the pop-pop-pop of an old Stokes B-2 tableting machine inside. Only 8 of the 16 punches were working, but the owner managed to produce 200 Miltowns a minute with a retail value of ten cents each—an after-hours project that paid far better than turning out Vitamin C.

Still, this was a penny-ante operation and Inspector Cohen was a long way from his primary goal—finding the source of meprobamate, the active ingredient of Miltown. (At that time it was legitimately produced only by the patent holder, Wallace, and two licensees, Lederle and Wyeth.) Inspector Cohen collected samples of raw materials and finished tablets with their tell-tale punch marks, and a few other clues. But the president of the vitamin company could not, under the laws in force at that time, be made to disclose his source of meprobamate. He said his records "had been lost in a recent fire." Eventually, he was sentenced by a Federal judge to six months in jail on each of half-a-dozen counts. Sentencing was suspended and he walked out of court after paying a small fine, totaling the equivalent of a few hours labor with his Stokes B-2. The restrictions on his resumption of drug manufacturing? One day's probation.

Although he had many other duties, Oscar Cohen never stopped looking for the source of clandestinely synthesized active ingredients for drugs being counterfeited. One day while conducting an inspection of a registered plant, he recognized slurry (an intermediate stage in the chemical process) of a drug that this particular company was not licensed to produce. Even with the approval of the patent-holder, FDA would consider this a new drug for which a New Drug Application (NDA) would have to be filed. Inspector Cohen came right out and told them, "I think you are making counterfeit raw materials here." He collected samples that became the basis for an injunction prohibiting further production of that particular substance in that location.

As all too frequently happens, this operation moved to a nearby state and the owner set up a laboratory where he claimed to be making only fine chemicals, not drugs. FDA has no jurisdiction over raw materials not defined as drugs in the FD&C Act or its Amendments. While there are only seven legitimate manufacturers of basic amphetamines and only ten legitimate manufacturers of basic barbiturates, there are countless producers of the basic chemicals used during the manufacturing process. These intermediate chemicals have many other nondrug uses— one being a component in jet engine fuel. Obviously, investigation of the 'diversion" of basic industrial chemicals is impractical. Yet FDA sometimes reaches the point where it has to prove that a certain lot of X intermediate is destined to make addicts, not jets, take off.

The complexities involved were demonstrated one day when Inspector Cohen took me along on one of his informal calls on a man who evoked certain ambivalent feelings. I'll call him simply:

THE CHEMIST

"He is brilliant, you see," Oscar Cohen said. "His particular talent lies in a remarkable ability to simplify production methods for complicated compounds at a lower cost than larger laboratories. Like many of these renegade professionals, I think he has a personality problem. He's an 'injustice-collector.' But when you view him as a chemist, you have to credit his abilities, law-breaker though he may be."

After working hours, using his own car, Oscar drove me to an industrial area on the outskirts of a large city. It was all the more dismal because of the sleet and heavy winds that buffeted us as we stood in front of an old brick building, waiting for an answer to the knock on the door. (I could see no reason why this man should talk to a writer, but I was told that The Chemist was a colorful character and not to be surprised at anything.)

Turning up the collar of his raincoat, Oscar really pounded

this time, calling, "Hallo, Doctor! This isn't an official visit—"
The heavy door swung open so quickly we almost fell inside.

A huge, red-faced man waved black rubber gloves toward a
small office, saying in a booming voice, "Come in, come in, I'm
very, very, busy, but come on in." Despite this disclaimer, he
seemed to have all the time in the world. Whenever we got up
to go, he motioned us back into our seats, and beamed at us as if
we were long-lost friends. I was particularly astonished at the
bantering small talk exchanged between the FDA Inspector and
the man he had at various times "seriously inconvenienced," shall
we say.

The Chemist, bundled up in spattered bib overalls, several
layers of ragged sweaters, and a woolen cap, apologized for the
lack of heat and offered to make some camomile tea. While preparing it in a back room, he shouted to us that he now owned this
building and the one on the corner, where he let a man live in a
rent-free apartment in exchange for help in the laboratory at
night. "He comes in to turn things off when the reactions are
completed," he said, handing me the tea. "As you can see," he
added with a twinkle in his blue eyes, "I'm an old man now and
I need my night's rest." Sitting at his ancient desk, puffing on a
pipe, he was the picture of contentment as he described his present
operation.

"I've stopped advertising in *OPD* [the chemical buyer's guide
published by *Oil, Paint, and Drug Reporter*]—I'm only interested
in making compounds that sell for over six* dollars a pound.
Things I can handle easily myself without a lot of paperwork."
There were only a few scraps of paper on the desk near the telephone; most, if not all, of his orders were called in. "I just got
an order from [leading rubber company] that will keep me busy
for awhile. Fascinating problem. And I've been making [cold
remedy intermediates] on a regular basis, for [medium-sized
ethical drug company]. But I don't make any *drugs* here, myself,
only fine chemicals. No dosage forms."

Inspector Cohen explained that I would like to have a look
around his laboratory, since I had never seen a small one before.
The Chemist did not hesitate, but said cheerily, "Well, yes, this

*He had been charging $30 a pound for one drug he was illicitly synthesizing, and
probably much more for others.

isn't like American Cyanamid—I do everything here." We were ushered into series of cave-like rooms that resembled old alchemist's shops. In one cubbyhole he made hand-blown glassware; in another alcove he stored tools. The largest room contained no expensive or elaborate machinery, just a couple of huge pots, a small grinder or mill, and wall racks holding assorted glassware. There was little indication of current production: a stainless steel pail was half full of wet powder, and one of the bottles had about two inches of a clear liquid in the bottom that, judging from the droplets on the sides, may have been freshly distilled. There were no powders or tablets on the trays in his tiny drying room, but I noticed chemicals stored in amber bottles on a shelf in his office.

The Chemist had been educated abroad and in the course of our leisurely conversation, I learned that several of his former classmates and later business associates were people I had interviewed: a major drug company president, a pharmacology professor, and a dean of chemistry. When he discovered that we shared a common interest in botanical drugs, he brought out his yellowing thesis on indole alkaloids, the chemical configuration that may be responsible for causing hallucinations in persons who take substances containing them—LSD, morning-glory seeds, certain so-called magic mushrooms, and the like.

When I asked whether he had done any work on ergot, the fungus that provides lysergic acid, the starting material for making the hallucinogen LSD, he quickly stated that he was no longer interested in indoles.

At that point, The Chemist recounted his previous troubles with FDA, almost in the manner of a naughty schoolboy who has had so much fun trying to outwit the schoolmaster that he'll do it again, every chance he gets.

Ignoring Inspector Cohen for the time being, he told me, "*You* know, of course, that last substance I was charged with making was known for hundreds of years as a constituent in hops. It didn't originate with [the patent holder]." He went on to explain that one day while listening to recordings of Bach, he thought of a way to make the drug that was much simpler, cheaper, and better in every way than the previously patented process. According to unbiased outside assays, it produced a drug identical to the one trade-marked by the big drug company. "Their chemists eventually worked out the same improvements on their own," he added. "I am not claiming to be a genius."

"What did you do with your own process?" I asked.

"Oh, I sold it abroad for thousands of dollars," he answered. "Naturally, I'm not allowed to go on producing anything like that here."

Then he told me that when he first came to this country, he had been very interested in developing new drugs. He worked as a bench chemist in a small, ethical firm with a man who later became head of one of the biggest drug companies. They had a joint project, but he said he walked out on it when they had a disagreement. He did not appear to be an embittered injustice-collector, but, rather, perfectly content in running his own business, with no apparent ill will for large companies. In fact, one of his comments could have been abstracted from a Pharmaceutical Manufacturers' Association (PMA) press release: "I don't blame Pfizer, Lederle, and Wallace for fighting what they consider to be patent infringements in court. They have every right to protect their investments—mind you, it takes millions to develop a drug before it goes on the market. Then it costs a fortune to advertise and promote it. No thanks, I wouldn't want any of *their* headaches!"

As The Chemist stood hospitably in the doorway, waving as we drove away, I realized that my only criticism of his laboratory was that it was dusty. Inspector Cohen reminded me that making chemicals was a messy business and the dust, in any event, would be removed during the later drug manufacturing process. As for rodents and insects, the chemicals tended to keep them away. Did this mean that there was no danger to the consumer from the products The Chemist was making? The FDA Inspector quickly pointed out that in any kind of unregulated operation there is a great disaster potential. "Suppose instead of intermediates, he is actually making LSD? Or the stimulant, methamphetamine hydrochloride, or some other drug that is distributed directly to users through black-market channels—and something goes wrong? He is a good chemist, but that's no guarantee against human error."

Inspector Cohen went on to explain that once a shipment leaves such a laboratory, it disappears without a trace and cannot possibly be recalled. "Even if he is making intermediates only, the people who buy from him may not assay his materials before compounding dosage forms from them. They should according to the law, but frequently they don't. Especially if they are operating clandestinely themselves."

After being behind the scenes at FDA during many drug recalls, I felt that the public is reasonably well protected where legitimately produced drugs are concerned. Through the use of lot numbers, shipping records, and other controls, a specific batch of a suspect drug can be traced with amazing efficiency. But here was another facet of the counterfeit menace I had not thought about: If a deadly substance happened—through human error—to be substituted for one of the ingredients, a staggering number of people could die before the cause of death was determined and traced to the source. If it ever were traced. Short of outlawing every dose of that type of medication, what could FDA do?

The mere existence of even one clandestine drug laboratory threatens all the protection we have gained through half a century of hard-won drug legislation. Cheerful entrepreneurs like The Chemist, no matter how benign they appear on the surface, could become mass murderers. And yet, these men are secure in their laboratories until FDA somehow proves that they are selling adulterated or misbranded drugs in interstate commerce.

The tracing of liquids and powders such as they might produce is one of the most difficult and important aspects of the FDA's detective work. Clues are hard to come by. Unlike monogrammed tablets or capsules, a pile of white crystals has few distinguishing physical characteristics. The labels and shipping invoices are frequently falsified as to sender's and receiver's true names and addresses; even the contents are disguised on the container.

At the outset of a raw materials investigation, there are a bewildering number of possibilities to explore: was the material synthesized by someone like The Chemist in a small, one-man laboratory? Was it stolen from a large legitimate producer? Did an apparently ethical manufacturer sell it out the back door without invoices to a black-marketeer? Perhaps it was an export-import item—but was it made here for legitimate shipment abroad, then smuggled back in—or was it produced in a foreign country and imported here? Or was it smuggled in?

The last ride with Bennie. Five persons were killed. Amphetamine was found in the stomach of this driver, and Bennies were spilled in the wreckage of the tractor-trailer.

Gifford D. Hampshire, FDA.

Undercover FDA inspector leaves scene of illicit drug "buy" ostensibly to get $6,000 for peddler. By means of a concealed transmitter, he is alerting U.S. marshals stationed nearby.

U.S. marshal places peddler under arrest.

Gifford D. Hampshire, FDA.

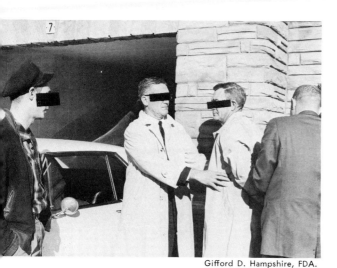

Inspector confronts peddler as marshals disarm and handcuff him.

Gifford D. Hampshire, FDA.

The arrest of a major pill peddler

As peddler is led away, he shakes inspector's hand and makes the oft-heard comment: "Well, you were just doing your job."

Gifford D. Hampshire, FDA.

Gifford D. Hampshire, FDA.

After issuing a Notice of Inspection to the peddler, the inspector takes samples of the illicit drugs in the peddler's car.

The young chemist operating this bathroom laboratory has been described as "a millionaire." His specialty: liquid amphetamine.

The Triumph electronic capsule counting machine.

Seized at Mannie's Stash

Trade-mark punches for tablet compressors.

A drum of active ingredients for counterfeits shipped under another chemical name from Italy.

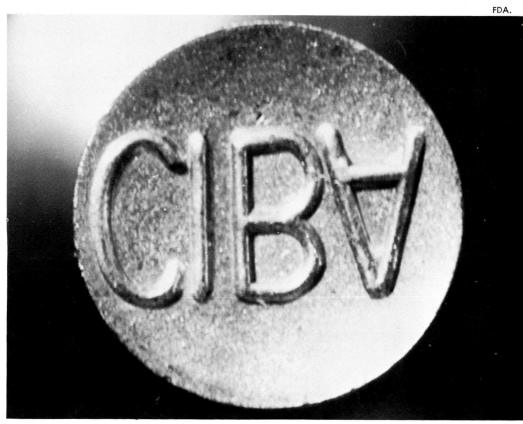

Magnified end of one of many counterfeit punches, showing raised letters of a legitimate company's name.

Counterfeit tablet imprinted from punch shown.

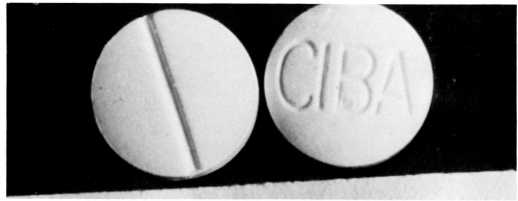

Author with Stokes B-2 tableting machine confiscated by FDA from moonlighting tableter, who smuggled it out of a legitimate drug plant piece by piece and reassembled it in his basement at home.

FDA's chief "pillistics" expert, Dr. A. H. Tillson, examines authentics in the Washington "drug library" of samples used as a basis for comparison with drugs seized.

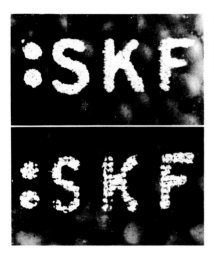

Non-branded "T-D" amphetamine capsules, generic drugs, which were turned into counterfeits via illegal "SK&F" imprints. (Photo below.)

Microphotographs compare monograms inked by Mark-em machines on real and counterfeit SK&F capsules. Faulty engraving on Mark-em roller gives a fuzzier imprint on counterfeits, lower photograph.

Sophisticated counterfeiting operations duplicate all legitimate packaging.

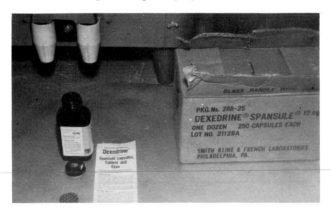

CHAMELEON

Chameleon, involved in almost every variation of black-market medicine, is, like his namesake, remarkable for the many changes in his outward appearance. He is qualified to practice a profession, but is not now practicing. Through professors, doctors, and chemists he has connections with the scientific world; one of his closest associates was employed by the government on classified research. Along with relatives, Chameleon operates an export-import company. He is also a partner in a firm dealing in new and used manufacturing equipment. He has been an officer in more than one drug company. Some of his operations have been cited by FDA for violations of the FD&C Act. Chameleon is backed up by a number of diabolically clever lawyers; one also represents a reputed Mafia leader. He has other advisers with good political connections. Devoted to his family and active in community affairs, Chameleon's chief asset may be his personal charm. Handsome, athletic, meticulously groomed—some underlings call him Mr. Polished Fingernails, Mr. Pressed Pants—he has extraordinary powers of persuasion. Otherwise astute business and professional men, even hardened ex-convicts, have been induced to take incredible risks because they believe in him, particularly what he promises to do for them.

Inspector Oscar Cohen sums him up thus: "He's a flimflam artist who flimflams the flimflammers."

Chameleon is so brazen that he once made a personal call at the FDA District Office to inquire about the latest changes in certain drug regulations. FDA was obliged to give him the details, although they knew full well that he wanted them for the sole purpose of working out ways around the restrictions. Drug company private detectives, their internal security men (some of whom are former FBI agents), lawyers, and top executives agree with my FDA interviewees that Chameleon is very high up in the black-market medicine racket.

Cases are being made against him, but he is still at large: the men working under him are the ones who get caught. Embittered as they must be, they keep returning to him for technical advice, for "contacts," and for help in "getting back on their feet."

Chameleon's varicolored occupational disguises allow him to move freely in many different circles. As a professional introducer of the like-minded, he seems to rival the late Elsa Maxwell.

For instance, it was he who saw the possibilities in linking "inky" barn facilities operated by S with Mauser's network of trucking outlets. Described by one detective on his trail as "thinking double-time all the time," it is no accident that loan sharks like S were shadowy figures in bankruptcy cases where small drug firms and drugstores were forced out of business. Nor is it mere happenstance when salvage-dealers like Mannie appear on the scene to spirit away equipment and raw materials. Not surprisingly, the same machines and men continue to turn up in new drug manufacturing plants in which Chameleon has an interest.

Excerpts from taped recordings of conversations with Chameleon—and about Chameleon:

MANUFACTURING CHEMIST: Whatever information he got some years back was from me on how to make [popular dosage form]. Then, two, three years later he got a patent on it. Made a lot of money in stocks, too. Never gave me a nickel.

FRIEND: Listen, I heard he was counterfeiting everybody's labels and packages. Must have good lawyers to get out of it. He once went into bankruptcy owing me money, $300.

CHEMIST: You should be glad it wasn't $3,000. Funny thing now is, *he's* suing everybody. All you hear around him is "Lawyer, lawyer, lawyer." . . . That guy is completely surrounded by lawyers!

A registered pharmacist, who lent his name and professional reputation to a project that later became involved in drug counterfeiting, complained:

R.PH: You made a monkey out of me, running me back and forth to buy that plant equipment. The impression I got was you were offering me a partnership in a wonderful place. You were lying—

CHAMELEON: I introduced [company's officials] to everyone, got them customers all over, and that's the last I knew. . . . It's unfortunate if people make mistakes, but human beings *do* make mistakes. Is it a crime to say, "I want you to meet so-and-so, I've done business with him for a number of years and if you feel you can do business with him, fine."? Am I legally or morally responsible if they are doing something wrong *after* that? Am I? I said, "Goodbye, you're on your own!"

R.PH (*Shouting*): Don't hand me that crap. I was right there.

CHAMELEON: Sure you were, it was *your* idea.

R.PH (*Angrily*): Where the hell do you get it was *my* idea! Who counted the money out? *You* did! You were the real owner, you *owned* the plant.

CHAMELEON: What plant? I don't know what you're talking about, owning plants—Dahlias? Roses? Come on now, isn't this an absurd conversation? Look, your coffee's getting sour. . . . You know, I still have great faith in your abilities. I want to *help* you. Now, I can get you some formulas—

R.PH: *Help* me? *Help* me? All I got since I first met you is headaches. You introduced me to *them*—

CHAMELEON: OK, so now it's a crime to introduce people. That's all. That's the last. I'm sorry. I apologize. I had no intention of creating ill will. It's too bad it all backfired. But I think you should go to *them* if you were not treated right. I am out of the drug business. Never again. . . .

CHAMELEON (In a lengthy discussion with a prospective patsy): Your best bet is [Mannie]. Then, probably, [Tom]. But why don't you get the raw materials and make it yourself? You can get [Rocco] to deliver, and some colored people to move the machinery. I say, if I can't make it myself, I don't want to be at their mercy. . . . The guy that *sells* is the guy in trouble. Not the one who makes. . . . Some of these suppliers, there was a time they'd pull you in, you know, off the sidewalk. . . . Find the manufacturer that needs money, he'll sell you something. . . . That building is still vacant in Jersey. The old miser wants too much, he started out asking over $45,000. All those lofts are still vacant and he has to pay the mortgage, the taxes. . . . Here's an item that costs, what to make, three–four bucks a thousand? [The producer's] getting, guess what—$80 a thousand. That's, I mean, a big spread. You want to cut in on that, go ahead. . . . You've got a lot of guys making seeds [tiny medicated pellets to put in capsules]. . . . They don't make the capsules, they buy them. Any idiot can buy capsules and put a name on them . . . what's there to that? You have the machines and you have the capsules.

QUESTION: Don't you have to be a pharmacist? Some kind of technician?

CHAMELEON: Oh, come *on*! To do imprinting? That's ridiculous! To print a name on a capsule, you have to be an *artist*? You don't have to be a genius for that!

A few days after this conversation, a dealer (apparently suspected of being a government informant) tried to buy bulk prescription drugs from Chameleon, who told him: "I have no time, interest, or desire to be associated in that in any way. If you can tell me where to sell 1,000 [pieces of machinery] we can talk business."

DEALER: Tell me where to get pills and I'll get you a customer.

CHAMELEON: If you offered me $500 a bottle, I couldn't give it to you. If you said, "Here's $2,000 cash, just

give me the source." I can't help you. Try that
and find out. [*When dealer persists*]. . . . I tell
you, I am *out* of it!

The FBI is interested in Chameleon because his group deals in
drugs stolen in interstate movement. The Federal Bureau of
Narcotics has been watching him ever since he started utilizing
the talents of Mauser and others with narcotics records. Customs
agents have their eyes on him as the result of a brief encounter
when he paid a small fine for importing an expensive chemical
under the name of a much cheaper substance. Interpol, the International Police Organization, is investigating his part in the theft
and sale abroad of a drug now in development. His contacts with
known Mafia members have brought him to the attention of other
experts on the international crime syndicate.

When I saw him last, he looked as if he didn't have a worry
in the world.

CHAPTER FIVE

From A Small And Dirty Business

ABE AND BERT

The Pure Food and Drug Laws of 1906 were completely replaced in 1938 by the Federal Food, Drug, and Cosmetic Act.
From the practical standpoint of the people we are discussing—
and they are eminently practical people—the FD&C Act meant
that they would have to figure on more overhead for lawyers, and
they would have to put up with more frequent Federal inspections. A man I shall call Abe said, "When your family's in the
drug line, you inherit a lot of grief along with the business; you
get troubles with FDA like a legacy. It's all in the game, take the
bitter with the better, as they say."

Abe dropped out of school in the 1920's to help relatives run
a little flavoring- and fruit-extract business. His first brush with
government came when there was trouble over a botanical extract
used in prescriptions—it was adulterated with a poisonous substance. (In a similar case, 30,000 people were paralyzed.) After all
the hullabaloo died down, though, business was better than ever
and the firm expanded into chemicals. Some of the things Abe
remembers from those days have stood him in good stead: for
instance, how the head of the company didn't panic, even when
the government chemist testified that their product had crippled
laboratory animals. Instead, he hired the most skilled lawyers to
try to get this evidence ruled out. When asked questions in court,

106

he always declined on the ground that to answer "might tend to incriminate" him. He didn't let business go to pot during the litigation—he rented a post office box, moved the plant to a hideaway, painted the windows black, and kept on filling orders— business as usual. His partner said, "Look they've *got* us. And the racket's over anyway. I say, let's close up shop and quit!"

Abe's relative replied: "I'm not worried. They may have us down, but so far, we're not out." Another of his favorite expressions was: "Everything'll be all right in the morning."

Abe inherited that business and that philosophy.

In the 1930's he had financial reverses because some of his products were like those highlighted in the best-seller, *100 Million Guinea Pigs*. Exposés of that type he naturally labels "a fabrication of lies, all lies," and like Tom, he loathes writers and fears them far more than government inspectors. The former "stir up the people and get laws passed." The latter, in his own words, are "poor working stiffs, dumb clucks—lookit the money they could make if they used *their* education in this business: they know *all* the tricks!"

During this period, Abe decided it was more profitable to go bankrupt. This was, in police parlance, his first "bust-out fraud." By having everything in his wife's name, and carting off machinery and materials before the auction, he salvaged enough to start up in another location. This time, his friend Bert was the official head of the firm, but the real moneyman was not connected with the corporation in any documentable fashion. Bank accounts were opened in little hamlets in the Catskills, and the whole operation, according to a later legal citation, was "conducted in a surreptitious way with guilty knowledge on the part of the appellants." ("Appellants" because by now they knew enough to keep appealing cases.)

Abe and Bert manufactured many supplies for the home medicine cabinet: cheap mouthwash and aspirin, plasters for lumbago, and the like. They catered to the bargain basement trade and cut corners wherever possible. The raw materials they used—oils, gums, botanicals like mint and eucalyptus—were invariably substandard. In their incessant bargain-scrounging, they formed a wide acquaintance with shady characters in the salvage business, a group categorized as The Forty Thieves, and not without reason.

When there was not enough genuine distressed merchandise from floods, fires, and trainwrecks, then freight-handlers and truckers cooperated in "liberating" merchandise. Either they stole it outright and fenced it; or they scuffed it up, dented metal bottle tops, or threw some water on it, to unload it as damaged goods.

One time when Abe and Bert were stuck with gallons of their own amber "antiseptic," they had an even brighter idea: Why not manufacture salvage? Why couldn't you buy up, say, empty Listerine bottles, fill them with your own stuff that was not moving at all and sell them to cut-rate outlets with the story that the wrappers and labels had come off when the firemen doused them with hoses. . . . "You *heard* about that big warehouse fire, didnya?"

The scheme worked.

At five dollars the case, Abe, Bert, and their ilk could hardly meet the demand for fake Listerine and similar bogus products. One druggist bought 100 dozen 14-ounce bottles and ran an ad in the *San Francisco Shopping News*:

> ON SALE MONDAY: Here is an exceptional buy on large size Listerine Antiseptic. Limit: One bottle to a customer. To eliminate store-keepers from obtaining it, we have removed the outside wrappers so that it cannot be resold, and so that our regular customers would not be deprived of this special. On sale MONDAY AND TUESDAY ONLY: 59¢, Large Bottle.

Lambert Pharmacal Company, the Listerine patent-holder, heard about this and hired Pinkerton's detectives forthwith. What an outrage! Millions in advertising being usurped. Who knew what the culprits were filling the bottles with? Ditch water most likely. (According to Lambert, analysis showed that the fake Listerine didn't kill as many germs on contact as did the authentic product. The Lambert lawyers weren't sleeping nights, visions of lawsuits danced in their heads.) The command decision was to prosecute the crooks—vigorously! But this was a complicated case. Tied in was the counterfeiting of Standard Brands' Royal Baking Powder. Fearful of what publicity would do to their "image," they quietly picked up the counterfeits and replaced them with authentics.

An eye-witness at the trial reported:

The judge proceeded on a discourse about how terrible it was to perpetuate a fraud of this kind, not only on the manufacturers, but upon the public who had relied upon Listerine and Royal Baking Powder for so many years. He exhausted his vocabulary in denouncing this scheme, apparently thinking his biting words would inflict greater punishment than incarceration. The 'mountain labored and brought forth a mouse': The defendants paid fifty dollars for counterfeiting Listerine and fifty dollars for counterfeiting Royal Baking Powder.

As a result, is it any wonder that in the years to come, the likes of Bert and Abe saw no reason *not* to copy whatever product they fancied? Among many other items, they counterfeited Johnson & Johnson sterile surgical dressings, Kotex, Vitalis, Arpège perfume, and name-brand vitamins (filled with sawdust). Surely, the all-time low came one week after Salk polio vaccine was introduced, when a bogus "Salk polio vaccine" appeared on the black-market.

Just before World War II, Abe-and-Bert types went into sulfas, palming off ordinary ointments as miracle cures. Immediately afterward, business boomed with the introduction of the Wonder Drugs. The public clamored for antibiotics. While The Forty Thieves could scarcely pronounce penicillin, let alone ferment it, they were eager to get in on a good thing. Bert had a druggist cousin in the Bronx who pointed out that the government permitted a deviation of 10 to 20 percent in the labeled potency of penicillin. There was money to be made in compounding these high-priced items at the minimum, say, 80,000 units instead of the 100,000 marked on the label. "Do this, and you can still be ethical," the consultant-cousin advised.

Abe and Bert wanted to be in the ethical drug business. It was all right in the old days to make money in *schlock* shops down on Fourteenth Street, or over in Hoboken, or out in Long Island City, but their families were growing up now, and they wanted to leave something that they could be proud of to their sons. According to the new laws, they would have to have a registered pharmacist in charge of their pharmaceutical manufacturing plant. Bert's cousin in the Bronx wasn't interested. What to do? They'd had their share of quack pill-rollers and bathtub chemists; this time they were going to "scientifically" test prospective employees in advance.

I looked up Abe and Bert's first "professionally qualified" pro-

duction manager, Charlie. Fortunately, he seems to have almost
total recall. First, he explained how he became a registered pharmacist, then how he started working for Abe and Bert, and what
misfortunes befell him in their employ. Charlie, by the way, has
stayed pretty clean. He has been plant superintendent for some
medium-sized and large firms in his day, and while his scruples
have had to be fairly elastic at times, he's managed to escape
FDA prosecution. Now a remarkably handsome man, along in
years but physically fit, he neither drinks nor smokes and—above
all—he takes no pills! "God forbid," he says, "after what I have
seen in my time. . . ."

CHARLIE: I started out in a little drugstore in my home town
—long-winded hours and short pay—trying to earn
enough money for medical school. One of my
teachers—may he rest in peace, he's since passed
away—said I was qualified enough to go to Johns
Hopkins, but I didn't have the means. If I knew
then what I know today, I would have managed it
somehow. Well, what I did was take some pharmacy
courses from an Institute in a nearby city and later,
I attended a course run by a shyster professor in
New York City. Mainly, I picked it up bit by bit
from books, and on-the-job in the pharmacies. I
never liked to stay in one place long, so I hit the
road, was a pharmacist's mate in the Navy, and like
that. In the 1930's they came up with this law, and
I had to go take an examination. I passed it and
I've been paying to keep my pharmacy license up
to date ever since, first two dollars a year, then five.

I got into pharmaceutical manufacturing when
a fellow came in with a prescription that had a lot
of poison in it, strychnine sulfate, I think it was.
He asked for a quick computation of how much
strychnine would be in each pill under the metric
system. (It was in avoirdupois.) After I gave him a
fast calculation, he took me to see the president of
his company, who asked me to take charge of a
problem. They were making everything under the

sun from barrels of liquid hand soaps to copies of brand-name corn plasters. Their formulas were mostly trademark imitations. They had a tank car, it looked like, of spoiled cough syrup they hoped to salvage—thousands of gallons they didn't want to take a loss on, y'know. I said I'd see what I could do, but first I wanted them to clean the place up. It was pretty dirty for a block-long plant. I figured if I couldn't do anything with the cough medicine, I would throw it in the sewer, myself. They put me on a nice salary for those days, fifty dollars a week.

First thing, I insisted they hire a chemist—they got a kid just out of Fordham or Rutgers, for eighteen dollars a week. Then I told them to fire the supervisor in the liquids department, he was spoiling everything that was made there. I don't have the heart for stepping on someone else, but this guy was the root of all evil. He didn't know what he was doing half the time, I think he drank the stuff. The tablet supervisor was *definitely* an alcoholic. He'd come back from lunch all woozy and anything could happen. He was twice my age and needed the job, big family and all, so I hated to say anything. But after a week, I talked to the boss. The upshot was, he threw out a lot of key people and put me in full charge. I said I'd get everything ship-shape in six weeks, or they could have the job. But meanwhile, I needed carte blanche to set up a system of controls and records so we could tell what we were doing. It was a mess, largely because the place was full of relatives with no qualifications, no experience. There were 35 girls in the packaging department, which was supervised by the owner's cousin, a real nitwit. So it wasn't easy to straighten them out. I'd say they had 75 employees, almost everybody related. But that's typical of these outfits. . . ."

QUESTION: Whatever happened to all that spoiled cough syrup?

CHARLIE: Oh, I revamped it—you might put this under the category of "product development." I took what they had, assayed it to see how much of each ingredient they had there, and how much it had deteriorated. Then I fortified it and put in a few more things so they would have a good palatable product. They used it all up and got reorders. Do you know, they still have that item in their catalog!

QUESTION: Were they making only over-the-counter items, or did they produce prescription drugs, too?

CHARLIE: Were they making only over-the-counter items, came on the scene and they were in a lot of hot water with FDA. They had a couple of dozen counts against them for substandard salves and ointments, and a citation to go to the FDA District Office for a hearing to explain their side of it. The boss lit out for Florida—every time he got a legal paper, he headed for Florida—and I had to represent them, since I was the only registered pharmacist in the place. All their lawyers came with me, of course, so I picked up quite a bit of useful legal know-how. Later, they sent me to Washington for hearings, and I got to know the Attorney General and a man who was Assistant FDA Commissioner, at that time.

QUESTION: Why did you leave that job?

CHARLIE: We got into a mess with another company, which is now much bigger and considered highly ethical: their executives are active in drug trade associations and all. Reformed. But in those days, they did cut a lot of corners. They supplied us with some substandard active ingredients like, well, oh, —I don't want to pinpoint anyone because they were all doing things like this. There had been no assaying going on to speak of. This material was supposed to be 100 percent active when it came to us and it was more like 60 percent. The supplier

and one of my bosses were buddies, so they made
an arrangement whereby I was supposed to doctor
it up, add things to bring it up to potency, so as
not to cause any more FDA trouble. *But* when I
went to do this, the other partner said, "Why
bother—who will know?" I said, "*I* will know,
that's who! I'm gonna do it so I can stand behind
it." I was wasting my breath, he didn't know what
an assay was and he didn't care. He arranged things
so that shipments went out before I'd ever get the
assay—sometimes they were sent out 50 percent
under strength. First thing you know, *I* am called
on the carpet to explain all this to FDA. But I'm
getting ahead of my story—in the meantime, the
supplier and his so-called research director are getting very nervous and they keep trying to take me
to lunch to talk things over at their fancy drug and
chemical club downtown. I told them I could buy
my own lunches. I wish I could have afforded to
stay that independent. When I was called to testify,
there they were with their lawyers in the back of
the room glaring at me. I knew they could black-
ball me in the industry. I didn't want to be a dead
pigeon, so I kept my mouth shut, quit that job,
and moved on.

Charlie described an experience he had on a later job:

That little shyster [one of the owners] didn't have
any consideration for people at all. He wanted me
to make up ten million dummy capsules. "We'll
make a haul, then we'll quit," this little phony
said. I listened to him, let him get through his
spiel, then I said, "I think *you're* the biggest
dummy I ever met, and if I didn't know you all
these years, I'd throw you down the stairs." Imagine! This was a prescription drug he was talking
about: a doctor would make a diagnosis of a condition and order a drug of a particular strength,
and weeks could pass with nothing happening.

People could die. Or a condition could become chronic that might have been cleared up in a couple of days. Did [this drug manufacturer] care? Not him! Now his partner is more of a decent sort —he doesn't know what's going on over there. He's like an absentee landlord, just signs the checks.

Further Adventures of Abe and Bert

Later, Abe and Bert had decided to dissolve their partnership and set up two apparently different corporations; actually, through relatives, they held stock in each other's firm and traded equipment, workers, raw materials, and orders back and forth as if the operations were under one roof. There were no written records of these transactions.

Their long-time friend and consultant, Chameleon, located a run-down chemical factory in the New Jersey swamps for Abe. The place was incorporated under his daughter's married name, and christened, shall we say, Barbara-Ann Laboratories. Business was very good right from the start: Abe tableted hormones, tranquilizers, and other prescription drugs for sale to generic distributors, who then sold them to druggists, hospitals, nursing homes, and government agencies. One of his friends tableted and packaged a famous tranquilizer for the patent-owner, a major drug company. The demand for the drug was so great that even the big company couldn't fill all the orders in their own laboratories, so part of the work was farmed out. The subcontractor, in turn, asked Abe to help him out on the Q.T. This type of thing leads to the lending of trademarked punches and dies for tableting machines.

As soon as Abe got his hands on these, he immediately sent them to a tool and die company in the Midwest to have duplicates made. Chameleon had told him these people would do anything for a price, even though they had a good business making punches and dies for a number of large ethical drug companies. They charged about $800 to copy this particular set. The originals were returned promptly to Abe's subcontractor friend and no one was the wiser.

Abe did little work involving capsules, but he was storing

Chameleon's Markem machine, which prints the trademarks on the capsules in ink. One day he was discussing the gravure rollers, or "wheels" for the Markem, with a former salesman for Chameleon:

ABE: This engraver wants $1,400 for putting "SK&F" on the blank wheel. It would only cost SK&F $40 for the same thing, but this guy knows it's an under-the-table deal. He figures we're going to make a bundle, so *he* wants to make a buck. It's not tricky work, it's just the idea of the thing. You can't get it done by Markem—Markem is legit. You can't go by them and say, "Here, make me an SK&F on this plain wheel." But with this guy—no questions asked. Give him the sample. Say, "Bill it to Joe Blow." He don't give a damn.

EX-SALESMAN: That's OK for you and Mr. Polished Fingernails, but you gotta have money to start with. I gotta throw some food on the table. I gotta pay the rent. I'm embarrassed to tell you how broke I am. Honestly.

Abe saw a chance here to help the fellow make some money fast, and at the same time take care of an important western drug distributor, Big Mex, who had been hounding him for "footballs," the oval-shaped orange pep pills fancied by some truck drivers. They could not be punched out on regular compressors that rotate while making round tablets because this would break the oddly shaped dies and upper punches. The machine's head had to be taken back to the factory to be "key-wayed"—fixed so the punches wouldn't rotate. In his plant, Abe had a line of "key-wayed" tablet compressors going full blast. But they were all tied up making heart-shaped green and orange pep pills of amphetamine for distribution to pharmacies.

SK&F had introduced hearts in 1949 as a prescription medication for obesity, depression, and other conditions; but the heart-shape was immediately copied throughout the country. Even some pharmacists were found punching out their own supply of SK&F

hearts on machines in their basements. Abe said, "Hearts aren't my biggest money-makers—but, it's a way of ingratiating myself because big distributors never get enough. They depend on my supply. Druggists have to have hearts to get people into the store. In the end, I get other business out of it." Abe was hardly operating at a loss: it cost him about 25 cents to make a thousand hearts, which he sold at the wholesale price of $6.

Abe gave the down-at-the-heels salesman an old single-punch machine (his busy heart machines had 16 punches), and told him to take it down to be key-wayed. He explained that it could be put in a closet at home and operated manually until the salesman got the hang of it. Then, hooked up to electricity, it could punch out around 5,000 tablets an hour, depending upon how hard one wanted to work. The speed was adjustable. Even a few hours a day would bring in what Abe called, "a nice piece of change." A set of punches and dies for hearts, as well as footballs, were passed along just in case.

Abe pointed out that it was incredible how many 5-milligram tablets you could get from just a pound of the active ingredients: something like 90,000 hearts, with the excipients (inactive sugars, binders, etc.) mixed in. The total cost of all raw materials shouldn't run more than $25 per pound, he said.

The salesman wouldn't need any special equipment, Abe explained. The dry materials could be mixed by rolling them on the floor in a small fiber drum, the kind chemicals are shipped in. Then the mixture could be dumped into a large enamel pan (the salesman had an old-fashioned baby bathtub that was just the thing). The food coloring had to be carefully added—this was the real tricky part—and worked in with the hands. "You have to get your hands dirty"(!). Next, he said to add a starch paste to dampen, just like for clothes. Then, rub all this through a screen —a window screen was fine. Dry the granules in a low oven, then put them through a Foley vegetable mill (the salesman used a potato ricer). Oven-dry overnight. Then the granulation was ready for the machine. The compressor exerted about four tons pressure, forming hard tablets.

The salesman would spoil a lot of tablets at first, they would be too thick, or too crumbly, or the color wouldn't be right, but after a day or two, it would be "as easy as tossing together a cake mix, and a heck of a lot more profitable!" The salesman told his wife that he was making vitamin C and it would bring in a lot of money, so she didn't complain about the mess in her kitchen. In fact, she helped him a great deal. Their children counted the tablets into the unlabeled plastic bottles, and the family car was used to haul raw materials and deliver the finished goods. The only problem seemed to be their nervous irritability and insomnia, which they didn't realize came from inhaling dust from amphetamine, the active ingredient, at close quarters. (A man who tableted hormones without proper ventilation developed enlarged breasts. Properly run drug companies, of course, take special precautions to protect workers from dangerous drugs)

Abe, the obliging subcontractor, now had his own subcontractor, a very common arrangement in these circles. He never turned down an order, no matter how busy. When a man came in wanting a poisonous substance made up in tablet form for use in a garden spray, he said, "No problem, I'll work it in." The customer was aghast when he dropped by to pick up part of the order; Abe wasn't bothering to clean his machines between runs of poison pellets and medications. It was unbelievable! This man went home extremely upset, knowing that he should *do* something. Acting on a good impulse, he called Chief Inspector Clem Westerly and described exactly what he had seen and where.

Inspector Oscar Cohen was immediately dispatched to inspect Abe's drug plant. It was a new corporation, therefore on the priority list for inspection during this first year of operation, but there were dozens of similar plants ahead of it, so it probably would not have been given an inspection for some weeks or months. The order for pellets would have been completed by then.

Down through the years, Oscar Cohen's negative reports had prevented Abe from shipping drugs in interstate commerce from one of his companies; and had caused him to lose a government contract in another. This time, surely, he would be barred from the drug business forever. After inspecting Barbara-Ann Laboratories, Oscar wrote:

> Quality controls virtually nonexistent. No control lab on the prem
> ises and no employee qualified to operate such a lab. No checks
> made of raw materials; almost none of finished products. Metal
> fragments from broken screens in coating pans might get into

tablets being made. Production carried on in crowded, congested, disorganized areas. . . . Samples were collected of [almost 200] different drug products manufactured by the firm. [Analyses revealed measurable quantities of poisonous substances X and Y in almost 100 of these samples.] Investigation showed manufacture of [poisons] in regular drug-making equipment without any cleaning of equipment afterward.

Since the firm had no batch records, there was no way for FDA to determine when the pellet production actually had begun, or how many medications were affected. Abe and his workers were uncommunicative, except to deny all charges in the face of the undeniable evidence in the FDA report:

> Multicolored powders in the Fitz Mill and skirts [cloth funnels] clearly showed the manufacture of more than one product without adequate cleaning. Workers insisted that equipment was always cleaned after each run, but this is false since the entire operation was observed. There was no cleaning, nor were there facilities for cleaning anything in the granulation room. Tablet compressor heads had green as well as pink material adhering to them. Coating pans contained thick encrustations. Floors throughout the plant were so filthy they could not be cleaned by washing—it was necessary to bring in pneumatic hammers to break up the encrustations.

A Notice of Hearing was issued to provide Abe with what can only be considered "an alibi hour," all part of the FDA gentlemanly aproach to regulating gentlemen. And alibi he did: "We have *tried* to do the proper thing and have never *deliberately* done anything wrong." His application for State Board of Pharmacy permission to operate this factory was reviewed and found to contain not only simple lies, but also fancy embellishments: he claimed to have a registered pharmacist superintendent—none other than Charlie, who had never even seen the place. He mentioned a nonexistent chemist operating an imaginary laboratory, and he went so far as to list the elaborate equipment contained therein. Why he felt compelled to conjure up a "working library and reference room," when these are not basic requirements, is anybody's guess. Perhaps he was just nurturing his lifelong dream of being "big and ethical" without going to the bother and expense of making it come true. Abe had made enough money by this time; his fabrications could have been realities.

Since 1962, FDA has required prospective drug producers to send in for a registration number, which is mailed to them free of charge. According to FDA, the assignment of the official number does not indicate that the drug plant has *passed* inspection, it simply means that it is registered *for* inspection, which is supposed to take place during the first year of operation and once every two years after that. FDA does not have enough inspectors to keep people like Abe under constant surveillance. But when they receive a complaint like this, they act immediately. They cannot, however, keep complainants informed on their follow-up, so public-spirited citizens sometimes are left with the impression that nothing is being done.

Few customers, and even fewer employees, make complaints. Nobody else really knows what's going on.

Before the charges were filed against Barbara-Ann Laboratories, state authorities recalled around 70 lots of drugs out of the un-determined quantity distributed and ordered the plant closed. One product appeared to be dangerous in itself, without the added threat of contamination from poison pellets. Apparently intended for weight-reduction, it contained 30 milligrams of am-phetamine mixed with several grains of thyroid. (The customary dose of amphetamine is 5 milligrams three times a day, or 15 milligrams to be released over a period of 12 hours.) The only reasonable uses for such a high stimulant dose might be in cases of narcolepsy, a rare disease characterized by excessive sleepiness; or, to counteract an overdose of depressants, but in such an emergency, stimulants would probably be more effective when administered intravenously. In any event, what was the thyroid doing there? Even in glandular obesity, where both thyroid and appetite-suppressants like amphetamine are prescribed, careful physicians prefer to have the medications taken separately. I checked with outside medical authorities to determine whether it was basically irresponsible to manufacture such a product, and concluded that this "shotgun mixture" was as disreputable as the man who produced it. Furthermore, it was so carelessly com-pounded, government chemists found that all of the active ingre-dients were released within one hour—a tremendous jolt that could have disastrous consequences for people with weak hearts or unstable nervous systems.

The FDA recommended prosecution. There was "adulteration" and, also, "misbranding" because poisonous substances X and Y were not listed as ingredients on the drug labels(!); and there was a violation of the New Drug Law since "there was no effective New Drug Application on file" for the amphetamine-thyroid concoction.

Abe was not brought to justice for almost a year. Federal case-preparation is time-consuming and exasperating, especially when the accused has taken every possible precaution against being held legally responsible. Handwriting experts had to be consulted in order to trace bank checks to accounts held under assumed names—that sort of thing. Abe's lawyers—one, a former Assistant U.S. Attorney; another, experienced in representing Chameleon— were masters of delaying tactics. In his first appearance before the Federal judge, Abe entered a plea of not guilty to all counts involving adulteration, and he was not in court again for six months. When he next appeared, the plea had been changed to guilty on two counts; the other counts were dismissed. Imposition of Abe's sentence was suspended and he was placed on probation for three years. The judge admonished him to "stay out of the food and drug business" during that time. The Secretary of Barbara-Ann Laboratories, a technician I'll call Dave, was told that he would not be permitted to own a drug firm, but since drug production was his only means of livelihood, he could continue to work in the trade. He had been in direct charge of the all-purpose production line.

Abe's attorney had asked for mercy on the grounds that the firm was now defunct and the unfortunate owner was "destitute." The Federal prosecutor representing the people, when asked by the judge whether he had any specific recommendations, had none. Yet the Justice Department had been informed by the FDA that this was an exceedingly serious matter. The only statement the Assistant U.S. Attorney appears to have made is one substantiating Abe's plea of poverty.

Abe, Bert, Dave, Erv, Dr. F., et al:

Abe has set up a generic drug business in a new building "owned" by a physician relative. He is there every day from morning until night, ostensibly just an interested observer, since his name is not connected with the firm in any way. The plant is supervised by a bright young man, Erv, who worked as Bert's production manager for several years after graduation from a New York school of pharmacy. (The current president of Bert's company, Dr. F., officially keeps an eye on that production line. But, actually, these professional figureheads spend much of their time as glorified salesmen. Dave is still the man-of-all-work "out back," where the manufacturing goes on.)

Abe, Bert, Chameleon, Dave, and others have held many discussions about setting up drug plants—it is, after all, something of chronic problem. They exchange information on small factories that can be rented for $1,800 a month. Fifty-thousand dollars buys a modern building suitable for drug production. Equipment is extra, of course, but one counterfeit operation made $50,000 a month with $900 worth of broken-down machinery. In another case, application for a Small Business Administration loan of $200,000 was considered the best financing bet. (This may turn out to be more in the nature of a government "grant.")

At any rate, Abe finally cast off his "*schlock*-shop" image. The company letterhead carries a typically reassuring slogan on the order of PUrity-REliability-ECOnomy, from which a firm name like PURECO Products may be abstracted. The ingenuity of pharmaceutical fly-by-nights is nowhere better demonstrated than in the way they come up with a dozen new corporate names in as many years, all the while playing musical chairs with company directors and hopscotch with the New York-New Jersey-Pennsylvania maps.

Where Abe is concerned, that slogan from the good old days has proved reliable, "They may have us down, but so far, we are not out. . . . Everything'll be all right in the morning." During an illicit drug transaction not long ago he remarked that he would never be "too high and mighty to be interested in making money." However, since he had made almost $20,000 legitimately the month before, he pointed out that he was confining his outside-normal-channels activities to "big hits." He was talking in terms of one million tablets per.

FDA's 14-page summary of evidence to support current charges against Abe includes this statement:

Recordings were made of every conversation and they are being retained under seal and in a locked cabinet until needed. All meetings . . . and, in most instances, transferring of drugs . . . were witnessed by New York District's surveillance team. Photographs were taken of the meetings on [dates] and the negatives have been submitted in sealed envelopes. . . . A "routine" inspection of [Abe's] company was made. . . . Invoices were reviewed. . . . No records were located covering any of [Abe's] sales between [dates]. . . . [The report concludes:] During the undercover investigation, [Abe's] remarks paint a clear picture of his attitude toward selling drugs illegally. He cautioned against dealing with truck drivers and others close to the end of the distribution line and suggested sticking to individuals further up. [From FDA transcript:] "when you're the chief source, and you're *also* involved in distribution, you're dead! How can you deny anything? You got the plant, haven't you, mister? You own the punches, don't you, mister? In fact, *you* run the whole business—*What* can you say to that? The closer you have the operation down to the roots, the more dangerous it is." There is no doubt that this man will violate the FD&C Act whenever the money involved is attractive enough, even though he violates his Federal probation in the process. He has the intelligence, experience, and connections to insure a good chance for success in any illegal operation of of this type. He is well acquainted with FDA's means of proving I. S. [interstate drug movement]* through identifying punch marks and with other techniques used by our agency. . . . We should make every effort to prosecute him for his flagrant violations of the FD&C Act and try to remove him from the drug business once and for all. In this way we may prevent him from negotiating any more "big hits" which result in millions of drugs getting into bootleg channels.

Abe's legitimate business is the production of nonbranded prescription drugs known as generics. Although these may be potent medications for sick people, he has always tried to get by with the cheapest available labor. His employees, judging from their em-

---

*Sales (witnessed by author) took place in New Jersey. Drugs purchased included amphetamine footballs for specified delivery to "truck-drivers out West and night-club owners in Baltimore," and amphetamine " 'crossroads' for a customer in Connecticut." There is no known manufacturer of amphetamine salts in New Jersey. Therefore, this case involves both interstate movement of raw materials and uninvoiced, unlabeled, finished dosage forms. However, some Federal prosecutors do not accept such recorded statements as proof of delivery for interstate shipment.

ployment histories, production fiascos, and recorded conversations, are an unstable lot. While running pharmaceuticals through machines some have 1,001 *other* things on their minds, such as setting up their own drug plant somewhere with stolen formulas, punches, and materials. There is little job security and few, if any, employees can look forward to a gold watch and a pension after faithful service. What they are more inclined to do is figure out a way to beat the boss at his own game.

Abe often complains about his personnel: "This coater [X] didn't show up again. I have to have [Y] working for two days on the coating pans, and [Z] doubling up until [X] comes back. This is killing me! There's lots of good business around! One of these days I'm gonna fire the lot of them and start over from scratch. I tell you, the *aggravation. . . .*"

Inspector Oscar Cohen expressed considerable aggravation himself as he described what FDA inspectors find in plants where the management is irresponsible or downright dishonest, and the supervisors and technicians are ignorant, poorly trained, disgruntled, or otherwise inadequate. Running oral medications through machinery contaminated with poisons is just one of many life-threatening practices all too frequently encountered. Here are some others that have caused deaths and serious illnesses in consumers:

—The production of drugs from recalculated preceding batch-production records, instead of from accurate reproduction of a master formula. This can be a little like jotting down a family meat loaf recipe for six on the back of an envelope, then scaling it up to serve 300 at a church supper or down for a twosome—it's hard not to end up with too much or too little salt. There is danger in on-the-spot, unverified calculations of types and amounts of drug ingredients, especially when some operators use the metric system, some the apothecary, and others, both. Hastily scrawled abbreviations can cause DES (diethylstilbestrol, a potent hormone) to be substituted for DAS (d-amphetamine sulfate, a stimulant). After a patient died from salicyclic poisoning, and others were made quite ill, FDA inspectors learned that sodium salicylate had been substituted by mistake for PAS (sodium paraminosalicylic acid). Other violations of good manufacturing practices in this same plant included running the granulation for Drug X into a drum labeled for Drug Y.
—Careless packaging, and, especially, mislabeling, account for most

drug mix-ups. To save money, labels for many different drugs are sometimes "gang-printed" in large sheets. The printer's mistakes may go undetected, and sheets are easily intermixed, as are cut labels stored helter-skelter. The practice of prelabeling empty containers increases the possibility for errors. One such container rolled off its pile, was misplaced on another, and subsequently filled with the wrong drug. A patient almost died as a result.

—Cross-contamination among several drugs occurs when clean and contaminated pieces of equipment are stacked together, or when dust from other drugs settles. Vitamins contaminated with hormones have caused preschool youngsters to develop puberty symptoms and to become sexually precocious.

—A common, hazardous practice involves the production of visually identical drugs—round, unmarked white tablets, for instance—in the same area and, even, at the same time. An aspirin bottle with penicillin tablets in it could have serious consequences. (FDA is currently cracking down on drugs contaminated with no more than traces of penicillin dust. Since penicillin is fluffy and hard to control, reputable manufacturers are spending millions of dollars to eliminate this type of contamination—some are even putting up separate buildings for penicillin production.)

Drugs in liquid form are subject to mix-ups, too. A pharmacy professor described what he found when he visited several generic manufacturing plants, after his university's hospital decided to economize by buying nonbranded drugs. He said, "They wanted to cut costs and look good in the eyes of the administrator." Since the school of pharmacy has no jurisdiction over the purchasing agent at the hospital, the professor's tour was strictly for his own information.

"One plant had an area as big as an aircraft hanger. In the middle of this were 500-gallon tanks of 70 percent alcohol, used to mix about half-a-dozen drugs being bottled separately. After the mixtures were squirted into identical pint bottles, they were stacked in crates. On top of each crate was a loose piece of paper identifying the drug. They waited until the end of the week to label the bottles. It was so drafty in there, I couldn't help wondering how often the pieces of paper were blown away. You couldn't tell the difference between the drugs just by looking at the liquids in the bottles. Not long ago a product labeled castor oil turned out to be turpentine oil. Usually, a whole bottle of several ounces of castor oil is quickly swallowed or mixed in juice to avoid tasting it too much. The difference wasn't detected and there were some deaths.

"The testing of a liquid product's stability before it is marketed is another neglected area. Antibiotic syrups for children have been found to be more than 50 percent deteriorated. Also, FDA warns that suspensions, ointments, and suppositories should be thoroughly blended to insure uniformity; some hormone suspensions have been encountered ranging from 50 to 140 percent of labeled strength because of improper mixing."

The professor asked several generic producers whether they assayed the products they produced, and they replied that they did not because they made them from materials that were up to U.S. Pharmacopoeia (USP) standards. What happened to the drugs during packaging hardly bears thinking about. The professor saw a girl filling bottles with drugs by using a measuring device operated by a foot pedal. Several times she accidentally bumped the pedal, spilling the drugs on a dirty surface. She scooped them up with her bare hands and put them into the container, which went on down the production line. In this plant, production workers were unable—even if they wished—to follow good manufacturing practices because facilities were so primitive.

An Army drug procurement officer and friend of the professor, checking on medical suppliers, found a drug firm producing generics for a large mail order company as well as for the Armed Forces without any pretense of following rudimentary public health measures: workers had to climb three flights and go to the rear of the building for the nearest washroom, where two of the three toilets were boarded up and the third wouldn't flush. Only cold water was available in the sink, and there were no towels, toilet paper, or soap in the room. When the Army officer asked the plant manager, a lawyer, whether drugs were assayed, he replied that they used "USP materials from reliable sources." Presumably, he thought nothing would harm them.

The professor explained that when an aspirin tablet is assayed by the USP method, it is checked only for the labeled amount of acetylsalicylic acid, plus a few other tests for such things as iron, which might have scraped off machinery. The drugs are not assayed for the presence of filth or contamination. The girl operating the foot pedal was supervised by a pharmacist. However, the professor said: "He was busy doing something else—guess you can't be all places at once. But he later went into a spiel about how they were going to produce a certain non-prescription drug in sealed, individual packets, so it would be 'more sanitary.' Since their manufacturing procedures were so unsanitary, there was no logic to this at all, except as an advertising gimmick to fool the unsuspecting public.

"I next visited the brand new laboratory of a manufacturer of duplicate prescription items," the professor continued. "In other words, they prepared USP aspirin and so forth for sale to pharmacists. I don't see how the employees stood the working conditions. In one room there were at least ten tableting machines pounding out various drugs, including penicillin and also saccharine, at an adjacent machine. You could hardly see across the room, the drug dust was so thick."

The professor of pharmacy summed up: "A drug company is only as good as the man or men directing it. In a small outfit, there may be only one decision-maker. If he is honest and well qualified—or if he hires competent people—there is no reason why his product should be inferior. If he is dishonest, or careless, it's a different story. His irresponsibility is reflected all down the line; he repels conscientious workers, attracts the type willing to go along with him. They may have been well trained, they may know the dangers to the consumer, but they just don't care. In major drug companies, among hundreds or thousands of employees, there will always be some who are careless. Despite the elaborate systems of checks and balances that are standard in these vast operations, not all human errors are caught in the plant. Mislabeled or otherwise mixed-up drugs do get out on the market and have to be recalled. When this happens to a Squibb, or a Merck, or a Lederle product, it becomes front-page news because their names make news. Many stockholders are concerned, for one thing. But it is ridiculous to imagine the president, board of directors, and key production people of such large corporations conniving together to turn out potentially dangerous drugs for the sake of saving production costs, cutting corners. They have far too much to lose, and there are far too many employees involved. In a small, privately owned company, the command decisions are made by one man or several partners. From what I have observed in such places, when the boss gives an order, there is precious little backtalk."

What is the connection between drug counterfeiting and production of generic drugs? Dr. Erwin Di Cyan, a consulting chemist, has spelled it out:

> Everyone wants legitimate drugs at illegitimate prices. That impossible demand creates the climate in which counterfeit drugs can flourish. . . . A price is not a thing apart—it depends on the value of the commodity it buys. . . . The present crusade for reduction of prices offers, without reflection, the use of generic names as a panacea. . . . The pressure to prescribe under generic name is purportedly to save the patient's pocketbook. But who will protect the patient? Public enlightenment is badly needed. And, above all, well-meaning individuals who agitate for generic name drugs should also be given all the facts.
>
> How many know that, although only rarely is a generic drug producer a counterfeiter, nearly every counterfeiter also produces generic name drugs?

BERT AND HIS T-D'S

Bert, Abe's erstwhile partner, hadn't been sitting on his hands. He went into what is known as the T-D business, dosage forms designed for time-disintegration, especially hard-shell capsules filled with tiny, medicated seeds. A scientist at Smith Kline & French Laboratories in Philadelphia created this type of slowly dissolving medication after looking at a candy display—his idea is based upon the penny jawbreaker principle with its multiple coatings. There now are countless imitative drugs on the market visually identical with SK&F Spansule capsules—70 products are made to look exactly like Dexedrine and Dexamyl, except for the SK&F monogram. Over 200 look-alikes compete with Contac, the cold remedy manufactured by Menley & James, the SK&F subsidiary.

SK&F pursues drug counterfeiters more actively than any other pharmaceutical firm; particularly commendable is their willing-

ness to share the results of company-financed investigations with
FDA. About the time SK&F was zeroing in on Bert, FDA undercover inspectors were making huge buys of counterfeit Dexedrine
and Dexamyl Spansule capsules, known in the gray market as
"green and clears" and "brown and clears," the colors of their
capsules or shells. Tiny green and white or peach and white seeds
contain the active ingredients inside.

A tour of SK&F's production line demonstrated that a Dexedrine Spansule is an extremely complicated drug to manufacture
despite its candy-dipping derivation. The ingredients alone are
given 150 tests for purity and consistency, while the finished
dosage forms are subjected to 1,170 checks and counterchecks. The
man responsible for SK&F's quality control is a Ph.D., formerly
head of the pharmacy department at the University of Kentucky.

Bert's methods of operation were revealed when individuals
suspected of patent infringement were subpoenaed for questioning:

FEMALE
EMPLOYEE
OF BERT: We've been in a constant state of change. There
            have been so many regimes, it's like a South Amer-
            ican country. I think the merchandise was given
            out for cash. I don't remember to who, it's like a
            million faces. Gee—there were so many mistakes!
            What's all this about, anyway?

BERT: Well, somebody bought, *theoretically* bought,
            capsules from us, which it is perfectly OK to manu-
            facture. But that somebody then went a step fur-
            ther and put "SK&F" on it, making it a counter-
            feit. They have to trace down where it was
            originally bought. Now nobody can remember who
            dealt with the counterfeiters—which is not a crime
            —but it *is* wrong.

EMPLOYEE: How would you counterfeit a pill? Why—

BERT: It's made for three cents and sold for three dollars
            on their name, SK&F, that's why they're complain-
            ing.

EMPLOYEE: Oh, now I get it. The manufacturers don't like it. Gee, I wish I could help you find these people, that would be marvelous! I'd like to find all the counterfeiters of currency and everything!

Bert was next asked whether he knew of a machine capable of marking the timed-disintegration capsules he produced with the initials SK&F. He denied ever seeing such a machine, but thought they were made by a company called Markem, for around $7,000. As an afterthought, he named three competitors who had them in their plants, but he neglected to mention the Markem machine in Abe's possession at that very moment. This convenient memory lapse continued.

QUESTION: Do you know [Lew]?

BERT: Is that a person or a place?

ANSWER: A person. [A wholesaler in a distant state.]

BERT: No.

GIRL (*Blurting*):   But that's a *very* familiar name—!

Bert now had to admit supplying Lew with large amounts of prescription drugs on special order. Extended questioning confirmed that Bert had just lately met with Lew in one of his retail pharmacies, described as "a busy madhouse," because of the tremendous business. However, as investigators continued to probe for more information about orders in the millions, Bert insisted that he was running a very modest outfit and was barely able to make ends meet. "We're not Rolls Royces, we're bikes!" he protested.

Inspector Oscar Cohen, meanwhile, was tying in information from confidential informants. He knew that a man who had picked up two million filled T-D capsules, which were imitation Dexedrine and Dexamyl without monograms, at Bert's company was "sorta short, sorta dark, sorta average." Probably he was the same man who arranged for the counterfeit labels and counterfeit punches with the printer and the engraver. It was not unreasonable to expect this mysterious stranger to turn up next in the Never-Never Land of drug distribution.

CHAPTER SIX

To The Never-Never Land

An FDA official told me:

To engage in a successful, extensive counterfeit operation, a means must be devised whereby the bogus drugs can be entered into legitimate channels of distribution. The primary target for the counterfeit drug producer is the wholesaler, who represents a large volume outlet with established retail contacts. The wholesaler may be a *sub rosa* operator who knows that the drugs are counterfeits; or he may be a wheeler-dealer type who buys if the price is right— no questions asked. Both types are obviously aware that the drugs offered have an illegal history of some kind because of the low price or circumstances of the transaction. However, their only concern is whether they can unload them at a substantial profit. The therapeutic quality is not questioned. They ask only that the drugs, be they stolen, distressed, or counterfeit, look enough like regular drugs to be saleable.

In addition to purchasing Bert's T-D dosage forms, Lew bought all his hearts from Abe and sold them to short-line jobbers as the genuine SK&F product for $22 a thousand, SK&F's own price. He rationalized this by saying that SK&F had no right to consider the heart shape their invention.

"Only God can make a heart," he declared. "Where does SK&F get off calling this their baby? It's ridiculous! I used to give my girl in sixth grade heart-shaped cinnamon candies for Valentine's

Day. The candy-makers have a right to scream that SK&F counterfeited *their* idea."

Various kinds of counterfeit drugs were being detected in pharmacies up and down the Eastern seaboard, as well as in California, Oklahoma, Texas, Illinois, North Carolina, Georgia, and Alabama. A good many of these had been traced back to Lew's wholesale headquarters. A major drug company, whose products were counterfeited, obtained a court order requiring Lew's appearance for the purpose of answering questions. The first depositions taken were unproductive; he refused to answer, demanded adjournments, would not supply records, broke dates, and, when threatened with contempt of court action, insisted that he was not refusing to answer the questions, he was just refusing to answer without legal counsel. But he would not call his lawyer.

When FDA sent inspectors to look over Lew's records pertaining to purchases and sales of the drugs in question, they reported that he "lied and used dilatory tactics" to prevent their obtaining this information. (The 1962 Kefauver-Harris Amendments make it mandatory that drug handlers, manufacturers, and distributors reveal to FDA their records showing origin and destination of all prescription drugs.) Lew went so far as to refuse FDA inspectors entry to his retail pharmacies. However, by sending in an undercover inspector with a doctor's prescription to be filled, FDA did obtain a drug sample and it proved to be counterfeit. The FDA report concluded that Lew is: "No novice in the illicit drug industry, he shows a definite criminal behavior pattern . . . arrests by local police for criminally receiving stolen goods . . . fines for selling misbranded drugs. . . . There is no question but that he is one of the more important principals in the nationwide distribution of counterfeit drugs."

Investigations conducted by drug companies and FDA in different parts of the country revealed that Lew had purchased large quantities of counterfeits from a number of sources. One was a buying and selling telephone service that never actually handled the drugs. Another was the shady dealer out West whom I call Big Mex. A third seemed to be connected in some way with The Group; Inspector Cohen and other men in the New York District continue to work on this facet of the case. But there were a bewildering number of other possibilities, as well.

It is becoming difficult to distinguish clearly between drug manufacturers and distributors, since there is a trend toward drug production on the part of large general-line wholesalers, and some manufacturers have their own wholesale branches. In between there are dealers, brokers, exporters, importers, jobbers, and others who handle drugs in wholesale amounts. Drug distribution is in a chaotic state, but three major selling methods emerge: (1) Sales exclusively through wholesalers. (2) Sales mostly through wholesalers, with a limited number of direct retail outlets. (3) Sales primarily through retailers.

Because a drug's price or discount can vary depending upon the status of the purchaser (druggist, hospital, government agency, etc.), the competition is like a finely honed two-edge sword; it works both ways. Manufacturers and wholesalers attempt to woo retailers by offering special deals, and by supplying extra services that may range from fancy displays to carpeting or piped-in hi-fi commercials. But, according to the Robinson-Patman Law, they must not discriminate between little drugstores in Podunk, and high-volume retailers in Times Square. There are other sticky wickets, such as the Supreme Court ruling in 1956 outlawing wholesale price maintenance, and so on. The retailers, on the other hand, are preoccupied with finding the best source for best-seller drugs. Take a leading tranquilizer like Librium, for example. Hoffman-La Roche, the producer, derives half of its $100-million-plus business from this product, offered to wholesalers for 15 percent discount off the list price, and to retailers at 12 percent. Commonly, an additional 2 percent discount is given for cash payment. Retailers would naturally like to buy all drugs at wholesale prices, if they possibly could. Some manufacturers and distributors may go along with this. It all depends. On what? There are no clear-cut answers. That's the problem.

One Western wholesaler said he sold prescription drugs for "not over 6 percent" of his cost. By his own admission, most of his supplies came from so-called diverters* in both wholesale and

---

*"Diversion" as used in the drug trade press has a broader application than FDA's "illegal sales." It has been applied to hospital prescription-filling for nonpatients; drug sales by mail; sales outside of sales territories, or sales by dealers lacking a franchise. When the drug handlers are registered or licensed, and keep proper records, these sales may still be legal.

retail channels. He also bought from exporters and distributors of repacked physicians' samples. (In addition, according to FDA, some drugs handled were counterfeit; he claimed he innocently bought counterfeits at the manufacturers' regular wholesale prices, thinking they were genuine.) FDA has found counterfeits of Diuril, HydroDiuril, Serpasil, Esidrix, Meticorten, Tedral, Miltown, and Equanil offered for *half the list price and less*—considerably cheaper than even the 6 percent above his cost offered by the Western wholesaler.

When major pharmaceutical manufacturers refuse to sell to certain wholesalers, they still manage to buy desired products through complicated cross-country rerouting systems involving dummy purchasers. Actually, drugs are often drop-shipped—that is, they can be billed to one drug store, but sent on to others. A private detective hired by manufacturers to trace their products, which included dangerous controlled drugs, reported that each of Wholesaler X's incoming shipments was "immediately stripped of all addresses, serial numbers, etc., and these were burned at the end of the day."

When questioned by FDA, such dealers state that where they get their merchandise is a "trade secret." They protest that franchise systems, minimum order requirements, and other trade restrictions "drive them to it." To maintain a Librium distributorship, for instance, it is necessary to purchase at least $30,000 worth of Hoffman-La Roche drugs per year in shipments of at least $1,000 each. However, the detective reported that Wholesaler X received as much as $50,000 worth of a single contraband drug at a time, and did a multi-million-dollar-a-year business.

Some companies, like Lederle, ship mostly through their own coast-to-coast branch offices. Carefully guarded, sealed refrigerator trucks with loads valued up to $500,000 make direct deliveries of large orders. Even so, diversion occurs through thefts from loading platforms, and armed robbery by hoodlum hijackers.

From the FBI and drug company security men, I compiled a list of hijacked loads of drugs. From among dozens of entries, here are a few cases: A Chicago wholesaler had $460,000 worth of Eli Lilly, Mead Johnson and other manufacturer's drugs stolen; part of the loot was found in a motel formerly owned by the reputed crime leader in Chicago . . . G. D. Searle reported hijackings of loads with wholesale values up to $75,000. Three armed ex-convicts kidnapped a Squibb driver in lower Manhattan and made off with $250,000 worth of antibiotics, which were recovered from a druggist who owned two stores. A Brooklyn mobster was arrested for an even more lucrative hijacking of Parke Davis antibiotics. Lederle Laboratories reported theft of $125,000 worth of anti-biotics from a tractor-trailer; nine men, including two pharma-cists, were arrested. In a West Coast case, a railroad car was moved from a drug warehouse siding and broken into. Hoffman-LaRoche products were hijacked by men conspiring with a pharmacist, who pleaded for mercy on the grounds that, "I did a lot of good things for people in my drugstore during the past 30 years." Wallace Laboratories learned that one unethical druggist was not content to sit by waiting for stolen goods. He approached one of their truckers and offered to buy "allegedly stolen" tranquilizers valued at $6,000 for $800.

No one knows the extent of drug diversion through hijacking and theft, but the total amount must be tremendous judging from these examples.

Regardless of where and how an unauthorized dealer obtains so-called diverted drugs, the "trade-secret" ploy seems his best way out, for if his sources were revealed they would probably be eliminated either by government or industry.

FDA is not concerned with fair trade, *per se*, but in the purity and safety of the drug products traded. The fact remains that clandestine transactions outside of normal business channels tend, by their very nature, to endanger consumers. Illicit drug distribu-tion gimmicks have involved the invoicing of one type of drug under the name of an entirely different one. Shipments have been sent to fictitious receivers, or to bona fide accounts without knowl-edge by that account, then intercepted by the sender for sale elsewhere. Drug company salesmen have rigged sales that even-tually permitted products to fall into the hands of price-cutters preying on their own companies. This is a type of hanky-panky similar to divergent forms of merchandising found in the home appliance and other fields. But there is a vital difference: the "merchandise" in question is life-saving medication. It may have a short shelf-life, or require refrigeration. It should be immediately identifiable and available for recall by the manufacturer in case of emergency. Drugs cannot be safely stored away like so many toasters until the best deal comes along.

At the retail end of the distribution chain, consider the plight of a community pharmacist who complained to a doctor, "This SK&F is a line very hard for me to come by. . . ." While a medical student, the doctor had detailed (sold drugs) for another company, whose local wholesaler might be able to help the pharmacist. This was the deal the wholesaler offered: the invoices were typed out as sales of a trade-marked hormone he was authorized to sell, but penciled lightly in the margin was "Dexedrine." However, the community pharmacist did not receive the drug then and there, but had to pick it up under an assumed name at another drug store. He became suspicious. After inspecting the Dexedrine, he decided that the white seeds seemed to cling together more than in another lot of the drug he had on hand. Maybe it was just his imagination—but he decided to discuss this with a colleague. The fellow-pharmacist advised him to arrange for an official analysis by the state drug people, but in a roundabout way, so his name wouldn't be involved. The drugs proved to be counterfeit.

The community pharmacist then had the ticklish problem of recalling some of his shipment that he had sold to *other* pharmacists. There were harsh words about liability, because the counterfeits had been dumped into large stock bottles and mixed with authentics. It was now impossible to tell how many had been dispensed, to whom, and with what results. Since the wholesaler who faked the invoices refused to divulge his source, that seemed a dead end.

But FDA was working toward this very source from several other directions, aided by a few guarded statements made by Lew in his depositions. (The wholesaler finally began to talk after some of his customers were investigated and started filling in the record for their own satisfaction.) One such was a rugged individualist I shall call the Mail-Order Man. He has drug discounts spinning around in his head like wheels in a clock: "Some manufacturers will give a discount ranging anywheres from 10 to 25 percent and wholesalers offer goods anywheres from 5 to 15 off list. Wyeth gives the wholesaler only 10. Mead gives 15. Jobbers offer you anywheres from 12 and 2 . . . sometimes 10 and 3 . . . and on and on."

Around the first of the year Lew had called to ask the Mail-Order Man if he would like a good deal on some "export" drugs. The drugs were a best-seller stimulant and a leading tranquilizer. Although Lew pushed especially hard to sell the stimulant, the Mail-Order Man ordered the tranquilizer, sending Lew $25,000 just before leaving on a short trip. Upon his return he was alarmed to find that the tranquilizer had not arrived. More frantic telephone calls followed, with Lew insisting that he was doing everything possible to trace the shipment, which he now suggested might have been hijacked. Lew said that he had called the such-and-such police precinct to report the loss. The Mail-Order Man, who did business in another part of that Western state, found there was no such precinct in Lew's city. He demanded his money back. Lew said he didn't have it, but, as security, he would ship an equivalent amount of the stimulant. The Mail-Order Man said that having this was better than nothing, but he still wanted the tranquilizer. He turned to the FBI for help on the supposed hijack, but since it wasn't an interstate matter, they couldn't intervene. Finally, he hired a private detective to investigate.

Meanwhile, the Mail-Order Man invested in special mailings to unload the extra stimulant, only to discover that Lew had offered the same advantageous discount to competitors who were buying only a few bottles at a time. What was worse, Lew was selling it direct himself at an even cheaper price! Enraged, Mr. Mail-Order called to tell Lew that he was "killing the market," but found himself buying up all the remaining stimulant Lew had in stock, to keep it from going to his rivals.

At this point, he learned from his customers that the stimulant he had been selling them was counterfeit. Some were wholesale druggists themselves who complained about being investigated by state and Federal inspectors and industry representatives. Customers were being driven from their doors by all the talk of counterfeits. And they were furious.

The Mail-Order Man insisted that he had bought the stimulant in good faith from a licensed wholesaler, and that all purchases

were billed by regular invoices and paid by check. He claimed
not to have heard about drug counterfeiting before. But when
questioned, he admitted that *something* seemed funny about the
stimulant before the complaints came in. The backs of the bottles
were sticky. When he had asked Lew about this, he was told that
foreign labels had been removed from the bottles. The story was
that "these drugs were left over from a mission of mercy abroad."

The Mail-Order Man decided he wanted nothing more to do
with this particular deal, so he agreed to take a dated check from
Lew for his $25,000, plus notes to equal the difference on the
additional stimulant purchases that were now being returned. He
was then almost immediately advised by Lew that the tranquilizer
shipment had just turned up (as if by magic?). "The wrong trucking company had it," was the explanation given. This was good
enough for the Mail-Order Man. Let by-gones be by-gones. This
was too good a deal to pass up.

Lew's counterfeit products were outward bound to still other
wholesalers around the country. Dealers receiving them lied under
oath, saying that they had never heard of the counterfeit drug
racket, even though FDA had evidence that they had previously
discussed counterfeits on three or four occasions while getting
their stories straight. Instead of pleading the Fifth Amendment,
they fell back on the I-cannot-divulge-trade-secrets plea. Some
distributors scoffed at the idea that drugs seized were counterfeit,
even after proof by chemical analysis: "FDA doesn't know what
it's talking about . . . All rumors. . . ." Others, knowing they were
dealing in counterfeits, still sent mailings to hundreds of pharmacists advertising rock-bottom specials. Some ran barter-and-
exchange operations, with virtually no records of drugs in and
out, or even of cash changing hands. "Only when we can't buy
an equal amount in barter, do we settle up by check," one said.
"If there's any kind of credit memo, it's written in Pig Latin—
some of my customers said they threw away the suspicious bottles
and took credit. They just sent me note saying—you could hardly
read it—'five dollars, subtract half-a-bottle disposed of.' You can't
argue with a customer. *Customers are hard to find!*"

FDA'S FOLLOW-UP SLEUTHING

Since FDA has no authority over the price of drugs, Chief Inspector Clem Westerly could hardly have been less interested in all the details on wholesale discounts, retail mark-ups, price-fixing charges, and anti-trust hassles that were forthcoming. What he wanted to know was—where did wholesalers like Lew get those counterfeit drugs?

Lew finally identified one source as a dealer in distressed merchandise who called himself "John Smith." He arrived out of the blue one day to offer a deal on "some export stuff" at several dollars cheaper per bottle than the going price. Lew gave him $18,000 cash, and agreed to pay the balance within six months, offering dated checks as notes. There were no records—not even Lew's bookkeeper knew of the transaction. Lew said this was not at all unusual. He made the checks payable to John Smith, but he had no idea where the man conducted his business. No business card was proffered. Smith was the "Don't call me, I'll call you" type.

A drug company attorney asked Lew: "Did he say where he obtained this salvaged material?"

LEW: Well, in salvage they never tell you exactly where they get it.

Lew explained that John Smith seemed to be a middleman, because he was continually checking back with his source. One day Smith saw a Triumph Electronic Counter worth almost $2,500 which Lew had bought to count tablets and capsules for a government order when he was still in the repackaging business. Smith asked if he could borrow the counter, with the idea of buying it later on. After some dickering, they agreed on a price of around $1,500. Smith said he needed it because he encountered a lot of broken bottles in the salvage business and he wanted to rebottle the spilled capsules. Lew observed that Smith ought to be careful because this was just a counter, not a cleaner, and gelatin capsules with glass particles in them "wouldn't be too good."

The counting machine was taken away, and Lew maintained that he completely forgot about it—what it was worth, how much he had coming on it—everything. In fact, he admitted its existence only after the attorney showed him the bill of sale from the company he had purchased it from. Next, he was shown a picture of Mannie—was this John Smith?

Lew said hundreds of people a day came into his place, how was he to remember! Deposition after deposition, he was shown the picture; never would he make a positive identification, nor would his attorney permit him to sign the depositions. The salvage dealer was described as having no outstanding characteristics: "medium height, medium weight, medium everything." However, the cashed check—which Lew eventually was obliged to produce— carried an endorsement on the back and certain scribbled notations that yielded valuable clues when compared with other handwriting samples being collected by the Chief Inspector. Lew did admit knowing Chameleon—he had had business dealings with him over the years. Too, he had ordered amphetamine T-D's from Bert, but he insisted that they were generics and not trademarked capsules.

When the last deposition was taken, 18 months had elapsed since the first, and what was there to show for it? Very little so far as the FDA was concerned. Slightly more for the drug company. They were asking a Federal judge for an injunction to prevent further counterfeiting of their products, pending the outcome of a civil suit filed against Mannie and others, including a printer.

THE PRINTER

The break came in the case of The Printer when private detectives, hired by pharmaceutical firms, trailed The Printer's young helper from Mannie's bar back to the shop. The bar was located near the diner where members of The Group liked to transact business over coffee, far from their constant fear of "bugging."

The Printer said that he first met Mannie when they were kids at the "Y" something like 30 years ago, and he hadn't heard from him for perhaps 10 years. Then one day Mannie telephoned an order—he was sending over a label he wanted copied. It was wrinkled and looked as if it had been soaked off a bottle, but after retouching with ink, reasonably good copies were reproduced. Next followed orders for package inserts, bottle sealers, and cartons. Had the printer noticed names on the labels—SK&F, Squibb, McNeil, Parke Davis, etc.? (Mannie was evidently dealing in, or preparing to deal in, potent antibiotics such as Mysteclin-F, Grifulvin, and Chloromycetin.) The Printer answered, "Frankly, with my glasses, I can't read small things too good." But he finally admitted that he had recognized Squibb and asked Mannie whether he was giving up his tavern and novelty factory to go into the drug business. Mannie retorted, "Look, anything we can make a buck with, any odd lots we can buy cheap and sell for a price, *that's* our business." The Printer observed: "It's not uncommon to find people dealing in distressed merchandise—even in spoiled drugs."

It developed that even in a small, job-lot print shop such as this, there were on hand all the materials needed for drug-counterfeiting "paper work." The Printer said: "We used Kromkote 70-pound paper for the labels; the cartons are the usual 16, 18, or 20 point clay-coated board; inserts call for a thin, lightweight bond, Ti-opaque; and the seals are printed on cheap waxed wrapping paper you can find in any butcher shop." For printing nearly 50,000 labels, he received about $2,000 in cash. He kept insisting that this was a legitimate order, one he made no attempt to conceal from his employees, but ran right through the shop in broad daylight. "Now, if I'd thought this was part of the commission of a crime—well, I may be stupid, but I don't think I'd consider $2,000 the price for my life!" he summed up.

The phrase, "price for my life," may or may not be significant. This case was dependent upon the testimony of The Printer's young helper who received the sample labels and payment in person. (The Printer said that he had never set eyes on Mannie or his representative during the entire transaction.) Just as attorneys were about to question The Printer's helper, they learned that he was dead.

As for the specific crime of printing counterfeit drug labels, this act violated a state statute prohibiting the counterfeiting of anything of value. (But only if the product is represented by the seller to the buyer as "genuine." If it is truthfully sold as a counterfeit, the state law does not apply.) It did not violate the FD&C

Act until the labels were actually affixed to containers of drugs in interstate commerce; then it was considered "misbranding."*

A drug company charged in its Federal civil suit that in one counterfeiting operation, drugs made by unknown persons and valued at $500,000 were misbranded. This caused "confusion, mistakes and deceptions" when purchasers were led to believe that bottles bearing the company's trademarks, address, and lot numbers actually contained the genuine product. The company asked for treble and punitive damages and for permanent injunctions forbidding the defendants from further counterfeiting their labels, packaging, etc., and from infringing their trademarks. It was two years before this injunction was granted. At a pretrial conference, the drug company was awarded damages of over $500,000, but they will be lucky to collect five cents.

Meanwhile, Chief Inspector Clem Westerly sent Oscar Cohen and other inspectors into the field for about eight months of grubby digging. Among other things, they were looking for facts on custom-designed cardboard dividers, which were used to separate glass drug bottles inside the cartons. These were not made up by the printer. The FDA, as well as drug company detectives, were searching through bank and other business records; consulting with police and FBI handwriting experts; and following through on chemical analyses of the white gravure inks used to imprint trademarks on capsules.

More and more counterfeits of all kinds were appearing. The Chief Inspector was particularly anxious to solve the mystery of the counterfeit metal bottle tops: when alcohol was applied to them, it dissolved a cover-up coating of black paint and underneath three small initials appeared. (The authentic bottle caps had no such initials under their black paint.) One day in a supermarket, he found a bottle of flavoring with a similar cap and those same three initials in plain sight. The flavoring producers bought the caps from Such-and-Such Company, which, fortunately, kept a decent record of its sales. One order from a trading company looked interesting—there was something about the signature. It

---

*The Drug Abuse Control Amendments of 1965 prohibit "the doing of any act which causes the sale of a counterfeit." All counterfeit drugs are subject to seizure under this Amendment but there is no criminal liability of an individual holding the drugs if he has no prior knowledge that the drugs were counterfeited.

proved to be one of Chameleon's many aliases, but his attempt to disguise his handwriting did not fool the sleuths.

Bit by bit, the pieces to the puzzle were falling into place. For instance, a Triumph electronic counting machine like Lew's had turned up in the raid on Mannie's drug stash. The Chief Inspector sent memos to FDA field offices from coast to coast advising them that there was only one distributor for this machine in the United States.

He explained:

> The Triumph machine consists of two separate parts with two different serial numbers on nameplates. The larger half is a turn-table-hopper unit. The smaller half is an electronic monitoring unit. . . . The turntable-hopper part has a nameplate attached to the front of the hopper; but, to read the serial number of the electronic unit, one must remove the unit from its cabinet. The serial number on this half of the machine begins with the letter "L." We are attempting to account for all Triumph counters sold in 1962 by visiting firms and recording *both* serial numbers. Please visit firms in your territories . . . if any have sold their machine, a follow-up should be made to the purchaser.

Mannie's machine had no nameplate on the front of the hopper, it had been removed. (The distributor of these machines alas, recorded only the outside number on his sales form.) But the serial number on the inside had been overlooked. The FDA investigation turned up a drug company—one that had other dealings with The Group—which had sold the machine to Lew. (The inside number checked with the one on Mannie's machine.)

Since FDA already had copies of that bill of sale, why was it necessary to go to all this trouble? Because the only serial number on the bill was the number that had been removed from Mannie's machine—the outside number. The burden of proof lies with the plaintiff; in this case, the United States. In court Mannie could have stood mute on the question of the machine, or he could have said that it was similar to, but not identical with, the one sold to Lew. Now the government had ruled out the possibility of two machines with this inside serial number—only one machine in the entire country had been unaccounted for, but now its history was documented. In addition, laboratory analysis of a few

T-D capsules still in it proved that they were made in Bert's manufacturing plant. The ink on the capsules was white gravure ink purchased by Chameleon, under an alias. Carton dividers were bought about the same time as the ink from a stock box company and the same type of payment was used, a check made out in Chameleon's disguised handwriting. The dividers were invoiced to a trading corporation that listed Mannie and Chameleon as officers.

The go-between in all these transactions was positively identified as the hoodlum known as Rocco. He was, indeed, "sorta dark, sorta short, sorta average." No wonder Mannie had been willing to pay him to "stay on the lam" while all these cases were being developed!

A New York District memo to the FDA Division of Case Supervision in Washington firmed up the charge of conspiracy:

". . . The fact that these [cartons, dividers, ink, etc.] were purchased on or about the same time indicates that this is more than a mere coincidence . . . it indicates a well-thought-out plan. . . . All this equipment was picked up by [Rocco], the same man who transported the counterfeit Dexedrine, Dexamyl and unlabeled Mysteclin-F capsules . . . to [Midwest wholesalers]."

Later sleuthing revealed that: "The account folder at [Bert's] Laboratories contains invoices made out to a dummy corporation doing business at [Rocco's] home address. Bills of lading for capsules received are signed by a 'Mark Raymond.' 'Mark Raymond' has been indentified from a photo as being [Rocco]."

Rocco also was probably using the alias John Smith, but there was no way to prove it so long as wholesaler Lew refused to identify him. Thus, Lew held in his own hands the power to elude the conspiracy charges. The best the New York District could do was to advise Washington that Lew had deposited to Chameleon's and Mannie's trading company account many hundreds of dollars via checks signed by Lew's sister. Inspector Oscar Cohen wrote in an official summary. "For the type of operation involved, they would need someone who could get large quantities of these drugs into legitimate channels. [Lew] sold drugs to [Big Mex, Midwest dealer mentioned earlier] at 15 percent discount. [Big Mex] cannot get them at a greater discount than 10 and 2 from any other supplier."

The General Counsel in Washington evidently considered this a tenuous connection, because wholesalers were not included in the conspiracy indictment against The Group.

Abe, too, seemed to be wiggling out of tight spots. Another FDA memo described how Abe's employees testified that they had overheard the company secretary Dave asking Chameleon about "cash or a certified check for that Markem machine." Abe first denied under oath ever owning a Markem machine used to imprint company names on capsules. Later, he maintained that he had purchased the machine for "a South American individual" and had received a commission. This story seemed highly improbable since anyone could purchase this machine directly from the company. When Markem service people visited his factory to make a routine check of the machine's operation, Abe said he no longer had it, and refused to divulge where it had gone. If he had, in fact, sold it to a South American customer, why would he not have told them? Over a period of time, evidence piled up from many sources indicating that single orders of 500,000 T-D amphetamine capsules had been shipped from Abe's place, although they were suspected of originating at Bert's.

What drugs did Abe produce? He refused to give FDA authentic samples. Without samples they were stymied and could not trace his products in commerce through comparisons in the "pillistics" laboratory. Thus, like Lew, he was able to thwart the government's investigation merely by remaining uncooperative.

There were other frustrations. While all of the criminals were "tail-shy," Mauser the trucker was especially adept at throwing surveillance teams off the trail by using small panel trucks, large trailers, and private cars for pick-ups and deliveries. One of his helpers described how cartons of drugs were shifted from over-the-road rigs (tractor-trailers) to straight jobs (one-piece units). At drops, the empties were ditched, a common practice for hijackers. "Inky" dealer S came into the picture again, delivering around 400 pounds of counterfeit drugs to airports at one time for shipment airfreight as "costume jewelry," "novelties," etc. The names of senders and receivers were invariably as counterfeit as the contents of the cartons, so it was necessary for FDA to maintain surveillance at airports on the other end to see who picked up the shipments.

All this tied up FDA manpower and vehicles that could scarcely be spared from regular assignments. And they were still a very long way from their basic objective: to stop the counterfeit flow, all unethical suppliers and distributors had yet to be located and their plants shut down.

Where were these plants? FDA still wasn't sure, but it was obvious that there was a lot of subcontracting involved, as when Bert manufactured generic T-D's, and Abe's Markem machine was used to imprint SK&F on them, turning them into true counterfeits rather than just look-alikes or imitations. Rocco, Mannie, and others in The Group attended to the packaging, elsewhere, while Mauser and S were involved with shipping. Tom, Chameleon, and others had their specialties too: masterminding the project, making contacts, selling, setting up new plants out West. Some plants may be single facilities where drugs are made from raw materials, packaged, and shipped on the spot. Lew, Big Mex, Doc, and countless others covered retail outlets. Drug counterfeiting, in short, is like a giant amoeba, spreading first in this direction, then in that, dividing, breaking off, and—for a time—vanishing altogether. Then, it comes again, a monstrous thing in our midst.

THE SMALL WORLD OF BIG MEX

It is not at all unusual to find wholesalers who, in addition to their regular business, also sell at retail. Because of the general confusion in this area, it is not surprising to find that while Lew bought drugs through channels from Big Mex, Big Mex buys directly from Lew and from Lew's suppliers—Abe, Bert, The Group, and others. Big Mex has frequently had dealings with Chameleon. It is, as these people often exclaim, "A small world!"

Big Mex is a traveling wholesaler from "out of the West." It is his habit to drive to New York, New Jersey, Philadelphia, and Baltimore periodically to freshen up his contacts among the gray- and black-marketeers. Big Mex stands only five-feet-two in his built-up boots and salt-and-pepper crew-cut. He always has to have an admiring audience—a girl friend, a young petty crook, even a hitchhiker. His air-conditioned car has a TV and bar in back and several ingenious sliding panels operated by inserting a stylus into the seat cushions. These hideaways are convenient for storing large sums of cash, or drugs to run across the border— either border, as he has business contacts in Canada as well as in Mexico. He also has police records in a dozen states.

Big Mex was convicted of dealing in counterfeits, but is appealing up to the Supreme Court. The FDA tried to get his bail bond revoked, but the judge wouldn't do it so long as Big Mex was still appealing. Picked up a few months ago for not having a license to handle drugs in an Eastern state, he said, "I was just on the way to purchase that license, see—I even have the $5 in my hand." When he was mentioned in an article on the illicit drug traffic, he promptly sued the publication. "FDA and newspaper people are tryin' to crucify me!" he complains. His womenfolk do an effective job of weeping softly in court whenever he appears, and his list of character witnesses seems inexhaustible—he contributes to worthy causes and heads committees for civic improvements. In his home town, Big Mex operates a distributorship and belongs to all the right businessmen's groups. One of his daughters is a pharmacist; he has set her up in her own drugstore on a choice downtown corner.

Actually, the distributorship is a front. His main source of income is from his "territory": a dozen states in America's heartland where he is one of the biggest suppliers of illicit drugs to truckstops, brothels, prisons, and bars. He also does a flourishing business supplying bulk prescription drugs to dispensing rural physicians.

There are no clear-cut lines defining the types of businesses engaged in by a Big Mex. He is just as likely to buy bulk raw materials from a dosage-form producer as from a broker; and brokers, supposedly dealing in basic chemicals, offered him such finished products as neatly prepackaged physicians' samples. Here, from dozens of different conversations, are typical glimpses of the undergrowth in the pharmaceutical jungle:

BIG MEX: Did you get in touch with your friend that used to be at Sandoz? I want to get some literature from him and see exactly what the score is on LSD—how to use it and so forth. There's dough in that. What was that product that other fellow in sales mentioned? Ergocornine—will they look into it?

ANSWER: It's too hot for him to handle, he said. You can't
            buy it from Sandoz—*

BIG MEX: Well, you said he knew someone that deals with
            them through a clinic or something. Maybe through
            them. . . .
            You know that salesman worked for [Abe] one time?
            He's in geriatric vitamins and the chiropractic line
            now. I happened to think of him because he's just
            brought me some stuff, Rauwolfia, and I need. . . .

Any drug in current use was likely to be mentioned, or any of
its components. Here we have Big Mex talking to Abe and another man about APAP, used in the production of Demerol, a
synthetic pain-killer subject to narcotics controls; spray-dried
lactose, an inactive ingredient; quinine for malaria; and business
in general.

BIG MEX: What gives? Everybody's talking about setting
            up a plant.

ABE: This is supply and demand. . . . I'll tell you
            very simply, half a million is a week-end's work.
            The price keeps going up, some guys have the
            gall to raise it double, you know. . . . They work
            around the clock and they have to get paid good
            for it. You got to pay a premium for materials
            so it's off the record since the new law. Every-
            body has to make a loan. . . . It's better than that
            loan shark. [They discuss loan sharks in the pill
            business.]

THIRD MAN: Let's look up this APAP. [Mannie] wants me to
            buy the powder for him, he wants a lot, about
            100 pounds a week. And no invoice. He's in a
            world of trouble, all those counts against him
            now.

*Sandoz has discontinued the distribution of LSD to researchers, and they never
marketed it.

ABE: He's supposed to be smart, but he keeps getting
                caught by the FDA. I think he's just a runner
                for [Chameleon]. That guy! I know him from
                way back. I can't understand it—he's been up on
                so many raps and he's still in operation. They
                can't touch him, for some reason I don't know.
                . . .

THIRD MAN (*Looking in The Drug Topics "Red Book"*): Here
                it is, Demerol APAP, how the Hell d'ya pro-
                nounce this company, Brawn? Comes 50 mg.
                tablets, but he wants powder.

BIG MEX: He must have a hot lead if he wants a hundred
                pounds every week.

ABE: That's cheap stuff that APAP. A dollar thirty-
                five a pound.

They argue about whether this is the same APAP that is used
in making antihistamines for over-the-counter drugs, or whether
it is, in fact, the narcotic, Demerol. One man observes that it is
sometimes easier to get narcotics than a simple inactive ingredient
like spray-dried lactose at 21 cents a pound. He has been trying
to buy it in quantity because, "it is wonderful stuff . . . direct
compressible, you don't need any ovens or granulation, all you
do is mix your active ingredients with it and it's ready to go."
McKesson & Robbins won't sell it to him, for some reason, he
complains. So, he is going to arrange to have it stolen.

BIG MEX: How's [Bert]? Haven't seen him in quite awhile.

ABE: He wants me to make up quinine sulfate. Quinine
            took a big jump from 35 to 60 an ounce. It's going
            up to a dollar. I picked up close to 8,000 ounces for
            55 cents an ounce. It's not obtainable you know, I
            got it from a guy that I sell. I had him buy it from
            them because they'd never give it to me. They never
            sold it to civilians. It's so ridiculous, you have no
            idea what's going on. I'm buying it from under
            the. . . .

BIG MEX: What—tablets, capsules, or what?

ABE: It's rationed. If you never bought it before, you
           can't buy a capsule. The government is stockpiling
           it on account of the war. Price is no object now.

[Quinine went from 20 cents an ounce a few years ago to $2
an ounce reflecting the urgent need for the drug in South Viet-
nam where a resistant strain of falciparum malaria has developed
that cannot be controlled by modern synthetics. This age-old
remedy still alleviates malaria's symptoms even when synthetics
fail to cure the disease, and, once again is a vital war matériel.
After World War II, quinine was considered outmoded; Cinchona
plantations were destroyed or neglected in Java and Latin America. Between 1961 and 1964 the United States Government sold
from stockpiles some 10 million ounces, mostly to Dutch companies at a rock bottom price. American firms—both large and
small—were able to purchase only about one million ounces from
the government. All of this has made quinine, and especially the
alkaloid quinidine, used in heart medications, a skyrocketing item
among the gray-marketeers.]*

THIRD MAN: I happen to know where you can buy quinidine
            anywhere from $7 to $10 a thousand tablets.

ABE: I buy only the quinine sulfate, the hydro-
            chloride nobody uses it. . . . If this southeast
            Asia thing levels off, quinine will plummet. The
            government will dump it and you'll buy it for
            $2 a pound, which is what happened before to
            me. I got stuck—

BIG MEX: Quinine doubled already. What else do they
            stockpile? It's a good idea to buy up raw ma-
            terials. . . .

ABE: [Bert's] the one to talk to, he's makin' money
            right and left.

The next time Abe and Big Mex got together, they indulged
in their usual trade gossip:

*The 89th Congress investigated the more than 400 percent increase in the price
of quinidine from 1964 to 1966.

ABE: [Chameleon's] a shrewd cookie. He'd stick his grandmother. I pulled him out of a real mess that time he was making hormones. So now he's got religion . . . country clubs. . . .

BIG MEX: A zebra don't change its stripes overnight. I don't care what country club he belongs to. . . . Say, I don't see [a gray-marketeer] around anymore. . . .

ABE: He's still in the drug game. Out West, I think. They made a small fortune with that natural vitamin liquid, and they didn't know the simplest things, as, f'rinstance, they asked me, "How d'ya make these drops, do you use extracts or rose hips powder?" And *they* were supposed to be in the drug business! Anybody knows the extract is 50 percent vitamin C. The powder, you got maybe one percent, two percent. You never know what the hell ya got.

BIG MEX: There's a lot of them doing what they did 40 years ago, nothing up-to-date. And still they have that old coin paw out. I went around to see your other friend. He must have rocks in his head. He had millions of assorted tablets in his Davey Jones locker that I have no call for and his prices were wacky. So you didn't give me too good a hook-up, there.

·   ·   ·   ·

BIG MEX: Don't think I'm just sitting on my behind . . . now that the guy has his punches and dies paid for, I'm getting the hearts and stuff cheaper.

ANOTHER
DEALER: Each one of these guys has punches but they don't have a record of it. Now this guy here, he must have a complete set of every kind of punch . . . off the record. How did he get that many? Those punches he keeps in his own drawer, private drawer.

BIG MEX: Once in a while they [legitimate manufacturer] destroy them and get new ones. SK&F buries theirs in cement now, I hear. But this guy makes enough money to get the new ones. $75 for a whole set of punches.

DEALER: What are you talking about! You don't get no set of rotary 16 uppers and lowers and dies for $75. What are you talking about?

BIG MEX: Not the uppers and lowers . . . just the uppers. He keeps the lower punches and keeps the dies. In Jersey, there's a standard source for $75, but I don't know whether they're any good or not. A fellow was making some stuff for me and when I saw the tablets I said what the hell kind of punches and dies you got? He had punches that he whittled down, you know—shaved off, and they didn't look good. My customer wouldn't take that stuff.

·　·　·　·

BIG MEX: Gimme one of your labels there and I'll put your home phone number on it.

MANUFACTURER: No, not one of my labels! Let me give you something else, I don't want this to get out.

BIG MEX: What's your [customers] name?

MANUFACTURER: Let's just call him The Greek.

BIG MEX: Doesn't he have a name? What do you say, "Hey, listen Greek."

MANUFACTURER: Look, I'll give him a code that nobody else would know, like I'll tell him your wife's first name. Then when he calls he'll give *that* to you and you'll know it's *this* guy. No, don't write my phone number like that. Be smart! Write it backwards, if you have to write it down. But can't you just remember?

On one of Big Mex's Eastern rounds, he stopped first to see a raw materials broker. The conversation took place in Big Mex's car, where he began by complimenting the broker on the vicuña coat he was wearing. The broker is generally considered legitimate; big ethical drug companies buy from him; but on this day he was delivering a relatively small amount of dextro-amphetamine powder, which he said was perfect. Big Mex complained about the price.

BROKER: You've got to go through three or four people, now, each one taking a cut for steering you. "Go and see so-and-so," they say. "He always had plenty—" Always *had* is one thing, always having is another. This is getting to be a real rat race. Would you believe it, a guy wanted 12 grand for two 100 pound drums of this yesterday? He's in business for himself. Making a million samples in his lab, there. 40 grams, 50 grams, 100 grams, said it was experimental stuff for Harvard, for Merck—I don't think [Ph.D., the researcher] has those kind of customers, do you? He's probably not registered with Food and Drug, since he claims he's just making experimentals for investigation. I think its applesauce. I had the money in my pocket—if he had said $24 a pound, OK. You should be able to get it for $12, $13. But he hemmed and hawed and asked for $60. I said "Give me a sample, not off the top, out of the middle of the drum, I want to test it." Could be powdered sugar or milk sugar, or something.

BIG MEX: Yeah, remember the guy that got stuck on the kilo of expensive hormone—was it cortisone? Turned out to be talcum powder or something else. Wasn't a damn thing they could do about it.

BROKER: I know how he operates. What he probably does, he pretends to make the stuff "for export" and for his records, he goes through the manipulation of shipping out a barrel, say, of milk sugar marked dextro-amphetamine, so according to his records, he shipped it to India or some fuckin' place. Then he's got it to bootleg, right?

BIG MEX: At his prices, he can shove it. I've got a real good source in Michigan. What I want to know is, What's new otherwise around? Is [The Chemist] still "chemisting"?

They immediately discussed the fact that LSD had gone up to $60 a gram, because "publicity over those Harvard crackpots makes everybody want it." The broker explained, "it's hot to handle, but you can make a real buck on it, students, you know." Big Mex has a larger, though less sophisticated clientele. He wants a quantity of chloral hydrate—knock-out drops—for nightclub owners. Also, he complains, "I went to six people in Philadelphia—couldn't get any footballs. I'm gonna have them made up of 5 milligrams of dextro-amphetamine colored with orange syrup. [They are supposed to be made with $7\frac{1}{2}$ milligrams of desoxyephedrine.] These truckers are funny, they put their faith in a certain color, certain shape, and you can't shake 'em. F'rinstance, my boys runnin' pills in Texas say out there they holler for 'blackjacks' [black and white hard gelatin capsules with 15 milligrams of amphetamine]. Through the South, it's crossroads, in the Midwest, orange hearts and the brown-and-green clears. There's a bunch won't take anythin' but those green square-shape they make in Philadelphia. Other guys say 'they're no good, gimme footballs!' There isn't one out of a hundred has the football-shaped punches, you know any? I told one fella—showed me his catalog, says in there 90 cents a thousand—'I'll give you $8 right this minute!' But he didn't have any on hand."

The broker passed the word that Chameleon's ex-salesman was making footballs for Abe, and might do a little business on the side.

"Well, a man can't drive a trailer if he's half asleep—and these truckers don't want to sleep when they're supposed to. . . ." Big Mex explained that some truckers want to play the pinball machines, and others just want to play—he needed sleeping pills for prostitutes to take in the daytime. The broker sold him half a drum of secobarbital. Many of his truckstops had motels that were the big attraction, "Some of them don't pump a hundred gallons of gas a week, and the coffee is terrible, but you should see the 'waitresses'!"

Big Mex had two especially popular items: a so-called "manhood restorer," and pills for "delayed" ladies. "This is a deal where you get customers comin' and goin'," was the way he put it. He needed some bulk hormones for his "restorer," Aphrodite Compound, manufactured to his order by XYZ Laboratories in a Southeastern state. This concoction contained: strychnine phosphate; the male hormone methyltestosterone; an orchidic extract from animal gonads; other hormones; and some yohimbine hydrochloride from an African bark with an international reputation as an aphrodisiac. This was XYZ's private label prescription drug sold directly to drug stores, and doctors, and bootlegged through bars and truckstops, as well.

"A lot of people are selling manpower pills," the broker observed. "There's real money in this. Piece in the paper the other day, two fellows on Long Island cleared $300,000 in less than a year with tablets made from Passion flowers—1,000 percent above costs. That's just a mild tranquilizer, the botanical, Passiflora— It was the name that got 'em."

BIG MEX: Look at this bottle. I saw a lot of them sitting on Sam's shelf, he's got the barbell customers [vitamin-consumers], but that's just a small part of his business. He sells to the big mail order companies. Then he has this little sideline mailing out the back door. He said to me, "When you open my back door, there's like, the post office. . . . This is strictly a nothing formula like you see advertised in these hoax newspapers and sexy magazines. Nothin' but goddam minerals and mineral salts. He gets $5 and the fuckin' thing isn't worth 25 cents. Made from dessicated liver, see, 30 miligrams. Big deal. Directions: "Take one each day. A month's supply for five bucks"—

BROKER: That's the kind of racket to look for! I wonder why he don't put it out in a fancy plastic bottle—

BIG MEX: No—no—no, this is supposed to be sent, you know, no fancy labels, so your neighbors shouldn't know what you're gettin—this is to improve your manhood, that sorta jazz—not the postman or your wife or anybody. It's hush, hush.

BROKER: It's two times nothin', that's what it is.

BIG MEX: He doesn't mail out a hundred thousand pieces, he advertises just once and people come to him. It's so worded, you know, say, Joe Bloe in Kokomo can't get it up. . . . He looks at this ad and he secretly sends away. He has to enclose a quarter for a free sample. With that quarter, Sam—the maker—makes money! Look, he sends it third class mail, it costs him four cents to mail it, right? All his cost is advertising. That small ad don't cost much. The trick is in the wording to stay in the law somewhere. The hooker is, he has literature, too. In order to get the literature, you have to subscribe to The Plan, get a bottle regular every month. Every month the package comes, see?

BROKER: In other words, even if he's only got a thousand customers, at five bucks each—

BIG MEX: Yeah, it's something to latch on to. Now look at this: "Peak power equals peak manpower. This means to be power ready. At all times your energy must be at its maximum." See? You read into it what you *want* to read into it. But *he* didn't say a damn thing. . . . "Your problems did not develop overnight. Therefore, do not expect them to be solved overnight. Continuous use month after month will bring your power up to its maximum." (You're hooked, buddy!) "Keep your marital relationship at its very best—"

BROKER: That's a better business than crossroads any day.

Big Mex was interested in another of Sam's products, one that grossed $2,000 a week. It was a Vitamin B and iron tablet, exorbitantly priced. Pegged to "Please Rush in Plain Wrapper" ads in publications offering "Genuine Sterling Silver Wedding Rings —50¢," "Rupture Easers" . . . "Magnetic Lodestones" . . . it was promoted as "A really effective doctor's prescription which may relieve you of a serious worry." A nurse was pictured circling four days on the calendar; the caption read: "Delayed? Don't Risk Disaster!" Again, a full month's supply of this "Doctor's Formula prepared by Registered Pharmacists" could be obtained for $5. That readers could ill afford to be defrauded was docu-

mented by the advertisement below: "Send $3.50 for 20 Ladies'
Dresses (slightly used)."

Prostitutes-Pinballs-Pornography. Frequently pill peddlers apprehended by FDA inspectors have in their possession pornographic literature and related materials. Part of Big Mex's world
seemed right out of Courtney Riley Cooper's lurid 1930's exposé
of "white slavery" *Designs in Scarlet.*

Before he left the broker, Big Mex asked whether the sodium
pentobarb shipment had gone out to the man who was going to
make the ten million "yellow jackets" for him. "Yeah, and the
fella's gonna lose his shirt doin' it," the broker answered. "He's
supplying the capsules and everything for $2.82 a thousand. Pay-
ing a girl $12 a day to operate the machine, and you know she
can't keep it running for eight hours straight. She's gotta go to
the john, she's gotta relax. And it's an old machine—I know
damned well he can't get more than 50,000 a day."

Big Mex did not want any trademarks or labels on these—his
truckers and prostitutes "had a fit" if they got any labeled drugs.
On the other hand, his druggists demanded them. So, while he
was there, he agreed to take some genuine Abbott Nembutal the
raw materials dealer just happened to have on hand. They quib-
bled over the price, the broker saying, "Don't call these 'yellow
jackets' they're original Nembutal, $15 a thousand is real good
price." They looked it up in the *Red Book.*

These drugs were supposed to have come from a bankrupt
pharmacy. Big Mex asked: "You know any more fellows getting
ready to go bankrupt? If I knew beforehand, I could get stuff
cheap from them. Or, you can get good buys when you find partners in a place and one is mad at the other. You pick up this 'n
that—"

The broker steered him to Max and Norman, who were on the
"outs" at M & N Drug Company. If there was a deal, he would
get a commission.

Basically, Max and Norman are drug repackers, who purchase
tablets and capsules in bulk from various suppliers, including
some fairly large companies, then repack them for pharmacies,
doctors and hospital supply houses. Small shipments are sent
parcel post to such consignees as Masonic Home in New England.
Local deliveries are made by Norman's wife, their bookkeeper, in

her station-wagon. Large shipments go out via common carrier. Max is an elderly, nervous registered pharmacist who established the parent company, Max Laboratories. However, FDA inspectors found letterheads, labels, and other material relating to six other firms beside M & N Drug Company on the premises.

Prescription drugs are handled exclusively, but when they arrive in bulk, they are never analyzed for purity, potency, or anything else—they are "looked at" and if they seem "all right," they are packaged and shipped. Max Laboratories operates its own small advertising company, which prepares mail-order catalogs and advertisements for all the "different" companies. An example: "We specialize in only one group of products—vitamins. All of our research efforts are concentrated in this one field, etc." So-and So Vitamin Company, with a mail-drop address.

BIG MEX (*On his second visit to M & N*):   How's business?

NORMAN (*A partner with Max in M & N*):   Listen, don't stand there with the door open! Did you happen to notice a blue car out there? I think we're bein' watched. Saw that same car a couple times today. . . . Are you sure you aren't bein' followed?

BIG MEX: What *is* this—

NORMAN: FDA was back here yesterday, Max is shitting green. They—you're gonna be mad at me, but I can't give you a thing. Nothing. I have no way of hiding stuff, other than making it from scratch and shipping it right out. I can't buy anything without a bill or sell anything without a bill. Everything has numbers now, do you know FDA traces invoices now? They hang you on that. And I sell to the government—I have quite a few government orders. We had a choice of either assigning our own lot numbers or keeping a separate record book or putting on the manufacturer's lot number. So, it's easier to put the manufacturer's lot number—we had two FDA guys in here that wanted records of everybody I ship to, from placebos to pento. They pulled out every—

BIG MEX: If FDA pulled out things, you can blame them for messing up records. You can say *they* mixed them all up, even *lost* some. Weren't they in here a coupla weeks ago?

NORMAN: Yeah, but this time, regardless, they looked at every month for six months back. What I used to protect myself on, I billed aspirin tablets and shipped pento —it's amazing what's happened to this market since the new law. Boy oh boy, if you had the nerve you could make a buck now. But I got to think it over. I mean honestly, I'm scared. Let me think this over for a week or so. I can't get the chemicals without a bill, that's my problem.

BIG MEX: How did you make out with that guy you were getting leery of, that big noise from Buffalo or somewhere? He was getting on your nerves—

NORMAN: He's one of those greedy druggists. Went from 1,000 to 5,000 to 25,000 bottles at a crack. I told him I couldn't continue to do it. He's very prosperous, well thought of in the community. And it's a nice bit of business for me. But my regular inventory, I wouldn't dare touch with those guys coming here all the time. They're suspicious of large quantities. Now, see, over in that corner . . . I *know* what I got in that special corner, that's *my* corner. But it's getting all confused. They look in every drum. "Where did this come from?" They insist that everything be properly labeled. You know, it's not like what it was. They tightened up on raw material.

Big Mex was getting restless, irritable. His big customer in Texas wanted to know what was holding up the order. One of his trucker-distributors was waiting for a load of M&N pills in a truck terminal. He told Norman, "I've got a doctor you can send them through, and a pharmacist. Split the order up between them."

NORMAN: It's too much, don't you see? FDA's looking at

quantity now, along with everything else! Besides, they just closed out that old pharmacist I was using, that one about 90 years old. The State Board shut him down. My regular druggists are good customers, but *they* don't like to be invoiced either—you've got to give them a thousand now and then so they can fill a prescription they're not supposed to fill. I get them calling me all day long on the phone. No kidding. You give a guy a few hundred, he wants a thousand. It's getting impossible! You multiply this by thirty, forty druggists—

BIG MEX: Well, they pay you for it—

NORMAN: Oh, sure, they're happy to pay extra. They charge more in proportion in their store. But they'll ruin me with this alone. For me, the headaches are druggists.

PART THREE

With the Profiteering Professionals

The vast majority of physicians and pharmacists are ethical. This section deals with the few renegades who despoil the images of many truly dedicated members of the health professions. FDA records indicate that a small number of dispensing physicians, in particular, are major sources for the mass diversion of dangerous drugs to criminal outlets.

In the early 1950's the Federal government could have taken steps to curb the burgeoning illicit traffic in amphetamines and barbiturates by enacting the first dangerous-drug bill proposed. But this measure, authored by Congressman Hale Boggs, was "talked to death" in hearings. Medical and pharmaceutical associations were among the vigorous opponents of 38 similar bills that failed to pass. In fact, the American Medical Association officially stated that it saw no reason for the 1965 Drug Abuse Control Amendments. Reason enough had existed since a brutal kidnap-slaying was detailed on the front pages of the nation's newspapers in 1953. The warning should have been clear to all: Carl Austin Hall murdered six-year-old Bobby Greenlease of Kansas City while under the influence of amphetamines. Briefly, from the files, this is what happened in that case.

When FDA's districts in the Midwest learned that Hall's companion, alcoholic divorcee Bonnie Brown Heady, had a bottle of amphetamine tablets in her purse at the time of her arrest, inspectors were assigned to follow up. The local FBI agents in charge of the kidnapping case insisted that alcoholics didn't abuse drugs and they believed that the amphetamines were only harmless reducing pills. "There are too many people butting into this case, anyway," an FBI man complained.

An FDA inspector continued to investigate the penciled "NO9516" on the bottle's label. The FBI thought this was some kind of druggists' code; the inspector, a registered pharmacist, disagreed. His sleuthing revealed that NO9516 actually was the telephone number in a pharmacy's public phone booth. From this telephone, Hall had made his first call for the $600,000 ransom, which he later collected after killing the child. Significant as this information proved to be, the FBI firmly requested that FDA drop out of the picture.

The persevering inspector next obtained Bureau of Prisons permission to interview Hall and Heady in the death house. Hall wrote the following statement for him:

> Since 1964 I have been an habitual user of liquor . . . as much as one-fifth gallon per day. In order to keep awake I started using Benzedrine tablets. . . . During this time [immediately before the murder] I bought seven bottles of pills. . . . I asked for Benzedrine tablets and was told I needed a prescription. I gave [a pharmacist] a $20 bill saying "This is my prescription." He said that would do and gave me a bottle of one hundred. . . . [Hall described several similar "buys" in various Midwestern drug stores.] At the time of the kidnapping I was under the influence of Benzedrine that I had obtained from a friend . . . he had an interest in a drug store. . . . It has been my experience that for $20 most anyone can make buys of Benzedrine. [signed] CARL AUSTIN HALL.

Hall told the inspector that he was certain he could never have gone through with the slaying of the little boy if he had not obtained his "courage" from the drug.

Just as FDA was on the verge of obtaining additional drug sources from the about-to-be-executed criminals, pressure was brought to bear in Washington and FDA's investigation was squelched. Static was exchanged at all levels in both Federal agencies for more than a year and the correspondence between top officials was sticky, indeed. No doubt there is something to be said for both sides, but this conflict had far-reaching ramifications.

Carl Austin Hall was a classic precursor of the contemporary berserk pep-pill addict who uses amphetamine to prevent "chickening-out." Although it was impossible to prove that he was under the drug's influence, the Texas sniper who slaughtered 16 people in 1966 had amphetamine in his possession. Jack Ruby admitted that he killed President Kennedy's assassin, Lee Harvey Oswald, after taking a heavy dose of amphetamine. These are only a few of the more sensational cases.

All too often FDA traces drugs used in violent crimes to so-called legitimate sources—small town family doctors and neighborhood druggists—who are apparently shocked by the misuse of their prescriptions.

At the time of the Greenlease case, it happened that Clemens Westerly was one of the FDA men assigned to follow Hall's trail from bellhops in Omaha to pharmacies in "St. Joe." His reports as a fledgling inspector provide insights into the situation on both sides of the prescription counter. For instance, by no means did all druggists agree to sell Benzedrine without a prescription. "I talked only to the pharmacist and told each man I needed Benzedrine. I put a $10 bill on the counter. . . . At [X Drugstore] the man said, 'Nope, not if the $10 had three oughts tacked on to it. . . . At [Y Drugstore] the man said, 'Not a chance, Mac. That's a *Federal* law.' . . . At [Z Drugstore] the man said, 'That could cost me my license, fella.' "

But enough over-the-counter buys of Rx drugs were made to implicate at least one physician and a number of pharmacists as Hall's suppliers. However, those cases were "PA-ed," put into Permanent Abeyance.

Fourteen years later, Chief Inspector Westerly and other veteran FDAers are encountering in criminal cases some of the same doctors, and pharmacists, who formed the pill-peddling cadre out in America's heartland. The counterfeiting of "hearts" and other forms of amphetamine to meet the demands of truckers and weight-reducers, in particular, marked the beginning of the staggering drug abuse problem we are faced with today. It started with a small number of illegal sales by careless or greedy professional men; then, the underworld muscled into the lucrative racket. But renegade professionals still play a vital role in obtaining huge supplies of drugs for diversion. The nationwide distribution network would collapse without them.

FDA's Lewis P. Lasher, one of the nation's leading authorities on the dangerous drug traffic, told me in 1965:

> Because we can employ less than 10 percent of FDA's total inspectional force in investigating illegal dispensing by pharmacists and physicians, it's not even possible to check out all the leads and complaints we receive. Who can guess what percentage of violative situations ever come to our attention in the first place—5 percent? 10? If both seller and buyer are satisfied, *who* is going to complain to the authorities? Drug abusers make every effort to hide their weakness and protect their sources. FDA's prosecution figures cannot be used to gauge the extent of this problem.

FDA needs help. Isn't it time medicine and pharmacy faced this fact and rid the professions of chronic offenders? As spokesmen for these groups are the first to point out, "There are only a *few* unethical practitioners. . . ."

CHAPTER SEVEN

Down At Rosie's Drugstore

It's funny about drugstores—if they're run-down, have their windows full of faded crepe-paper roses left over from Valentine's Day, fly-specked hair coloring charts, cheap plastic toys, and douche bags—you can't help but wonder what's going on back there where the prescriptions are made. There are some stores in New York City in the West '40's and down in Greenwich Village that are notorious for another type of eyesore: the extraordinary variety of strange denizens who inhabit their premises. Wild-haired "girls" with chalky faces and purple claws, who actually are boys; tough looking "boys" with sullen mouths, motorcycling jackets, and heavy fringed driving gloves, who really are girls. And older men, who look as if they had spent the last 20 years under a rotten log. Here is where the "queens" camp it up, the junkies seek word of their connection, and solicitors of all stripes ply their trade.

You don't wade through society's dregs when you visit "Doc," the Cosa Nostra apothecary. On my first visit, the FDA men pulled up to the curb in front of a fine hotel and said, "That's his place, over there, next to the lobby." It was sleek and gleaming. Even from the street you could see every corner of the store through the sparkling windows. The interior was flooded with light from recessed fluorescent bulbs and along the walls were orderly rows of brand-name drugs lined up behind sliding glass panels. Two pharmacists in the back were busy compounding

165

medications, but they were in full view. Up front, Doc stood near
the cash register, while a younger pharmacist waited on a customer. Two other customers were sitting just inside the front
door in a lounge similar to a doctor's waiting room. There were
magazines like *The New Yorker, Fortune, Réalités,* on the table;
and potted plants lavishly massed for dramatic effect against a
pecky cypress wall were tall, their leaves not the least bit dusty.

Doc's bright smile was unnerving. It was almost 11 o'clock at
night and he had been in the store since early morning. I asked
for a blood-builder, a bottle of Geritol, specifically.

He was very sorry. "We only fill prescriptions here." (It was,
after all, called an "ethical prescription pharmacy.")

However, he walked me to the door and pointed to a side street.

"Turn down there, half a block, on the other side, and you'll
see a discount store, I think it's called [Kurly's Kut-Rate Korner,
or some such]. They'll probably have just what you want."

Doc should know. He owns both stores. And some others
besides.

That day, if it was typical, he filled over 400 prescriptions in
the store I entered. (The average pharmacist fills around 48 per
day.) Since many were made up of stolen drugs that cost him
nothing—he is, primarily, a fence—his profit was almost 100 percent on those items. The others undoubtedly included a fair share
of drugs that had been bought very cheaply, either because they
were "distressed" or counterfeited. Doc is a crook, no doubt about
it.

Let's visit a druggist I'll call Rosie, in another part of the
country. Is he really an ethical, conscientious pharmacist? He
does go out of his way to cooperate with the local authorities and
the Federal Narcotics Bureau. He has never been in any kind of
trouble with the State Board of Pharmacy, nor has he attracted
attention from the FDA.

Rosie's drugstore is the place to lurk if you want to hear what's
really going on around town. The slice of life dished up with the
club sandwich is apt to be on the raw side.

"Kicks, kicks, nothing but kicks, I don't know what the world's
coming to," Rosie told me one night, though he had served his
apprenticeship in the swingingest drugstore on Broadway. "You
know, I could understand this drive for kicks back in the old

place, when the girls would come in and demand 'B-B's'—Ben-zedrine and barbiturates. They were kids who had to sleep days and play nights, so they reversed the usual order by taking Bennies at night so they could enjoy their work, and sedatives in the morning to rest up." He held out his hand, "But look here, what do you think these are being used for, right here in this nice neighborhood?"

He was holding a little box that contained a dozen objects I couldn't identify. They resembled, in size and shape, penlight batteries wrapped in a thin layer of cotton wadding, over which a yellow silk mesh was tightly stretched. "The companies that produce these, strangely, just doubled their price. I say strangely because this is amyl nitrite inside a glass ampoule. All this stuff on the outside is to keep you from getting glass in your fingers when you snap it in half and sniff the vapors. It's a very powerful heart stimulant. Some jokers have discovered what they believe to be sexual effects and they were cleaning out stock as fast as I could replace it. This drug is nothing to fool around with, though. It could conceivably be fatal. But that doesn't stop them. They say, 'It only takes one or two sniffs, and it drives women wild—men, too.' "

I asked him if the manufacturers had any idea of this specific abuse of their drugs. (Afterwards, I wrote to one medical director, who said that they did not.)

"Beats me. Before I knew what was going on, I was ordering the stuff by the case—but manufacturers ought to realize there's no epidemic of heart attacks going on around here. That's why I say, it's funny, they doubled the price."

Rosie had some thoughts on drug prices: "A lot of the doctors are now prescribing cheaper generics—you know, meprobamate, say, instead of specifically Wallace's Miltown or Wyeth's Equanil. It's especially common in hospitals to do this. Well, so far as the patient is concerned, it saves them money, no doubt about it. They can get twice as many pills, sometimes three or four times as many, if I fill their prescriptions with generic drugs. But instead of making two or three dollars for myself, I may end up with twenty or thirty cents. So I'm against generic prescribing for sound business reasons."

One of Rosie's pet peeves was the amount that physicians charge for their services. "I always try to get back at doctors who over-charge, like some psychiatrists I know. For instance, I'm making a nice piece of change right now with a psychiatrist out in a suburb. When he found I couldn't get LSD for his patients, he kept after me and after me to come up with something he could substitute, something that would cause hallucinations. I'm now selling him Sansert, used in migraine, because I figured out that 6 or 8 of these tablets just might cause LSD-type effects. I now send 500 tablets for $400 out to his clinic regularly, charging him 80 cents a pill instead of 18 cents. I figure, *he's* charging those patients $50 an hour! I put him on to a good thing, so why shouldn't I get something for *my* professional 'know-how.' "

I asked about the risk involved; whether the hallucinations weren't a form of toxicity.*

"That's *his* lookout—he's the doctor, isn't he?"

About this time, a once-attractive brunette came behind the prescription counter, threw her arms around Rosie and clung to him. In one hand she held a sheaf of five prescriptions.

"I just got out of the hospital today," she said, nibbling Rosie's ear. "And I don't feel so good. Let me use your bathroom." She didn't look so good, either. In fact, she looked ghastly. Great dark circles under her eyes and loose grayish skin masked her basically good features. However, she was wearing a beautiful beige leather ensemble and if her eyes didn't sparkle, her jewels certainly did. "You are a real kook," Rosie cheerfully called after her. "A *real* kook."

Then, turning to me he said in disgust, "Imagine, we've got here Compazine, Thorazine, Valium, and two other new drugs, one a psychic energizer, the other a nonbarbiturate sedative. All from the same doctor."

As he put her "medications" into bottles, he listened sympa-thetically to her complaints. And after his customer left with her Pucci bag stuffed with pills, he grew nostalgic. "I remember all

---

*Sansert should only be used for severe headaches by patients who will return to their doctors for check-ups every three months, according to a Harvard Medical School report on 33 patients who developed severe overgrowth of connective tissue and inflammation while on the drug. Disorders cleared when it was discontinued. But overdoses of this drug could have fatal results, a physician in FDA's Bureau of Medicine told me.

those gorgeous showgirls who used to come in for their B-B's. And their men, too. One of my first nights on the job, this sharp-looking character walked in. You know, the white-on-white shirt, pale tie, French cuffs, diamond links, big diamond ring on his pinky, the whole bit. He shoved $20,000 in cash at me and said, 'Keep this 'til Saturday.' It had to be some kind of loot, but before I could ask questions he was gone and I was stuck with the stuff. What I did was wrap it up good and wear it at all times next to my skin. Sure enough, Saturday, this character came back, peeled off a healthy chunk of the green for me and departed. This got to be a regular thing, don't ask me why, and pretty soon I had a couple of these 'depositors.' I learned they were sort of middle-class Mafia when they were arrested for running a multi-million-dollar stock swindle, one of those boiler-room operations. They didn't come around for a couple of months. Then, one of them dropped in to see me about a personal problem.

" 'I have this beautiful girl and I'm having some trouble,' he explained. 'Can't you mix me up [an aphrodisiac] that will really work?' Well, at the time the big thing in that line was a vitamin B_{12} injection mixed with Methedrine, a potent stimulant. But I worked out a formula on my own, using several other ingredients not generally known to have that specific action, which was *so* effective I sold it for $20 a half-ounce. Once a big Mafia boss came in and plunked down enough money to buy a quart of it. It took some doing, but I mixed him a batch and from what I hear. . . ."

Though Rosie was telling me his stories, he hardly neglected his customers. Interspersed with the normal drugstore traffic, he dealt with the addicts. In the course of the evening, he turned away two sulky teen-agers who wanted a cough syup that he refused to stock any more because it was habit-forming. He quickly *gave* his only supply of morphine to an addict, warning him, "That's all there is, take it and get out. Come back and I'll turn you in." And he handed over for my inspection two prescription blanks filled out for a powerful barbiturate, saying, "Did you ever see counterfeit prescriptions?" These had been printed up by drug abusers who used the name of a physician who had been dead for two years. He told me that he has been given Xeroxed prescriptions, and that the problem of stolen prescription pads from careless doctors was serious. Before I left, I asked Rosie if he ever had any trouble with counterfeit drugs. He said that he had not, to his knowledge, been sold any, but that he had read about cases in the trade papers. "I decided to play it safe, so I always ask to see the shipping carton label, so I can check the lot number on the bottles. And when I buy generics, I get them from manufacturers who supply the government, or hospitals."

I looked at some of his bottles. One bore the name of a company currently under FDA investigation for supplying Big Mex with illicit drugs, another carried Bert's private label.

They *do* supply the government—and hospitals too.

CHAPTER EIGHT

Pharmacy's Conscience

The only point in going to the trouble to counterfeit a trademark on a generic drug is so you can sell it to a druggist. Truckers and pill heads wouldn't know Mr. Kline, Smith, or French if they stepped on them.

A COUNTERFEIT-DRUG DISTRIBUTOR

The President's Advisory Commission on Narcotic and Drug Abuse charged in its November, 1963, *Final Report* that:

On the basis of current study, retail pharmacies and pharmacists appear to be a major source for the diversion of dangerous drugs to illicit channels in the United States. . . . In the ten-year period ending December 30, 1962, there were 1,658 firms and individuals convicted under the Federal Food, Drug, and Cosmetic Act for the illegal sale of amphetamines and/or barbiturates. Of these convictions, 1,298, or 78 percent of the total, involved retail drug firms, pharmacists, or their employees.

That statement elicited many rebuttals from pharmacy trade associations with their own statistical analyses of the 1,298 convictions. It was pointed out that, "This is an average of 130 cases per year among more than 100,000 active practicing pharmacists dispensing almost 800 million prescriptions, and is no just basis for the Commission's indictment of the pharmacy profession." (The Commission, as a matter of fact, *had stressed* that offending pharmacies and pharmacists represent only a small fraction of the nation's total.)

171

Item: From AMA *News*, February 14, 1966:

HEARINGS PLANNED ON WELFARE DRUGS . . . Open hearings are planned
by the Louisiana State Board of Pharmacy into reports of irregu-
larities among pharmacists who provide medicine for aged welfare
recipients. An audit of 48 pharmacists handling welfare cases turned
up 25 instances of fraud. Some made restitution totaling $33,000.
The State Board of Pharmacy President issued this statement:
"There are 2,500 pharmacists in Louisiana and the Welfare Department has filed complaints against only 17 alleged violators". . . .

Item: Two California Pharmaceutical Association members
were threatened with expulsion for writing letters critical of unethical practices. They were told they shouldn't wash their dirty
linen in public.

When any vested-interest group is attacked, "image-building"
is only to be expected of the public relations arm. The crucial
question here is, How do the most responsible people within the
pharmacy profession feel about the renegade druggist and what
are they doing about him? What does it mean when they say in
their press releases: "The profession abhors those in it who violate
the law even more vigorously than does any law-enforcing
agency" . . . ?

To find some of the answers, I visited schools of pharmacy in
various parts of the country and interviewed registered pharmacists who serve as professors, editors, consultants, and trade association officials. I also talked at length with pharmacy owners and
employees. Every conscientious pharmacist I interviewed from
Los Angeles to Clinton, Arkansas, to Columbus Avenue on Manhattan's Upper West Side, agreed that it was in everyone's best
interests to expose a situation that is becoming increasingly dangerous to the public and damaging to the profession, in the hope
that something constructive would be done.

First, I had attended the Remington Award Dinner, an annual
gathering of pharmacy's most respected leaders. Dr. Robert J.
Gillespie, the immediate past-president of the American Pharmaceutical Association, raised several provocative questions:

Why is it that so many enter pharmacy with so little *professional*
motivation? . . . I challenge you to visit community pharmacies at
random—and 90 percent of all pharmacists are community pharma-

cists. How many would *you* say are professionally motivated? Or don't we want to be involved? . . . Professionally motivated pharmacists have never been in the majority—never! Do we have 1,000, 10,000, or 25,000 ethical pharmacists in this country?

What *is* "ethical"? Obeying the local, state, and Federal drug laws for a beginning. This may seem simple, but there are few druggists who are not pressured by respectable customers to break the law. "Please refill this prescription, I'm too busy to go back to that specialist, he's so expensive, and he'll just give the same prescription I've been getting for years." "I can't sleep, I've got a big day tomorrow, please give me something just for tonight . . . *just* for this trip . . . *just* for this pain. . . ." So it goes, every day in drugstores across the land.

"If you refuse to help them out 'this one time' they take the family's business down the block," a retailer explained. "You can deliver a tin of aspirin in the middle of the night and give good service for years on end, but turn them down *once* on an unauthorized Rx refill and you're dead."

Much of the time, nowadays, the pharmacist finds that he is reduced to being, as one put it, "A mere counter of pills and measurer of liquids"—a role fraught with frustration. In choosing his profession he obviously wanted to be in a position to help sick people. Yet the struggle to be more than a merchant is complex. Unlike the physician or dentist, the pharmacist-drugstore owner has a stock of goods that cost him something, and on which he must make a profit. The merchandising factor is always present. And pharmacist employees have to face similar dilemmas. Often they are obliged to adopt the profit motive of the employer.

About half of the nation's registered pharmacists are struggling small businessmen: after investing approximately $15,000 in their college education and an average of $37,000 in setting up their own drugstore, they work around 60 hours a week. According to a recent U.S. Public Health Service survey, they earn, on the average, less than $10,000 a year and their work is hard. The public gathers up cartloads of nonprescription drugs at supermarkets or discount stores, orders huge quantities of vitamins through the mails, but expects the druggist to have on hand at all times the most rarely needed exotic items.

The average prescription costs around $3.50. We complain
that this is exorbitant, even to save our lives. Magazine articles,
books, and accounts of Congressional hearings have led us to
believe that our pockets have been picked every time we leave a
drugstore. Actually, although the drugstore mark-up on the typical
prescription is between 40 and 50 percent, the average net profit
after taxes on the entire business is about 5 percent. Some 200
neighborhood druggists lose their stores through bankruptcy each
year and many are forced to shut down because, among other
reasons, they are not able to cope with competition from price-
cutters and renegade druggists like Doc who sell stolen or counterfeit drugs at an enormous profit.

By working closely with The Group, Doc is able to sell prescription drugs at rock bottom prices. In an FDA recorded interview, he explained: "I buy swag [stolen drugs] for half-price; for
HydroDiuril, that would be $27 [per thousand, wholesale] or
thereabouts. When Tom offered me Hydro for $23 I told him if
it was swag, he wasn't asking enough, and if it was counterfeit,
he was asking too much. I said you can sell counterfeits for $20
and still make a lot of money."

A former practicing pharmacist, now in an important government post, told me: "I long ago gave up pharmacy as a profession,
having become completely disillusioned about the opportunities.
On one of my early jobs, I was hired at the same salary as a
pharmacist who had been in that store 20 years—this gave me an
inkling of what the future held. Further, there was little cooperation and much competition. For instance, the two drugstores in
that town could have taken turns closing on Sundays or holidays
to give us some respite, but no, they both stayed open to make
the business pay off. I finally applied for a job in a pharmacy in a
supermarket because the drug department would honor the same
hours as the grocery store, and, for the first time, I'd have Sundays
off with my family. The store manager remarked that he knew
what the going wages were in town, but he wanted me to know
that he was not going to discriminate between his employees. It
turned out that what he meant was, he was going to pay his
pharmacist just as much as his grocery clerks, even if it was more
than the going rate. After four years of college and two years of

apprenticeship, is it any wonder that at that point I walked out on the profession of pharmacy?"

Today's graduate pharmacists have spent five years studying the sciences of materia medica, chemistry, biology, and pharmacology. In fact, there is a trend toward a six-year program leading to a doctorate. But according to law, pharmacists must not diagnose or prescribe. That is the province of the physician, who often turns to the pharmacist for specific information on new drugs. Doctors obtain most of their information about pharmaceuticals from the *Physician's Desk Reference* (*PDR*) sent to them free by the publisher, who charges companies for their listings of drugs. Pharmaceutical salesmen—known as detail men because they supposedly are able to provide detailed information—discuss their company's product with the doctors. However, even under the new FD&C Act "full disclosure" amendment, the paid ads in medical journals don't give *all* the details. These are printed on package inserts accompanying drug shipments from manufacturers to druggists. The procedure whereby doctors often call upon pharmacists to obtain many of the vital details about drugs has been criticized as too roundabout. But this is one of the few areas where pharmacists can utilize their professional judgment and training.

It is no wonder that pharmacists fear anything that threatens to make further inroads on their professional status. "The Rx file," spokesmen have stated, "is as sacred as the doctor-patient relationship. Why should it be opened to any FDA inspector who comes along?" Pharmacists objected to clauses in drug bills that require record-keeping and precise inventories on the grounds that, "Dispensing physicians have stocks of drugs on hand. If *they* are given professional exemptions, *we* should have professional exemptions. We are just as professional."

They do not welcome any measures that will put additional controls on drug sales, such as the transference of certain over-the-counter medications to the prescription list, because this is another way of contracting their sphere of influence. Pharmacists legally can and should counsel customers on remedies for minor complaints and serve as health educators by urging medical checkups for symptoms that could indicate a serious condition. They would like to see a third category of drugs become their exclusive domain—nonprescription items that could be dispensed only by a licensed pharmacist. They have a good point: dangerous non-prescription drugs should not be sold from grocery shelves like so many boxes of corn flakes. Already 40 percent of proprietary drugs are bought in nondrug outlets.

Pharmacy leaders are troubled about pharmacy's future as a profession, and individual pharmacy owners are worried, also, about their livelihood. But men like Doc do not share these concerns.

Doc graduated from an outstanding college of pharmacy in the city where he has operated drugstores for many years. I asked the dean of this school and several of Doc's teachers about him. They told me that he is "a great embarrassment" to them, but that there was nothing they could do. They are an educational institution, not a law-enforcement agency. Licensing and revocations or suspensions are handled by the state board people. (The FDA has no jurisdiction over licenses.) If Doc belonged to a state or national pharmaceutical association, as about three-fourths of all pharmacists do, they might privately reprimand him, but fellow members could not actually force him out of business. It could become quite sticky, since they own drugstores in direct competition with him.

Doc has a police record for grand larceny, narcotics violations, and half-a-dozen other crimes. His name and the addresses of his pharmacies have been published in his local papers, since he is perennially involved in drug thefts, mass diversion of dangerous or spurious drugs and illicit sales. His state board of pharmacy did try to lift his license, but he was successful in obtaining an injunction to prevent them from harassing him!

Is there any way to prevent people like Doc from becoming pharmacists? How closely can a school of pharmacy screen an applicant? In Doc's case, the dean said, "He was, of course, interviewed, but his grades were what mattered, both when he was admitted and when he was graduated. Actually, he was a very bright student. The only black mark on his record was suspicion of theft of some lab material."

More pharmacists are being trained than ever before. The American Association of Colleges of Pharmacy reports that enrollment in the nation's 74 member colleges increased 16 percent in 1965 over the previous year. There are now almost 12,000 students enrolled in the last three years of professional training. Dean Joseph B. Sprowls of Temple University, who is chairman of AACP's executive committee, assured me that all pharmacy school graduates are exposed to a discussion of ethics before they are sent out to practice their profession. Whether the exposure "takes" depends largely upon the home training and personality of the individual. As Dean Sprowls put it, "A few students, unfortunately, have already established an attitude that it is more profitable to break the law than to live by it. . . . I suppose that we occasionally make a convert, but I am afraid that it does not happen too frequently with people who are 18 years of age and upward. As for detecting these traits in students, we do, but not with any degree of accuracy. Sometimes the ones whom we think are most respectable go out and break the law. Others, thought to be untrustworthy, never commit a recognizable offense. I might point out that it would be very improper for us to refuse to graduate a student because we feel he is dishonest. In order to refuse graduation we would have to have unquestioned evidence of some violation of an academic rule, such as cheating on examinations. We cannot act merely on suspicious evidence any more than the police or any other governing authority."

Dean Sprowls pointed out that the pressures which cause pharmacists to violate the law are the same as those causing physicians to perform abortions, lawyers to handle unethical divorce cases, etc. "Pharmacists are no worse than any other group," he stressed. "But the offenses they commit are easier to detect, and people make a great deal more fuss about them because they relate to health. I always emphasize very strongly that pharmacists must be particularly careful to abide by the law and to observe all ethical standards. But I might as well save my breath with some students who have a totally different moral code established at some earlier point in their lives."

Convinced that professional ethics are best demonstrated rather than talked about, the AACP and the National Association of Boards of Pharmacy have jointly produced a *Pharmacy Preceptor's Guide*. (A preceptor is a practicing pharmacist who supervises students during their on-the-job training in drugstores.) It explains:

The student . . . is not ordinarily exposed in college to actual events involving ethical judgments of a professional nature. . . . The preceptor can teach more by his skillful handling of real life situations than can ever be taught in a college lecture. The preceptor's pride in the service rendered in his pharmacy can be the most potent factor in engendering comparable pride in the pharmacy student.

About 10,000 of these guides have been distributed since they were published in 1964. That they are badly needed was confirmed by the recollections of a number of pharmacists who described their own apprenticeships to me. An associate professor of pharmacy, who spent this period in an Army post dispensary near Washington, D.C., found the realities of practice so harsh that he forthwith took refuge in the academic life.

"About 95 percent of all our prescriptions were for officers' wives and children. The pharmacist in charge was a civilian of long experience, and, although I was a naive, young apprentice, I began to apply my basic mathematics and soon determined that he was only putting in about one-fifth of the penicillin required in prescriptions, making them worse than useless—actually, harmful in that low potency could cause fatal shock reactions when the drug was given again. This man stayed after everyone left and he always had his car backed up to the rear exit. But I didn't put two and two together until later. After I had proudly exhibited my mathematical skills and corrected his errors in compounding, he, of course, promptly told me I was mistaken. Within a few days, and despite a critical shortage of help, I was declared surplus in that particular pharmacy."

At least one other error was noted by this neophyte apothecary: "Another civilian pharmacist was preparing nose drops for General Omar Bradley. I thought it strange when I saw him going to the poison cabinet for one of the ingredients. In checking further, I found he had misread *camphoris,* Latin for camphor, in the prescription, and he was putting in the extremely irritating *cantharides,* Spanish Fly. General Bradley doesn't know the debt of gratitude he owes me—one of those 'nose drops' might well have changed the tides of war!"

Other pharmacy professors expressed grave concern about the bad influence some preceptors have had on students. One decided to conduct an informal study of the situation (not heretofore published) after a senior came into his office visibly shaken.

He said that he was in an extremely delicate situation. It was almost incredible, but he had evidence to prove that the pharmacist-owner of the store he was working in was selling and not recording gallons of paregoric to individuals without prescriptions. [Paregoric is an opium derivative usually prescribed in small doses for intestinal upsets.] He was also selling dangerous ergot preparations, 100 pills at a time, for abortion attempts. He even referred people to a local barber who performed abortions; there seemed to be some kind of "fee-splitting" involved.

The poor student was quite distraught, for he told his professor, "My boss sells Benzedrine, 1,000 at a crack! Everything you can think of! Except, he draws the line at morphine because he wants to stay clean, I guess." The student wondered: "Is this the way it is? . . . Will I run into this type of situation someplace else?"

The professor told me, "The answer to that question was a difficult one to give. In any case, I tried to do something about the situation. I approached an officer in the local pharmaceutical organization, saying that I did not want to make a formal complaint as a faculty member because I didn't want to implicate the university; but, I thought that if *he* knew about it, he could pass it on to the County Board of Grievances. I gave him the proof I had and that's the last I heard of it. When I checked into the matter later, I discovered that the unethical druggist was, himself, a member of that Board of Grievances!"

In an attempt to determine the extent of such activities, another professor asked his juniors and seniors in pharmacy to fill out a questionnaire, ostensibly about wages, hours, and working conditions, but actually designed to document malpractice in the profession. This was on a voluntary basis, answers were to be typed to avoid identification through handwriting, and no names were to be signed or mentioned. "I didn't want anyone to feel he was being put on the spot," the professor said. "We asked, 'Do you work for a relative?' If the answer was 'yes,' we discarded that questionnaire. I realized this was a restricted sample that could be somewhat influenced by our geographic area [a large state university located in a metropolitan medical center], but I was really *shocked* to learn that at least 30 percent of our students were working under pharmacists who violated the law. Maybe not as a general rule, but on occasion, and under the direct observation of a trainee."

Some of the survey questions were: "What do you think of your preceptor as a professional person? Have you ever observed your preceptor or any other registered pharmacist in the store refilling prescriptions illegally? Dispensing, without any prescription whatever, Rx legend drugs such as amphetamines, barbiturates, tranquilizers, thyroid and other hormones, antibiotics, ergot preparations, sulfas?"

There were also queries about narcotics. The professor suspected from the answers given that several supervising pharmacists were probably addicted to drugs. "This is an occupational hazard for us," he explained, "as it is for doctors and nurses. In this school students have much freer access to drugs than in a nursing school where I lectured. There, if a student nurse is found with even a single unauthorized prescription drug on her person or in her room, she is immediately expelled. Campuses across the country are plagued by problems involving illicit drugs—pep pills during exams, kick drugs, experimental substances like LSD, even things like Spanish Fly." (A co-ed in another university died a horrible death after her boy friend gave her some of that to make her "more responsive.")

A survey reported in *Modern Medicine*, March 28, 1966, showed that nearly half of all medical students resort to amphetamine during their training, usually while studying or to keep going after long hours on duty. Pharmacy and medical students are undoubtedly the source for some black-market medicines—in fact, an apprentice pharmacist was recently given a 18-month jail sentence for selling pep pills to fellow students. This young man may have taken the first step toward becoming another Doc. Or, he may have learned a lesson as a result of being caught committing a crime.

A professor-consultant concluded our interview with some qualifying remarks about "crimes committed by pharmacists." "It is hard to know where to draw the line," he said. "Infractions are not always a matter of greed, or entirely the pharmacists' fault.

When a chronic disease sufferer keeps returning regularly for refills of the same medication, often his doctor has not indicated how many refills may be given, and physicians do not always appreciate being called on this. If a druggist takes a chance and refills without calling the doctor—it's usually done to accommodate a customer, I think, rather than from the profit motive—and if there is a crackdown with the violator's name in the paper, this druggist will come out looking like a real crook. Yet he was only doing something that is done every day in probably every pharmacy in the United States."

When I returned to the New York FDA District, I asked Chief Inspector Clem Westerly about this fuzzy area of refills. He said the FDA considers it illegal for a pharmacist to refill a prescription without the physician's specific authorization. He feels that pharmacists are passing the buck when they imply that the fault lies with uncooperative doctors or demanding patients. Actually, statistics show that druggists do more business on refills than on filling first-time prescriptions. So economics as well as ethics are involved. It may be "an accommodation" to save a good customer a trip to the doctor for a new Rx, but the saving may be costly in terms of health if a physical examination or laboratory tests should be made before more medication is taken.

The Chief Inspector defined a prescription as "a specific order by a physician to a pharmacist calling for a *limited* number of doses of a drug, or drug combination, to be dispensed to the patient in a container bearing directions for use." A prescription is not, as common usage would have it, a kind of permit to have all the drugs of this type that the patient feels he needs. He said, "We have found unauthorized refills of potent drugs, capable of causing serious side effects or addiction, dispensed under the same pharmacist's supervision for five years or more. If a physician has been careless in the amounts prescribed, the pharmacist has a professional responsibility to consult with him. Sometimes people are sold a lifetime supply, 'just in case.' And after they die, their heirs come in to get refills!"

The volume of drugs handled by a single pharmacist can be staggering. Doc ordered 9,000,000 amphetamine tablets from three manufacturers over a period of a few months, maintaining that he needed them for his prescription customers. However, over a quarter of a million of these tablets were seized by FDA when they apprehended a peddler supplying truck stops; subsequent investigation and laboratory analysis proved beyond doubt that these were the very same pills sold for Doc's so-called legitimate distribution.

In another case, a North Carolina wholesale druggist purchased and illegally distributed during a three-year period about 6,000,000 units of drugs, mostly amphetamines—enough to supply the legitimate needs of all the drugstores in that state for 12 years.

A druggist in the Kansas City FDA District was fined several hundred dollars in 1962 and placed on three-year probation. In 1965, FDA inspectors were able to purchase as many as 1,000 red birds (sleeping pills) from him on a prescription calling for only 20 capsules.

Pharmacists have been caught sending huge orders of dangerous drugs by mail to individuals in other states. The selling of excessively large amounts of drugs is of course a violation if the purchaser is not an authorized wholesaler. One recipient of thousands of goof balls was the dean of men in a small Midwestern boys' school. Another was the wife of an Army sergeant who used the pills to commit suicide; another, a college student who died from an overdose.

The following documentation was presented to Congress, February 10, 1965, to support the argument that additional controls were needed to prevent what FDA called "substantial" diversion of depressant and stimulant drugs from retail drugstores:

—In 1962, a Kentucky drug salesman purchased 1,371,000 amphetamines from an East Coast manufacturer, and most of these were subsequently sold to a Tennessee pharmacist for illegal distribution. This man's license to practice pharmacy was revoked and he was placed on probation for three years after prosecution in state court.

—A factory laborer in Maryland peddled drugs to other employees in 1960. A pharmacist had surreptitiously obtained the drugs for him from a store where he worked. FDA undercover inspectors made buys of quantities up to 3,000 tablets at a time. A criminal action, which included conspiracy charges, was filed in Federal court. The pharmacist was fined $750, the accomplice, $250; both received sentences of three months imprisonment.

—In 1964, the general safety manager of a large trucking firm reported to FDA that as many as 100,000 amphetamines and barbiturates could be purchased at a time from a Chicago woman who obtained them from a drugstore. Two inspectors made separate buys from her. The drugs were delivered to two lockers in the Illinois Central Railroad Station. After discovering there were only 98 bottles of 1,000 tablets, an inspector and the woman went to the drugstore to complain and an employee gave them two more bottles. FDA is prosecuting the drugstore.

—A druggist in Alabama was fined $750 on nine counts of illegal sale of amphetamines and placed on three years probation in Federal court. He had sold 9,000 tablets in a period of eight days. Drugstore files covering receipt of drugs for a year revealed no invoices whatever, yet records of two local drug wholesalers showed shipments of 407,000 amphetamine tablets to this druggist during that period. A former employee indicated that even larger quantities may have been received from other dealers. This FDA investigation followed leads from the State Board of Pharmacy, the State Department of Public Health, the State Department of Public Safety, and the Federal Bureau of Investigation.

In another FDA case, a pharmacy owner in business for 22 years sold large quantities of amphetamines to agents posing as night workers in a nearby garage. He instructed them to go to a neighborhood physician and get a special prescription, "just for the record," then to keep on bringing back the labeled vials so he could "fill 'em up." The FDA men told him they were re-selling the stimulants to their co-workers, who had no prescriptions. Nonetheless, and without ever contacting the physician again, he gave them 27 refills in a month.

After the close-out, when FDA inspected his invoices, they learned that he was covering up many illegal transactions with

fictitious bulk shipments of drugs to nursing homes and hospitals
—institutions that had never heard of him. Unaccounted for in
this store were: 60 percent of the Tuinal purchased; 90 percent
of the Dexedrine; 30 percent of the generic 10-milligram amphetamine sulfate; 50 percent of the Butazolidin, used for arthritis,
and so on. This man's attorney argued that his client could not
afford to pay the fine. Later the real explanation came out: "If
the fine is large, state authorities will think this is a *serious* case
and my client's license might be placed in jeopardy." Notwith-
standing earlier pleas of poverty, the druggist paid the $1,000 fine.
But he went away complaining that his record had been clean,
except for "a little substituting" of one drug for another 'way
back in 1930.

This was a typical FDA drugstore case for many reasons. One
is that the violator had a history of "substituting." This practice
falls into a gray area that looks jet black to producers of brand-
name pharmaceuticals when their products are replaced by cheaper
generics, but it appears lily white to some Congressmen and
writers, so long as it's done in the name of saving consumers'
money.

Honest druggists do, of course, try to pass savings on to customers through careful buying of generic drugs from reputable firms
that employ quality controls and stand behind their products.
But unfortunately, according to FDA observations, there are
other pharmacists who buy bulk unbranded drugs from anonymous sources, substitute without approval by the doctor (illegal
as well as unethical), and simply pocket the difference between
the cost of the cheaper generic and the price they can charge for
the well-known brand the doctor had prescribed.

An East Coast pharmacist substituted aspirin tablets on a
prescription calling for cortisone. If this was to save the patient
money, why did he charge cortisone prices for aspirin tablets?

In any event, it is not legal in any state for a pharmacist to
substitute even a so-called "equivalent" brand without first obtaining the prescribing physician's permission. FDA prosecuted
this druggist. For all this man knew, the patient could have had
a violent allergy to aspirin. Suppose the physician had just discovered diabetes or serious heart disease during his last examination? Even substituting another brand of cortisone might have

been hazardous if it contained sugar or sodium, contraindicated for patients with diabetes and heart disease. Physicians don't necessarily give patients or pharmacists all the details.

The substitution of altogether different types of drugs has resulted in fatalities.

In a Western state in the mid-1950's, a druggist purchased sulfanilimide left over from World War II. (This form of sulfa has not been sold for human use since 1948 because of its serious side effects; the pharmacist was well aware of this.) He obtained the tablets for 7 cents a hundred, and used them as substitutes for other sulfas costing $1.45 per hundred. One patient died as a result. The attending physician had no way of knowing that he was dealing with a systematic sulfanilimide reaction—the other sulfa acts only on the intestinal tract's flora.

The druggist was given an 11-month sentence in a country-club–type prison, while a relative managed his business. When released, he began violating the law again almost immediately. As for the action taken by the State Board of Pharmacy: "We reprimanded this fellow *very* severely, we really *chewed* him out!"

FDA's monthly report of illegal sales frequently mentions antibiotics. In one case not long ago, a woman died because of a reaction to penicillin tablets not prescribed by her doctor.

An FDA inspector, who is a veterinarian formerly employed selling veterinary medicine, said that he has found a number of druggists palming these off on people. (Quality controls in plants producing drugs for animals are supposed to be just as high as for human drugs. However, one iron preparation manufactured to the prescription of a veterinarian was recalled when 168 steers of the 172 injected died.) Diversion of veterinary medicine is easier because distribution controls are somewhat less stringent. "There is a brisk sale of such antibiotics over the counter for the treatment of venereal disease," this inspector said. "Aside from the fact that these drugs may well be ineffective or dangerous through improper dosage, or because they are outdated, there is an additional public health hazard in that the venereal cases are not reported and contacts are not treated."

Whether any human beings have died after being given veterinary medicines is not known—in fact, the death toll from any type of black-market medicine cannot be estimated. How can one even compile meaningful statistics on deaths from legal medications?

One thing is certain. In the opinion of FDA officials, it was the practice of substituting by pharmacists that led to prescription drug-counterfeiting. The two practices have been historically intermingled. The first Federal substitution case in 1908 involved the sale of silver nucleinate for Argyrol, but in the 1880's, even before there was an FDA, *American Druggist* was calling attention to the substitution swindle. And in its July 6, 1953, issue, the magazine published a pioneering study of the problem. Here are some hightlights of that survey that still warrant our attention:

Manufacturers reported that substitutions on their Rx specialties ranged as high as 25 percent, and that the primary motive was "greed" on the part of pharmacists who palm off cheap drugs at high prices. Retailers countered with the charge that unnecessary duplication of identical compounds was to blame, because it is impossible to keep every brand of every specialty on the shelves.* One druggist said there should be an arrangement among manufacturers that no more than three produce any one therapeutic product. A drug producer even agreed, saying that "the catalogs of most national companies could be pruned 75 percent and the nation's health would not be impaired in any way."

At the time of the 1953 study, 39 of the nation's 49 pharmacy boards had already ruled that the substitution of one drug for another, or of one brand for another, was illegal as well as unethical. Almost 70 percent of the major drug manufacturers had taken steps to curb substitution and counterfeiting of their brands by incorporating identifying characteristics, called "tracers," in their products, and by designing distinctive shapes for capsules and tablets.

Violators are detected by company "shoppers" who have prescriptions filled in various parts of the country. If laboratory analysis proves that there has been substitution, manufacturers are more and more inclined to sue their druggist-customers. A. H. Robins, Inc., caught four Florida druggists filling prescriptions

---

*A 1966 Federal report says that there are 15,000 different dosage forms of prescription drugs legally produced in this country. Hundreds of new variations appear each year.

calling for their antispasmodic Donnatal with drugs of other firms. It was the liquid form of the medication, and the druggists colored the substitute so that it looked like Donnatal. Robins sued each druggist in Federal court for $10,000 damages, claiming that their trademark was violated. Obviously, the druggists would not have gone to all this trouble unless there was a considerable profit to be made.

The profit motive is so strong, that repeated surveys of the same substituting druggists have shown that warnings to cease and desist are, in the words of one drug company executive, "Like telling a pickpocket, 'Don't do that again,' then turning him loose at the track."

A 1963 survey in one of the better-regulated states—New York, where 13 of the State Pharmacy Board inspectors are pharmacists —gives some idea of the scope of the problem. That year, 7,172 samples were collected and analyzed; 131 were reported to be "spurious." These included so-called: Robins' Donnatal; Abbott's Nembutal; Squibb's Raudixin; Ciba's Serpasil; SK&F's Dexamyl and Dexedrine Tablets, Spansule capsules, and Elixir. Also bogus were: Cheracol Syrup, Kaopectate, Unicaps, Elixir Butisol Sodium, Syrup Histadyl E.C., Amesee Capsules, and Neo-synephrine Solution. The drugs were sampled either from pharmacy stocks directly or on prescription, and were analyzed by the state chemist. According to New York Pharmacy Board Secretary Kenneth S. Griswold, penalties in excess of $70,000 were assessed for these and other violations in 1963. In several instances, licenses were suspended or revoked during this period.

The American Journal of Hospital Pharmacy, July 1961, published results of the only nationwide investigation of counterfeiting conducted by the FDA. (Isn't it high time they got busy on another one?) In one phase of the survey, FDA had prescriptions for six drugs known to be counterfeited (Diuril, Equanil, Hydro-Diuril, Meticorten, Miltown, and Serpasil) filled by retailers under suspicion in various parts of the country. Of 59 prescriptions analyzed, 42 were counterfeit. In 900 drugstores selected at random for a second phase of the study, nine drug samples from nine retailers were found to be counterfeit; six of these drugs had been made by a notorious counterfeiter; three were from an unknown source or sources.

At that time, FDA did not feel that the facts warranted disturbing sick people about the quality of their medications, so these findings were not publicized to laymen. However, the report concluded with a warning to pharmacists:

"The origin of counterfeits and the possibility that they have not been properly manufactured leaves us no room for apathy or complacency. Potentially, the problem is an explosive one. . . . Marketing of counterfeit drugs is a bootleg operation easily detected by the retail pharmacist. . . . The racket could not exist without the cooperation of unethical druggists."

Many others, themselves pharmacists, have made similar observations. The American Pharmaceutical Association's 1966 President, Dean Linwood F. Tice of the Philadelphia College of Pharmacy and Science, has said: "There would be no such thing as counterfeit drugs if every pharmacist in the United States practiced his profession ethically!"

No practicing registered pharmacist could possibly escape all the warning alerts for counterfeit medications. These have appeared in local and national trade papers, newsletters, and professional journals. The peril in "Special deals" has been particularly underscored. A few years ago, bogus drugs were peddled in paper or pliofilm bags; but druggists have been cautioned that nowadays counterfeiters are duplicating cartons, bottles, inserts, and labels.

The Distribution Protection Section of Smith Kline & French Laboratories in Philadelphia has an extensive educational program underway to alert pharmacists, law-enforcers, and the public to the counterfeiting problem. One of their pamphlets gives the following suggestions under the heading, "What Can Pharmacists Do To Combat Counterfeits?"

1. Buy drugs only in original, sealed containers. Don't buy a small supply of a drug which the seller claims was taken from the big-sized original bottle.

2. Beware of any person who offers to sell a drug at an unreasonably low price, with the claim that it is a close-out or distress merchandise. Always get invoices from your suppliers.

3. Report to the department of health or pharmacy board, local FDA office, and the manufacturer, the name of any person who

offers to buy empty original manufacturers' containers—particularly of fast-moving and expensive drugs—of large sizes as 500's and 1000's.

4. If you encounter a suspected counterfeit drug, get the name of the seller, and any other information you can (car license number, description, etc.). Report at once to the department of health or pharmacy board, the local FDA office, and the manufacturer of the product concerned.

To avoid counterfeits:

KNOW YOUR SUPPLIERS AND BUY ONLY
FROM REPUTABLE LOCAL SUPPLIERS YOU KNOW.

How widespread is distribution of counterfeits through pharmacies? We really don't know. The FDA doesn't know—doesn't even have access to the information locked up in drug company files. A sharp, unprecedented drop in sales of a leading product, in a territory where legitimate competition has been closely monitored, may mean that counterfeiters are cutting in. Prescription audits of brand-name specialties dispensed—which exceed the amounts of invoiced manufacturers' sales—offer other clues. But, as Tom and Doc pointed out, the really smart operators keep on buying some legitimate drugs from their regular sources in order to avoid being pin-pointed on sales charts. In any case, sales facts and figures, the loss of business, and similar bits of intelligence are closely guarded trade secrets in this highly competitive industry. There is little inclination to share them with the nearest chief inspector, even though he may be working hard on the very same cases.*

There have been isolated instances of FDA/Industry cooperation with good results, but by and large, as a matter of policy, drug companies refuse to tell FDA anything unless forced to by Federal statutes. For instance, two major producers of barbiturates and amphetamines declined to supply vital information needed by FDA in formulating its recommendations to the Congress on drug abuse control. Their specific production figures could have been buried in the totals from many companies that did respond

---

*However, drug counterfeiters manage to obtain much inside information. A drug company executive was dismayed to learn that Tom's estimate of a "hot" drug's monthly sales was only a few dollars off the actual amount running into many millions of dollars.

to the call for help. They did *not* have to be identified. The FDA
Commissioner at that time, Mr. Larrick, estimated that nine and
a half billion amphetamine and barbiturate pills are produced
annually in the United States, but he pointed out, "if the production of two major ethical drug companies were added, this amount
probably would be doubled." One of these companies was voted
"most ethical" in a consumer survey but, certainly, in this instance, they were hardly public-spirited.

Where counterfeits are concerned, some executives, however,
are speaking out. Merck's Western Sales Manager G. Wayne Bye
told drug officials at a meeting: "There are distributors pushing
counterfeit drug merchandise to some degree in practically every
large city in the country. . . . If counterfeiting continues unchecked and becomes general public knowledge, it could under-
mine public confidence in the integrity of the profession."

SK&F's Assistant to the President Carl K. Raiser has stated:

> Our investigations, covering hundreds of prescriptions filled
> throughout the United States over many years, reveal that 9 out
> of every 10 substitutions are filled with counterfeit products. Not
> with other distinct brands, but with direct, unmistakable counter-
> feits! Such druggists do *not* exercise professional judgment, nor do
> they indulge in a magnanimous gesture to save customers' money.
> Nine times out of 10, they delve into a bottle of counterfeits and
> palm them off as the original. They perpetrate a fraud. . . .

Is there any way a customer can spot these druggists?

It is very difficult. As noted, Doc operates several kinds of
drugstores. His major outlet is a purely professional pharmacy,
prescriptions only. Down the street he has a cluttered discount
outlet, a bazaar of dusty bottles, dented cans, and cartons of
miscellany. After picking one's way through brand-name items
marked only a few cents off list price, and a lot of much cheaper
merchandise of unspecified origin, one finds a small prescription
counter in the rear of the store.

It was at this point that I recalled John Ruskin's observation:
"There is hardly anything in the world that some man cannot
make a little worse and sell a little cheaper and the people who
consider price only are this man's lawful prey." If it is true, as
one survey states, that the average family spends only around $50

a year on *prescription* drugs, it might be worthwhile to reappraise the household budget and try to save pennies on less vital items. Of course, where there is serious illness or a chronic condition requiring large amounts of drugs, the total cost can be quite staggering. Some people must choose between medication or a proper meal.

Pharmacists feel that leading manufacturers should drop their prices when "they've skimmed the cream off" a best-seller drug. According to *American Druggist*, it was the tempting price differential that caused up to 30 percent of all pharmacies in their survey to substitute some items, either occasionally or habitually. While I do not argue for needlessly high prescription prices, from my own investigation it is difficult to see how any ethical manufacturer could reduce his research, production quality control, and marketing costs *to the level of successful competition* with Abe and Bert for the business of druggist-customers like Doc.

Whether the consumer must save money on drugs, or whether he seeks the best that money can buy, he is either way threatened by the possibility of substitution and counterfeiting.

An executive in a leading drug company told me that he had difficulty picking out imitations of his firm's own products without benefit of chemical analysis. "Since I have to take some of our drugs on doctor's orders, and sometimes must buy them on the outside when traveling, I admit the situation makes me quite uneasy."

Few of us can obtain our drugs fresh from the production lines inside Eli Lilly, Parke Davis, or Squibb. Nor is it possible to have them routinely checked out by FDA's "Pillistics" experts in the Division of Microbiology in Washington. (During the analysis, drugs are dissolved, in any case.) We are forced to take our chances in this game of pharmaceutical roulette at the corner drugstore.

Since counterfeits have been found in all types of retail outlets in every part of the country, there are precious few inside tips. As soon as I thought I had one, something seemed to discredit it. For instance, in theory, an owner of a prosperous pharmacy might be less inclined to increase his profits illegally, than a man about to lose his business. But a spokesman for a major pharmaceutical manufacturer said, "Our experience shows that the substitutor has a better-than-average store, so far as sales volume, appearance, and location are concerned. One could speculate as to how great a role substitution played in the success of such stores."

Very well then, the struggling pharmacist-owner down the street should be the man to patronize. A reliable consultant made a most disturbing observation, "An *unethical* pharmacist running a relatively small business is more likely to give the customers *he knows* counterfeits or substitutes than total strangers, for the stranger might be a 'gum shoe' making buys for a drug company or a regulatory agency."

Should one favor a quaint one-man Apothecary Shoppe over a large chain that employs dozens of pharmacists, who are all likely to be nicknamed Doc? Not necessarily. Leading chain stores, according to *American Druggist*, are inclined to crack down on substitutors because one case, if publicized, could give every store in the chain a bad name. One national chain's pledge: "Substitution is not only a dangerous practice but most pernicious, and under no circumstances will it be countenanced," was published to illustrate this point in the magazine.

On the other hand, the wealthy owner of a chain of more than half-a-dozen pharmacies was arrested not long ago on the charge of being a contact man and fence for a hijacking mob. He was caught disposing of looted drugs. I wonder whether he has any framed pledges against substituting hanging in his drugstores.

These have been generalizations, of course. The important thing is the integrity of the individual pharmacist purchasing and selling the drugs, and whether or not he has double-checked to make certain that his sources are reputable. Consumers who are suspicious of the drugs they are receiving should take samples to their doctors and describe anything unusual about the appearance, taste, or effects. They could also bring the matter to the attention of the Bureau of Drug Abuse Control. (See Appendix E, for addresses.)

Meanwhile, the best advice is ancient, "Let the buyer beware."

CHAPTER NINE

And Pharmacy's Controls

The actual guardians of pharmacy are not FDA inspectors or narcotic agents, as one might conclude from newspaper articles about isolated cases. The men responsible for the licensing of pharmacists—and for suspending or revoking these licenses—are themselves pharmacists.

How well does the pharmacy profession regulate itself? This depends upon the individual state board inspector in the field and the board members supervising that particular state at that particular time. If, as the authorities I consulted agree, the statement is valid that "There would be no counterfeit drugs if there were no unethical pharmacists," we can suggest further that there would be no unethical pharmacists practicing their professions if state boards were doing their jobs.

A pharmacy professor with years of drugstore experience in at least four states said, "I can tell you about some state boards I have known. First you must realize that the members of state boards, while they must be pharmacists in every state, are political appointees and this is reflected in the type of governing you get. The state inspectors in the field are not usually pharmacists: they may be housewives, retired people, beauticians, barbers, what have you. Some are not above wanting a box of cigars or a couple of cartons of cigarettes as they make their inspection rounds. And, to show you the stupidity of employing people who are not pharmacy-oriented, once when I was in a new store, the state inspector came in with a list of minimum requirements for technical equipment, the reference library, and so forth. He looked at the current [XVI] edition of the USP on the shelf and actually asked, 'Where are the other fifteen volumes of this *set*?' In order to upgrade the enforcement of pharmacy regulations in any state, the board should include some academic people, as well as political appointees, if these are a necessary evil. It would keep them on their toes and provide additional sources of information."

An FDA supervisory inspector in a Western district stated: "I know of several instances, first-hand, where the state board members printed warnings to pharmacists in their newsletters on the order of: 'The Feds are in the state making undercover buys, so watch out. Don't sell to them.' In one state, when we were making OTC cases against pharmacists diverting large quantities of dangerous drugs, a State Board member tried to ruin our cases by sending out a notice giving our names and such descriptions as, 'One of the Feds is wearing a cowboy outfit!' "

From these, and other examples, it seems clear that while the National Association of Boards of Pharmacy (NABP), headquartered in a Chicago skyscraper, is trying to upgrade the image and effectiveness of state boards, some individuals and groups are undermining the effort at the grass roots level.

Surveys by NABP show that members of state boards, or commissions, as they are sometimes called, must have from three to ten years of professional practice as registered pharmacists before their appointment, usually by the governor of the state. Local pharmaceutical associations frequently serve as consultants. Members are paid from $5 to $35 per diem, plus expenses, and serve from three to six years. The state office may consist solely of part-time clerical help supervised by a board secretary elected by other members. Some states have only one inspector in the field checking all pharmacists and pharmacies.

Basic sources for anyone interested in knowing more about state pharmacy boards are the published *Proceedings* of annual NABP conventions held in conjunction with the American Pharmaceutical Association. In them, I read that "The most important responsibility of a board member is to determine, by examination, whether a candidate is a safe person to be entrusted to perform pharmaceutical services in a manner which will always be in the best interest of the health and safety of the public."

While we are concerned here with the pharmacist's honesty, rather than with his technical skills and general competence, the very wide variation in minimum standards for registration of pharmacists from state to state has some bearing on black-market medicine. Theoretically, a "composite pharmacist" could now be licensed who was graduated from college as early as 1905. He need have no prior practical experience. For an examination fee of $5, and an annual renewal fee of $2, he could be registered without an examination in one state if he were a graduate of that state's college of pharmacy. In other cases, temporary certificates could be given if applicants were deemed "qualified." Lastly, a most pertinent footnote in the *Proceedings* states: "Good moral character required, but not mentioned in statutes of 15 states."

About 11 percent of the pharmacists practicing today are not college-trained. Some have had no formal education beyond two years of high school. (Remember how Abe's first "scientific" production manager, Charlie, just went in and took an examination back in the mid-1930's?)* One can't generalize about "qualified registered pharmacists" with licensing laws as chaotic as they are. No two states are alike. The same applies to requirements for pharmacy-operating permits. The NABP survey noted: "In some states it is not mandatory for pharmacies to have any reference texts or special equipment that is used to weigh, measure, compound, dispense, and store drugs."

Seventy percent of the prescription drugs available today could not have been had at all in 1935, according to industry sources. Pharmacists must keep up with the latest advances and research data in the field. Professor V. N. Bhatia of the Washington State College of Pharmacy told NABP members in 1964:

"Most seminars or refresher courses have programs that are uninspired and uninspiring. They consist of a few high-sounding speeches by some nationally known persons, followed by talks on insurance, merchandising, etc., with perhaps one or two unrelated talks on scientific topics thrown in as an afterthought."

The black-market diversion of extremely potent, dangerous

---

*According to the 1964 NABP census, of the 100,697 registered and practicing retail pharmacists, 5,326 are nongraduates and 8,958 are graduates of two-year schools.

drugs may, in some cases, be due to the ignorance as well as the economic need and/or greed of a pharmacist. To be realistic, ethics cannot be taught and morality cannot be legislated. If all the warnings ever published have no effect on willful violators, the statutes must be invoked and these people put out of business. Not for a day or for 30 days, but permanently.

In January 1964, NABP reported the total number of pharmacy licenses in good standing in this country was 183,501, including a number of pharmacists who hold two or more licenses. During 1963, 1,201 licenses were suspended or revoked. In Colorado, 92 licenses were "lifted" out of the 3,020 in good standing, while, strangely, in New Jersey not a single practicing pharmacist of 5,146 lost his license, although a number have been investigated for selling spurious drugs there.

A comprehensive analysis of all state boards conducted by the Public Administration Service for FDA revealed in May 1965:

> A review of the 50 states was made in terms of extent of activity, using the following criteria: (a) very active—large field staff, some undercover work, many hearings and court cases; (b) active—more than one inspector, apparently alert to infractions, some revocations, suspensions, prosecutions; and, (c) inactive—one inspector or none, prosecutions or reprimands of pharmacists rare or nonexistent. These criteria were applied generally and liberally. For example, in one instance, a state that has only one inspector was labeled "active" on the basis of other criteria. Results showed 14 State Boards very active; 14 active; and the remaining 22 "inactive."

What do all these statistics *mean* to the consumer? The first duty of a board of pharmacy is to protect the public, not—as many pharmacists think—to protect pharmacy's commercial interest. State boards have regulatory power through license suspension and revocation. Obviously, they are not fully utilizing this authority.

As a result of the $250,000 survey of state boards, FDA has appointed Regional Assistant Commissioners to promote state and local action. FDA's case-making is focused on apprehending as many big-time operators as possible. Federal agents find that their limited manpower can best be used in breaking up whole rings of criminals. Thus the FDA has deemphasized investigations of individual pharmacists suspected of dealing in illicit drugs. The responsibility is being left more and more to local and state agencies. Unfortunately, no two states have the same drug laws, and within a state there are usually several health and law-enforcement groups with overlapping authority. The picture is even more confused because the interpretations of laws vary so greatly.

Even in Federal cases involving almost identical violations, one finds a pharmacist in Indiana paying a fine of $4,000, while a Tennessee pharmacist gets a suspended sentence, no fine, and a year's probation. Typically, penalties are light. And, of course, cases may be appealed. It is almost unheard of for a pharmacist to be sent to jail.

Some incongruous Federal-state views of drug law-breaking exist: in one city, while the state attorney general was levying $50 fines on dozens of variety stores for "selling iodine by unregistered clerks not under the supervision of a pharmacist," a Federal judge was lightly fining men convicted of making and distributing counterfeited drugs. He even let some of them off scot-free.

Clearly, such a chaotic situation demands the passage of a uniform drug act by every state legislature. It should be modeled on the Federal statute, as amended in 1965, and such crimes as counterfeiting prescription drugs should be considered felonies in all courts. A 1961 study of drug counterfeiting and state laws, conducted by Stanley M. Grossman of New York University Law School, revealed that very few state pharmacy laws specifically mention counterfeiting, and in most states all other unlawful activity related to nonnarcotic, but dangerous, drugs is in the misdemeanor category.

New York City Health Commissioner Leona Baumgartner, M.D., has pointed out many advantages of uniform legislation, among them the lowering of drug prices at the retail level:

Uniformity of food and drug legislation would give the consumer the greatest possible benefit of all advances and impose the least burden on industry. Drug companies doing business in several states spend enormous amounts of money on accounting and legal fees in order to comply with conflicting requirements. Savings here might well be passed on to consumers through lowered drug costs.

All states have now adopted the Uniform Narcotic Act, patterned on Federal statutes. But passage of laws applying to non-narcotic drugs, while ostensibly supported by every major trade and professional organization, is concurrently being undermined by some of these same vested interests.

It's the old story—pharmacists feel the laws should apply to manufacturers, while manufacturers demand tighter regulation of pharmacies. As a result, consumers are not protected and pay higher than necessary prices for prescriptions.

Even if the laws are not uniform, they at least should be up to date. One of the most archaic is the District of Columbia's Pharmacy Act—this "current" statute predates the Pure Food and Drug Act of 1906. One legal expert's verdict: "Our drug laws are a crime!"

This is an old problem. I have seen pleas for the enactment of uniform drug legislation, with particular emphasis on drug counterfeiting, that were written 30 years ago. The medications being copied then—Musterole and Grove's Bromo Quinine—were nowhere near as potent as those being pirated now. Today counterfeits are in the life-saving or death-dealing category.

Why has so little been done? An excerpt from a 1932 letter from a Lambert Pharmacal Company lawyer gives several clues:

> It is urgently necessary that various organizations promptly unite to promote passage of such amendments . . . since counterfeiters prey on leading products, and have retailers as accomplices, substantial profits are made before schemes are detected. After ten years' experience . . . punishment meted out in State courts where I've been compelled to bring civil action was farcical.

The various warring factions in pharmacy have spent too much valuable time in petty vendettas and "image-building." After attending the National Drug Trade Conference—a gathering of pharmacists, drug manufacturers, and distributors—the NABP president reported:

> NDTC has suggested uniform state legislation . . . little progress has been made between groups whose objectives and purposes are incompatible. Every time an attempt is made to approve wholesome uniform legislation for the protection of public health and safety by professional organizations, there seems to be opposition from

other member groups opposing such legislation as monopolistic. My personal observation of the NDTC is one where leaders from the drug industry as a whole can debate their differences of opinion and agree to disagree.

In discussing the need for legislative reform, a Pharmacy Board member told NABP:

"The only people who would oppose us would be the [X] Association and a certain few manufacturers. But I take heart in this. The [X] Association was against the first Pure Food and Drug Bill. The [X] Association was against the Harrison Narcotic Act. The [X] Association is still fighting us . . . over a drug safety bill. It almost seems that we are on the right side if we are on the side opposite the [X] Association."

For "[X] Association," one could substitute any one of several dozen associations. All segments of pharmacy, pharmaceutical manufacturing, and their regulatory agencies, like FDA, are either being attacked or counterattacking most of the time, as an hour's reading of current periodicals in any pharmacy library will prove. Having read these journals and attended these meetings as a science writer for a decade, I see no heroes emerging from these interminable battles.

It seems to me that measures, both preventative and punitive, are required: screening pharmacy school applicants more carefully; clearly delineating to students what is ethical and what is not, rather than lecturing vaguely on "professionalism"; prosecuting producers and dispensers of counterfeits, and publicizing the crimes and the criminals who tend to be repeaters. Only a few pharmaceutical manufacturers vigorously and publicly pursue the wrong-doers—it takes money, initiative, and a fair amount of courage, because their own products may be cast under a cloud in the process. But it is in the public interest to do so.

In order to increase and insure public support, I hope that organized pharmacy and individual pharmacists will find some way to implement this pledge from the American Pharmaceutical Association's *Code of Ethics*:

The pharmacist will expose any corrupt or dishonest conduct of any member of his profession which comes to his certain knowledge . . . he will aid in driving the unworthy out of the calling.

Drug News Weekly, January 9, 1967, made this forecast about the 90th Congress:

> On Jenkins Hill in Washington, D.C., this week 524 men and 11 women resume the yearly task of helping mold American destiny. They also preside over the special interest clashes which invariably keep the city jumping. . . . Senate Commerce Committee chairman Warren Magnuson (D., Wash.) has a plan for beefing up the truth-in-packaging law, plus a look at Federal, state and private industry roles in consumer protection. . . . Normally, drugs might be wrapped into this consumer protection drive. Except drugs are even more volatile an issue. A Senate Small Business subcommittee headed by Sen. Gaylord Nelson (D., Wis.) is liable to hold televised hearings on drug prices. Senate Finance Committee Chairman Russell Long (D., La.) might focus his own spotlight on drug prices as part of any handling of Medicare proposals by his group. And Rep. L. H. Fountain (D., N.C.) plods along, heading a House Government Operations Subcommittee which delves into the interrelationships of the drug industry and the Food and Drug Administration.

Elsewhere in this issue it is noted that the grass-roots consumer movement, rallying under the banner of The United National Consumers Association, Inc. (TUNCA), has "drug prices high on its list of targets."

Because of the truth-in-packaging and automobile safety measures it passed, the 89th Congress was characterized as "a consumers' Congress." During the next two years of the 90th Congress there is some indication that this trend may continue. And a good thing, too, for we should be at least as concerned about what is really in our package of Chloromycetin as we have been about our boxes of corn flakes.

Consumers should continue to ask questions and to expect straightforward answers, not only about drug prices, but also about drug safety, purity, and potency. One could begin by asking one's own pharmacist about the *source* of the specific medications being put into the prescription bottle. Does he know the name and address of the actual producer? Or was the drug repacked and sold by others? What about the distributor he bought it from, is he sure of his reliability? How does the pharmacy check on the quality and authenticity of the drugs it buys?

Such questions may be hard to answer, if not actually embarrassing for some pharmacists. But consumers of life-saving drugs have a right to know what they are buying and taking. If pharmacy owners hear enough of these questions from their customers, they will tend to be more careful in their purchases and practices than some of them have been. They should, in turn, demand more information from *their* sources, thus making it more difficult for black-market medicines to flow into legal distribution channels.

A bill was introduced during the last Congress that would set up a separate cabinet-rank Department of Consumers. So far as prescription drugs are concerned, it seems to me that we should support and encourage the people who are already trained to guard our drug supply—the nation's pharmacists and the FDA— rather than create another watchdog-type bureau in Washington. Of course, if pharmacy and the pharmaceutical industry don't meet these responsibilities, the government will have to take a stronger position.

The President's Special Assistant for Consumer Affairs, Mrs. Esther Peterson, didn't mince words when she told the American Pharmaceutical Association that consumers ask her:

"Is this man in the white coat behind the prescription counter making a huge profit on my illness? Is he in cahoots with the drug companies? Is he pushing this particular over-the-counter drug because his inventory is high? Or is he acting as a professional in all his transactions?" She underscored the fact that patients entering pharmacies with prescriptions must act on faith alone. "The average person is completely dependent upon the honesty, integrity, and competence of pharmacists. . . . You pharmacists cannot sit back and sidetrack these issues to the manufacturer, the wholesaler, or the physician. . . . Pharmacists are the important *final* link in the drug distribution chain."

As this final link, the pharmacist has more contact with the general public, day in and day out, than anyone else involved with pharmaceuticals. What use he makes of this opportunity is entirely up to him. Dr. Melvin R. Gibson, Dean of Pharmacy at Washington State University, wrote on "Patient Instruction by Private Consultation" in the December 1966, *Journal* of the American Pharmaceutical Association:

> The Pharmaceutical Center provides the place for a pharmacist to be a professional and deal professionally with the public. . . . Every

new prescription order should be discussed with the patient. Every renewal, which the pharmacist believes needs checking with the patient, should be discussed with him—in private. . . . The pharmacist is not in a position to discuss diagnosis and the ramifications of diseases. However, he is capable of discussing the drug as a drug with the patient.

An FDA official reports marked improvement in cooperation since the regulatory agency held a pharmacy leadership conference to explain the problem of dangerous-drug control. He is especially hopeful that pharmacists still in school will enter practice as *responsible professionals.*

"It is in this direction that pharmaceutical education must move without delay," agrees Linwood F. Tice, President of the American Pharmaceutical Association. "The pharmacist not only must be a custodian of drugs, he must also be involved in their control— not just in preventing their theft for illicit use, but in preventing excessive use or misuse by *bona fide* patients."

Dr. Gibson reported that the Pharmaceutical Information Center has caught the imagination of professionally-minded students more than any other development in community practice. "It is a most exciting challenge," he said.

There is a challenge here for the public, also. If we want good advice, good service, and good drugs from our neighborhood pharmacist, we should examine our roles as "good customers." Are we doing anything that might, eventually, help to drive a good pharmacist from the field, for either economic or personal reasons? There is nothing abstract or altruistic about this, it is largely for our own benefit. The ancient and noble profession of pharmacy is ailing. It needs and deserves our consideration.

Let us keep in mind some of the basic problems in pharmacy's struggle for survival as we are deluged with data and opinions on drug prices. Drug prices are important, but focusing on drug costs to the exclusion of all else is a dangerous oversimplification.

We should try to determine, as best we can, what lies behind the perennial exploitation of "drug prices"* as a political issue.

---

*According to the United States Public Health Service, Americans spent an average of $21.00 each for all medicines including prescribed drugs during the year ending June, 1965. Costs per person increased with age, from $6.40 per year for people under 15, to $41.40 for people 65 and older. These statistics were based upon a nationwide sampling of 42,000 households.

During the last election campaign a number of Federal, state, and local office-seekers made the lowering of drug costs a major part of their platforms. Do these people really have sound programs based upon extensive research, or are they riding along on hackneyed slogans?

The Pharmaceutical Manufacturers' Association has published for its members a summary of Federal legislation of interest to the industry, 1965–1966. Congress introduced 16,566 bills and enacted 800. PMA followed 104 primary bills on their day-to-day progress because they had direct or indirect importance to drug producers. They were also of vital importance to all of us, and many will undoubtedly be reintroduced in one form or another during future sessions. We may never have a Secretary of the Department of Consumers sitting with the Secretary of Health, Education, and Welfare and the Secretary of Commerce and other cabinet members, and we may not even need one if we make it our business to keep informed.

What we must have is more reliable information about pharmaceuticals. We should ask our Senators and Representatives to scrutinize the total prescription drug picture in this country, with special highlighting of the black and gray areas.

CHAPTER TEN

Drugs In Distress

The perils of counterfeit drugs are clear. But closely related practices that involve doctors, pharmacists, and hospitals are in gray areas and not strictly illegal, but dangerous to health; they, too, need to be controlled.

The sales pitch most frequently used in peddling counterfeits is that they are "distressed" drugs salvaged from fires, floods, train wrecks, or bankrupt stores. The FDA has found, also, that dubious drugs of all kinds are being passed off as "physicians' samples you can have cheap."

Whether the drugs are counterfeits, real salvage, or, even, repacked physicians' samples, they are bad medicine for the consumer and their sales should be outlawed.

The whole question of what happens to pharmaceuticals when rivers overflow, hurricanes strike, forests burn, or other natural disasters occur, needs to be explored. Theoretically, no damaged drugs should be sold at all, and yet we know, just from the salvage dealers encountered in The Group—Chameleon, Mannie, Abe, and Bert—that this is an old, old form of black-market medicine.

Ethical drug producers replenish lost or damaged uninsured stock after such catastrophes as the earthquake in Alaska. (Even in bankruptcy cases, a pharmacist can return unused supplies of prescription drugs and receive what he paid for them.) Major manufacturers will pick up this merchandise, destroy it, and make good on the loss because they want to protect their brand names. Thus, there is no excuse for the peddling of so-called "distressed" drugs and medical supplies.

Evidence of the dangers abound in FDA records. In November 1965, the Los Angeles District reported the seizure of gauze bandages, labeled as "sterilized," that were contaminated with mold. They had been packed for an Army contract in 1943; but they were offered for sale 22 years later by a surplus store operated by salvors.

Dr. Rupert Salisbury, Secretary of the Ohio Board of Pharmacy, exposed the salvaged-drug hazard at the NABP Convention in New York in 1964. The problem first came to his attention when some prescription legend drugs were shipped from an underwriter's warehouse not licensed as a wholesale drug distributor under Ohio's new laws. He said:

> Upon investigation, my eyes were truly opened. I fully realize that this is old material to many of you present, but I had no idea that there was such a market in distressed merchandise, including food and drugs. The problems inherent in an operation of this sort upset me very greatly. I submit that this is a simply dreadful state of affairs which someday will rebound disastrously when an item "approved" by an enforcement agency is discovered to have caused loss of human life! The public reaction will be overwhelming.

Dr. Salisbury was referring to the fact that his committee's 50-state survey showed that not one has adequate controls over the identification, reclamation, and further distribution of salvaged drugs. Neither the FD&C Act nor the Uniform Food, Drug, and Cosmetic Act being considered by individual states contains sufficient guidelines for handling drugs exposed to calamity. He could only conclude that—drastic as it would seem—all foods, drugs, and other medical or cosmetic preparations used internally or externally should be eliminated from the salvage operator's list of goods for sale. "There will undoubtedly be opposition—such bills have been defeated—but this is the *only* way in which the public health can be adequately protected."

Here are some reasons why the halfway measures now enforced in some states, and proposed in others, should be replaced with proper safeguards:

Merely requiring that food and drug officials be notified of a disaster is meaningless. Too often inspectors arrive at the scene of a fire in a pharmacy or warehouse and find nothing left but the shell. All goods and merchandise have long since been carted off and may have been dumped in unsuspecting surrounding states. (States with the best of these none-too-good laws are victimized by the flow of damaged goods across their borders.)

The control of salvage operators by licensure and inspection, including prior approval of each lot of salvage before it is introduced into commerce, sounds workable when applied to large salvage companies. However, fast-profit operators—among them small country auctioneers and shady fly-by-nights—tend not to apply for licenses. In states where licensing has been tried, these people, when caught, simply pay small misdemeanor fines.

The whole idea of on-the-spot evaluations of distressed pharmaceuticals, particularly those exposed to heat, is unscientific. The various components of a batch would have been exposed to a greater or lesser degree of calamity. The only valid way to determine the amount of alteration is to assay chemically each and every item in the batch. Not only would this require an enormous expenditure of funds and manpower, it would also destroy any possibility of resale. Bottles opened for sampling would have to be condemned.

As Dr. Salisbury pointed out, "There are grave shortcomings in sampling large lots of drugs exposed to high heats. . . . Very few medications of any sort are inorganic chemicals. And almost any organic chemical is subject to partial or total decomposition by heat . . . so, [these drugs] are undoubtedly altered whether or not the external container shows evidence of charring." He explained how dosage forms could be changed physically: High heats can crack enteric coatings, so that tablets dissolve in the stomach rather than pass intact into the intestine, the purpose for which an enteric coating is designed. Effervescent salts would no longer effervesce. Ointments, after melting and resolidifying, might have all the active ingredients in the bottom of the container. The contents of gelatin capsules could be drastically changed without the capsules actually sticking together in one gooey mass.

Since the consumer cannot tell whether or not he is getting salvaged drugs just by looking at them, Dr. Salisbury suggested that at least they ought to be labeled with a stamp indicating that they are "distressed merchandise." Many states now require this for salvaged beer and alcoholic beverages.

He continued with another shocker:

> As you know, such merchandise is sold as the regular item *at the regular price*, in spite of the fact that it usually has been purchased at about 30 to 50 per cent of cost from the salvage operator, or even at lesser amounts from an auctioneer. . . . Whether such a [labeling] requirement could be enforced or whether this would require additional legislation is a question which legal talents must decide. I submit that the normal history of the drug has been altered from the usual manufacturing and distributing procedures to a point where its actual market value has been decreased and I am convinced that the public interest demands that the buyer be informed of this fact.

Where lives are at stake, it may seem strange for so much emphasis to be placed on purely economic factors. But the people who lobby most vigorously—and successfully—against such vital measures are those who are financially threatened. I was surprised, therefore, to get a somewhat "business-oriented" reaction from an FDA inspector when I asked for comments on Dr. Salisbury's proposals:

"If you had ever been faced with the decision to release or condemn an entire stock of goods representing a man's total investment, you would understand that this is no simple matter. Should a businessman be forced into bankruptcy because of a relatively small fire in the basement of a pharmacy or drug warehouse? Where and how do you draw the line?"

Difficult questions. But in the absence of well-defined regulations, should not the guiding philosophy be on the order of "the greatest good for the greatest number?"

Prescription drug manufacturers spend an estimated $100 million annually sending small sample packages of new drugs—or new dosage forms of old drugs—to doctors free of charge. The practice of sampling is on the increase because it has proved to be the industry's best method of reaching their primary advertising target—the prescription-writing physician. The idea is to familiarize the doctor with the drug itself and to give him an opportunity to observe its effects on patients through the use of these trial doses, usually from one to seven days' supply.

The FD&C Act requires only that the samples be packaged with complete and accurate labeling. This label is frequently removed by the doctor before the drugs are given to the patient. On their own, some ethical companies have stamped each pill or capsule PROFESSIONAL SAMPLE or PHYSICIANS' SAMPLE: NOT TO BE SOLD. This is rather easily removed, however. In some cases saliva-dampened fingers have been used successfully, one indication of what is meant by "contamination."

Few doctors manage to use all unsolicited samples as they were intended to be used. It seems wasteful to throw expensive, life-saving medications away, so most store them, hoping a charitable organization will come collecting. When the stockpiles keep growing, exasperated doctors say "get rid of this stuff!" The drugs then may be sold to a man-who-comes-around, to a pharmacist, or bartered for cigarettes, cosmetics, and small appliances.

An FDA inspector, who formerly was a pharmacist in a store where the owner had "arrangements" with many doctors, described what happened to physicians' samples:

"In order to get back to the prescription area, we had to step over piles of samples scattered around the floor. Whenever the help wasn't busy—and this included the high school girl who sold cosmetics, the errand boy, and the janitor—they were expected to pick sample tablets and capsules out of their protective cellophane covering and sort them by hand into the large manufacturers' stock bottles from which prescriptions were filled. To say the least, drugs with different lot numbers were intermixed. This pharmacist-owner even dispensed his prescriptions in used containers such as old cold cream jars. Anything would do, so long as it had a lid. Besides samples, he bought distressed merchandise, dubious drugs of all kinds, and thought nothing of substituting."

Particularly dangerous is haphazard drug scavenging by persons entirely outside the health professions. In a typical case, two doctors were approached by men who represented themselves as the owners of a drug wholesale company, although they had no legal partnership or corporation, no warehouse or other business property, and were not registered to handle prescription drugs. Nevertheless, they had been purchasing samples from physicians in New Jersey, New York, Connecticut, Pennsylvania, Delaware, and Maryland for five years or more without any difficulty from the law. One of the doctors packed three grocery cartons, a suitcase, and two shopping bags full of samples in return for $15. These drugs would bring about $120 when resold to a drugstore. The doctor who refused to sell his samples telephoned the police and this particular operation was broken up—for the time being, at least.

For years FDA *Annual Reports* have cited many mix-ups that illustrate the extremely hazardous nature of sample repacking:

> . . . Repacked bottles bore names of drugs different from those they contained. . . . Different strengths of the same drug were actually in one bottle. . . . Outdated antibiotics and overage drugs were encountered, as were new drugs still in investigational status. . . . In two serious mixups, potent drugs had been substituted for milder ones shown on the labels. . . . Drugs were found in completely unlabeled bottles.

According to recent Federal court decisions, the selling of free drug samples by physicians is not illegal. It is, however, irresponsible. Such drugs become black-market medicines when they are diverted from normal channels of drug distribution. All the FDA can do is to charge that such repacked drugs are "misbranded" because of the absence of labeling required to maintain their integrity and safety. After U.S. district courts ruled against FDA, word spread that it was not against the law to buy or sell physicians' samples, and the racket flourished:

> *Item:* New York State Board of Pharmacy Inspector Max Goldberg conducted an intensive investigation in Harlem a year or so ago that resulted in the apprehension of an unlicensed drug-peddler who had been selling assorted samples for eight years. He had 50 open cartons of various pharmaceuticals stored in a tenement.
>
> *Item:* About the same time, FDA obtained a Federal injunction against a drug company to cease repacking various samples and applying counterfeit copies of a legitimate firm's labels to the containers. (Another example of how unethical practices lead to drug counterfeiting.)

According to FDA's March 1966, *Report*, donating sample drugs to charity is not without its dangers:

> *Item:* A seminary collected 4,000 pounds of samples for overseas missions from the Minneapolis area alone. Unfortunately, this humanitarian project was so poorly supervised that it may well have caused a great deal of harm. The FDA learned about the drug stockpile after a state policeman arrested a drunken driver and discovered in his car a large quantity of dangerous drugs. He was a handyman at the seminary, where pharmaceuticals of all kinds were stored in the unlocked basement of a dormitory. Students, lacking knowledge of the drugs' compositions, just sorted them according to size and trade name (if known) before repackaging for shipment to missionaries. In this instance, the seminary agreed to stop collecting drugs until there could be proper controls, and FDA supervised the burning of all drugs on hand. Minnesota officials are prosecuting the handyman for theft and illegal possession of drugs. But if he had not been drinking while driving, this mass diversion of drugs would not have been detected, nor would the potential dangers to sick missionaries and natives have been curtailed.
>
> *Item:* A church group in the Midwest, sent children to collect drugs from physicians. A housewife who was collection supervisor filled 75 large grocery cartons in her teen-ager's rumpus room with drugs before the secretary of the state board of pharmacy intervened. Doctors had handed these drugs over without ever questioning the youngsters, who had simply announced, "We are collecting for the missionaries of [such and such parish]."

The opportunities for student drug abuse, as well as fatal mistakes, are obvious. Yet these are typical examples of "innocent," noncommercial drug salvage operations in which charity is the objective, rather than personal profit.

The fact that some sample-repackers use proper controls while handling drugs merely provides an umbrella excuse for countless irresponsible scavengers to operate within the law. By not comprehending the dangers inherent in this practice, Federal courts have actually encouraged the spread of a major health menace. But the primary blame lies with those physicians who sell their free samples, or who are so negligent in disposing of them that others sell them. Doctors must assume more personal responsibility for the destruction of all samples not given to patients. If they prefer to donate their drugs to charity, they should first investigate the qualifications of the people who will be handling them. And, they should report scavengers and diverters to the nearest FDA office.*

The problems stemming from misuse of physicians' samples are serious. President Johnson seems to recognize this, for in his 1966 Special Consumer Protection Message to Congress he called for controls over the distribution of drug samples to physicians. He proposed that every sample pill and capsule bear a distinctive mark; that each type of drug be sent to a physician only after he requested it by name; and that manufacturers keep records of who gets how much of which sample and when. Canada already has such a law. However, a bill to implement these proposals died in our 89th Congress.

*See Appendix E for list of BDAC Field Offices.

CHAPTER ELEVEN

Generics:
Panacea or Political Football?

Our nation's drug supply will not be safe until the FDA can continuously provide adequate inspection of all drug plants so as to be able to guarantee the public that *every* batch of drugs marketed is safe.

PAUL A. PUMPIAN*

There is a long-neglected area of drug use and abuse that warrants discussion here—the deplorable situation in many hospitals in regard to medication. First, let us consider the problem of dangerous-drug diversion; then, the in-hospital use of dubious drugs of all kinds; and, finally, the question of generic drugs and the need for more uniform regulation of all drug producers.

The 1965 International Narcotic Enforcement Officers' meeting was devoted entirely to the problem of nonnarcotic drug abuse. It is significant that many narcotic experts feel that illicit amphetamines and barbiturates are a greater threat than opium derivatives (such as morphine and heroin). Mr. Pumpian stated at that meeting:

It is my belief that the "leakage" of dangerous depressant and stimulant drugs from nursing homes and hospitals, operating without the services of a pharmacist and without maintaining "proof-of-use" records, is far greater than drug "leakage" from the pharmacies

*Mr. Pumpian, a lawyer as well as a pharmacist, was the first expert appointed to FDA's new Bureau of Drug Abuse Control. At the time he was Secretary of the Wisconsin Board of Pharmacy and Chairman of the NABP Legislative Committee.

of our many states. The availability of such drugs in these institutions, and the lack of accountability is, in some states, atrocious.

Mr. Pumpian explained that:

An estimated 60 percent of our 7,000 hospitals have no registered pharmacist on any basis, full or part-time. Some of the others operate with a pharmacist 40 hours a week and without one 128 hours a week. No retail pharmacy would be allowed to operate in this manner—the practice is illegal and it presents a health hazard.

The situation in nursing homes and other institutions is even worse. According to Dr. Rupert Salisbury (the authority on distressed drugs mentioned earlier): "All the political 'Sunny State' Institutions, County Homes, and small hospitals have been in existence since the flood without Pharmacy, and at this time, in all states, they have lay persons administering drugs." Dr. Salisbury was particularly critical of geriatric nurses who permit patients to take sleeping pills "like popcorn" from ward stocks where there are no prescriptions for individual patients. When the keeping of records is so lax, overdosage, illicit diversion—anything—can happen. And does.

FDA prosecuted a hospital administrator who diverted huge quantities of drugs to illicit channels—and who even continued to order drugs "for the hospital" after it went out of business. Federal, state and local drug officials have described many instances in which drugs intended for sick patients were used by addicted hospital personnel, including supervisory nurses, or were sold on the black market. The ailing received injections of plain water or other bogus medicines. Frequently, when nursing home or other long-term patients die, their drug orders are continued for years just so there will be a surplus of pills to turn into cash.

Mr. Pumpian waged a battle in Wisconsin against doctors who write prescriptions for a year's supply of drugs at a time. He found out-patients at a welfare clinic, who received 1,000 tranquilizers during three-month periods. One patient required 600 tablets in three-months for his asthmatic condition, but he received 1,000. A woman traded her excess Miltowns for meat at the butcher shop. Another regularly sold 70 pills for $8.50 to anyone who wanted them. Some of the patients bartered the drugs for drinks at bars. When the medical director of the hospital was questioned about these practices, he explained that it was easier to dispense drugs in packs of 100's, and even 500's, to cut down on visits.

Untrained laymen—and this includes many hospital administrators and their purchasing agents—cannot judge the safety and effectiveness of drugs, or evaluate their dangers. Registered nurses receive some training in this field, but the real authorities on drug constituents are pharmacists. Yet in hospitals, where the choice of the right drug in the right dosage is most critical, pharmacists are few and far between.

Some two thirds of all hospitals have Pharmacy and Therapeutics (P&T), Committees, but according to surveys in the drug trade press, they exist mostly on paper. Furthermore, there is a system known as the Doctrine of Prior Consent, in which physicians permit hospital employees to substitute so-called "equivalents" for brand-name drugs prescribed. In some cases, if doctors do not agree to sign away their rights to control therapy, they lose their privileges in that hospital.

Delegating responsibility for prescription drugs to persons with no scientific training in medicine or pharmacy is extremely hazardous for patients. As Mr. Pumpian has pointed out: "It is well known that hospitals and institutions purchase generic drugs that are not always as effective therapeutically as the brand-name drugs. Hospitals have the right to promulgate reasonable rules for the orderly administration of the institution, but rules can only be justified where they are productive of better patient care."

There have been few studies of what goes on in hospital drug procurement and dispensing. One report by the University of Arkansas Medical Center showed "a surprising degree of error in hospital dispensing." Nearly a third of 5.5 billion doses of medicine prescribed for hospital patients each year have an ingredient omitted, or are given at the wrong time, or contain the wrong quantity, or have deteriorated, or are otherwise improperly given and taken, according to this two-year survey sponsored by the United States Public Health Service.

Against this background of the purchasing of questionable drugs; carelessness in dispensing; lack of control over large stocks; willful diversion to illicit outlets; medical consent to substitution; and a host of other evils, consider:

—*The New York Times*, April 19, 1966: Drug Induced Ills Held Increasing. Doctors Warn of Diseases Resulting from Treatment. Such diseases may manifest themselves as hepatitis, urinary tract infection, severe inflammation, shock, depression, etc. . . . A Johns Hopkins University Hospital study disclosed that 11 percent of patients suffer adverse reactions to drugs while hospitalized. In half, the reaction is severe enough to require longer hospitalization and special treatment. Some lives were threatened.

A registry of tissue reaction to drugs has been established within the Armed Forces Institute of Pathology, which has the world's largest repository of pathological material. It will supplement existing drug reaction reporting programs. At present, FDA receives reports of suspected adverse reactions from about 150 Federal and military hospitals, and 215 civilian hospitals under contract; and AMA receives similar reports from private physicians, some hospitals not reporting to FDA, and other sources. According to a press release, such information is to be catalogued and filed by data-processing methods, then made available for identifying drugs possibly associated with adverse reactions; assisting physicians to diagnose possible adverse reactions; and scientific investigations.

The World Health Organization is currently organizing a global reporting system for adverse drug reactions.

My question is: *Can* adverse reactions be scientifically detected and meaningfully tabulated when counterfeit, contaminated, subpotent, outdated, and otherwise substandard drugs are intermingled in hospital and pharmacy stocks?

The most elaborate computer systems in the world become merely expensive gadgets when part of the data they are processing is spurious. How many cards dropping into the slot marked "Dexedrine, SK&F," or "Miltown, Wallace," or "Diuril, Merck," represent Dexedrine and Miltown and Diuril produced by The Group or other counterfeiters? Was the allergic reaction or bizarre side effect noted in Patient Y caused by an ingredient in the drug dispensed, or was it the result of cross-contamination with another drug, or filth, from careless manufacture by the likes of Abe, Bert, and other gray-marketeers?

The physician faced with an adverse change in a patient's blood, liver, or kidney function can discontinue that therapy, start another course of medication, and, if he has time, send in a report and be wary of the drug in the future. It seems to me, though, that he has further responsibility. While pharmacists are the experts when it comes to the composition of drugs, only physicians can evaluate drug effects in human beings. Thus, only the medical profession can really pinpoint the nature and extent of the adulteration of our drug supply. Doctors might consider utilizing what has been called "the greatest grass-roots lobby in history"— the AMA—in a drive against substandard drugs.

One proposal is that the government certify each batch of the *most vital* drugs marketed. This is not unheard of—all antibiotics, food coloring, and insulin are now certified before marketing. The manufacturers pay a fee for the FDA inspection, so this is not a direct burden on the individual taxpayer.

Patients frequently require a continuous source of reliable drugs for everyday living—insulin for diabetics is a good example. Others are steroids, anticoagulants and nonantibiotic bacterials. President Johnson favors closer checks on vital drugs of this type. If Congress agrees with the administration, the Secretary of Health, Education, and Welfare will have authority to place additional drugs on the list requiring batch certification for identity, strength, quality, and purity.

During a Congressional hearing in 1965 George P. Larrick stated that it was his "purely personal opinion" that FDA inspectors should be permanently stationed in plants where the most important drugs are being made. Representative Delbert Latta from Ohio introduced a bill that year calling for continuous FDA inspection of drug manufacturing operations. He noted that all meat and poultry in interstate commerce must be government inspected on an animal-by-animal basis, but that drugs are inspected only periodically. He listed 14 instances in the previous three years where FDA detected critical flaws in drugs due to manufacturing. "Difficult to believe," he said, "is the fact that the most potent drugs given in life-threatening conditions are being produced under a system of spot-checking or spot-inspection by the Food and Drug Administration, whose inspectors now get into the drug factories on an average of only once a year. Such a situation is shocking to say the least, and cries out for immediate action."

Spokesmen for some drug companies that probably couldn't survive closer inspection react to these threats in a variety of ways. Frequently, they launch smoke-screen crusades for generic prescribing, "to save patients and the government money, and to fight monopolistic threats to small business."

Mr. Larrick, while describing the development of the concept of "good manufacturing practices" in drugs, stated: "The point I would like to emphasize is not whether drug manufacturers are large or small, but whether they have the scientific personnel and laboratory controls to produce pure, reliable and safe drugs. The law imposes the same responsibility on them all."

Medicare makes the whole question of "What drugs—for how much?" vitally important to patients and taxpayers alike. The amounts of drugs purchased will soar. In England, the National Health Service increased the flow of prescriptions from 74 million a year before enactment, to 201 million the year after. To cut costs, our Department of Defense and other government agencies have already instituted generic-name-only prescribing policies. A number of Congressmen introduced generic-only legislation during 1966 for all drugs used in Medicare and other medical programs financed by the Federal government.

One sponsor said that under his bill, even if a physician designates a brand-name on the prescription, "the druggist is not only empowered, but is *obliged* to fill the Rx with the lower-priced generic product." He said the legislation must be passed or, "for all practical purposes, we will turn our backs upon small business and reject their competitive participation in the vast drug procurement involved in this program."

There is nothing wrong with generic-name prescribing, *per se*, if the drugs themselves are good drugs. How, though, can we be sure?

—*American Druggist*, December 6, 1965: "If You Can't Test Drugs, Buy Only The Best . . . The practice by some very large hospitals of buying drugs from second-grade manufacturers . . . on the assumption that savings will result in dealing with firms that do not support expensive research programs . . . can be dangerous.

This is one of the points made by Dr. William E. Hassan, Jr., associate director of the Peter Bent Brigham Hospital in Boston and chief consultant in hospital pharmacy at the Massachusetts College of Pharmacy . . . in a new book called *Hospital Pharmacy*. Dr. Hassan cautions that the practice of buying from manufacturers who are not listed as "Class A" should not be followed "unless the hospital is in a position to establish a small control laboratory for the purpose of analyzing products purchased from these firms." He adds that, "often times, the cost of operating such a laboratory will far exceed the cost of purchasing under tight specifications from a reliable manufacturer."

Traditionally, VA, military, Public Health and other government agencies do large-scale buying on competitive bids for some of their drugs. Quality is controlled in these cases by government specifications, plant inspections, and pre-acceptance testing. Even so, one learns from FDA inspectors and other reliable sources of contracts being given to companies that have good programs on paper, but poor actual controls. Certainly, it is unwise for Congressmen to generalize about the high quality of generic drugs and to imply that all small hospitals and all physicians, everywhere, are safe in dispensing generics just because it is done in government institutions.

Instead of permitting laymen to make a political football of the use of generics, it seems to me that doctors should be doing the evaluating and prescribing.

As Paul Pumpian stated before the National Association of Boards of Pharmacy:

In the final analysis, the hospital is less able than is the physician to judge the purity or effectiveness of a particular drug. At least the physician, in observing the effect of drugs upon his patients, can often detect the fact that the product of one manufacturer seems to be more effective on his particular patient, even though another manufacturer markets the same generic product. A physician can be told many things about a drug, including its chemistry, its mode of action, and, to some extent, its toxic properties. But ultimately he must judge its effectiveness. To turn this responsibility over to the hospital, the pharmacist, or even a committee of the medical staff, would result in poorer quality medicine and violate one of the basic principles of medicine. . . .

Mr. Pumpian further noted that hospital employees who substitute generic drugs for the brand-name drugs prescribed "are in a precarious legal position and will be until meaningful standards and tests for dosage form efficacy are developed and utilized in the selection of pharmaceuticals from groups of so-called generically identical products."

The dilemma, as I see it, is not a choice between generics and brand-name drugs, but, rather, how to put illicit drug producers out of business without imposing unnecessary burdens on companies that voluntarily comply with present regulations. Two measures have been proposed: (1) extending batch certification to our most vital or "life-saving" drugs, (2) stationing FDA inspectors permanently in plants where these are made.

Obviously counterfeiters and black-marketeers would not be affected by such procedures because locations of their plants are unknown and they would not submit samples for testing.

Ethical drug company spokesmen I have talked with feel very strongly that batch certification would waste an enormous amount of money and manpower and handicap their operations. Further, it was pointed out, "FDA simply does not have that many scientists to look down that many microscopes." Another man asked, "How could an agreement be reached on which drugs belong in the 'life-saving' category without lengthy hearings?"

Dr. Karl Bambach, Senior Vice President of the Pharmaceutical Manufacturers' Association, whose 138 member-firms produce about 95 percent of all prescription drugs *known* to be sold in this country, told me: "The FDA does not have the inspectors, the scientists, or the police authority to enforce the laws that now exist. I would like to see these laws really enforced before imposing still new requirements upon the conscientious manufacturer. As for government certification of every drug batch, irresponsible producers probably would not submit samples representative of the messes they are putting out."

Is there anything to be said for batch certification, so far as black- and gray-market controls are concerned? I asked Weems L. Clevenger, Director of FDA's New York District, to explain the effects of the present limited batch certification requirements. His District has jurisdiction over the largest number of legitimate drug producers, as well as what seems to be the heaviest concentration of willful violators in the country. He said:

> In order to follow defined good manufacturing practices, a drug manufacturer must analyze a representative sample of each batch of every drug produced. Marginal operators frequently don't follow this practice. Under batch certification such as is now required for antibiotics and insulin, samples are submitted to FDA for testing *prior* to release of the batch for sale. Subpotent or otherwise deficient lots are thus withheld from public distribution. In order to determine whether the samples submitted by manufacturers are actually representative, we schedule routine sampling in the market of some of these same batches and compare the analytical results with those previously obtained.
>
> We also inspect the plant. If we find substandard conditions or practices, we can—and have—withheld certification of the drugs produced. If a clandestine manufacturer markets a drug on which batch certification is now required, we can remove that drug from the market. In addition, we have located and immediately enjoined them from further shipments.
>
> Similarly, new drugs and those undergoing pre-marketing clinical investigation may not be sold without FDA approval.
>
> These are, in effect, licensing systems with which we can act administratively to withhold and remove questionable and outright illegal drugs from public distribution.
>
> The present section of the FD&C Act, which requires drug plants to be registered, is not a licensing system. It is for information only. We cannot withhold, suspend, or revoke registration privileges for any reason whatsoever.

It would seem reasonable to suggest, in view of all this, that pharmaceutical manufacturers be licensed as a first step toward more uniform regulation. Licenses would be subject to revocation and suspension, and they should not be issued simply upon request, as registration numbers now are, but only after the prospective drug producers are proved qualified. While the FDA would still have the task of tracking down clandestine operators, the gray-marketeers *now* registered would have to bring their marginal practices up to standard or be forced out of business.

At the same time, licensing should not prove too burdensome for manufacturers presently passing inspection.

Licensing is not impractical or unreasonable. Executives of major ethical companies have admitted, "We could live with it." And more than one FDA official has told me, "Licensing would drive out a lot of shady producers almost overnight."

CHAPTER TWELVE

The Pill Mills

"Physicians must exercise more caution in prescribing stimulant drugs of the amphetamine type. . . . It has become increasingly clear that many physicians have not fully appreciated the inherent dangers in prescribing these medications and that in many cases their presumably therapeutic actions can constitute misuse of drugs." The Committee on Alcoholism and Addiction of the AMA went on to explain that "misuse" refers to the physician's role in *initiating* a potentially dangerous course of therapy. "When a physician prescribes stimulants, he should do so for a limited time and for a specific purpose. He must also assume responsibility for frequent reassessment to ascertain whether the drug is effective," the Committee stressed. The Committee said prescriptions should only be written for the smallest possible amount of stimulant needed.—Abstracted from *The Journal of the American Medical Association*, September 19, 1966.

Included in the medical practitioner category in the United States are 276,000 Doctors of Medicine, and 12,700 Doctors of Osteopathy. FDA's prosecution figures show that only seven doctors in 1965 and seven in 1964 were convicted of violations of the FD&C Act. Why publicize the failings of a small number of professionals when the vast majority are law-abiding and, in many cases, self-sacrificing?

The answer came from Weems L. Clevenger, when he was Director of BDAC's Division of Case Assistance: "We have found that *a single* unscrupulous physician can peddle enough pills in wholesale amounts to wreak havoc in a tri-state area."

Most ethical physicians seem to have no idea of the nature and extent of doctor-involvement in black-market medicine. (Some of my physician-interviewees had not even heard that brand-name drugs are being faked.) Doctors need to be informed so that they can help to remove criminally inclined persons from the profession.

Dr. Robert Mayo Tenery, Past-President of the Texas Medical Association, has divided unethical physicians into two groups. The first are "the uninformed"; he feels that organized medicine can direct their rehabilitation through education. The second, he describes as "the pathological, who have a completely warped attitude toward others. They *cannot* be rehabilitated and they utilize every loophole that can be found in disciplinary procedures. The etiology of this condition is worship of the almighty dollar, and the only treatment is radical amputation from the profession!"

This is the most delicate form of surgery and a rare operation, indeed. Let us get down to some cases that demonstrate why law-enforcers insist that renegade physicians are the original "untouchables."

In Seattle, Houston, Philadelphia, Chicago, New York, many Florida cities, and elsewhere, so-called "obesity experts" have set up a number of "get-slim-quick" clinics that the AMA's Department of Investigation says are primarily concerned with helping the physicians in charge "get-rich-quick." As everyone has heard, obesity is a major health threat. Medically supervised weight-reduction programs that employ amphetamines and other drugs in conjunction with a low-calorie diet, frequent physical check-ups, and counseling based on a true doctor-patient relationship, are *not* what we are talking about here.

The quack clinics, regardless of how many figurehead physicians and registered nurses are on the staff, operate quite differently. Preliminary examinations, history-taking, laboratory tests of blood and urine are supplanted by a mere taking of the pulse, or no contact with the patient at all, except to exchange a box of potent drugs for $5, $10, or $15. Although dishonest doctors insist these drugs are "perfectly harmless . . . will melt fat away

. . . count calories for you . . ." they are usually shotgun mixtures of amphetamines, barbiturates, thyroid, and perhaps digitalis and diuretics—all of which require close supervision and periodic reevaluation.

Patients with diabetes, high blood pressure, heart disease, nervous disorders, and other conditions are being harmed by ruthless diet-pill racketeers. Yet the business is booming—a metropolitan clinic has thousands of patients paying $5 per visit. One physician has opened more than a dozen suburban offices to handle his patient overload. Often, the doctor is never even seen and his spiel is recorded. Nothing is said about the basic need to consume less food in order to reduce. The idea is to make the patients utterly dependent upon the pills. If they stop taking them, their appetites will return, they will gain weight, and back they will come for more pills—a perennial source of profit. Countless respectable people are being turned into "pill-heads" by men and women whom they trust and respect as doctors and nurses. Yet this extensive trafficking in stimulants and sedatives is managed under a perfectly legal cover.

The next step down in medical practice is the "thrill-pill" mill, which may or may not have an obesity clinic "front." The entire operation is geared to supplying pep-pill and goof-ball addicts with drugs as quickly as possible. One "patient" received 450 amphetamines and 257 barbiturates during a month's visits. The elapsed time, per visit, ranged from 30 seconds to four minutes. There was no professional advice given, no equipment used, even the overhead expense of mailing out bills was eliminated, as cash was required. The doctor probably didn't even bother reporting such income, although his nurse said that he sold close to 10,000 pills a week at ten cents each. The amphetamine tablets cost him less than a tenth of a cent, or about $1 a thousand. Some of his "regular patients" had averaged a dozen pills a day for years. This is the next thing to coining money.

But it has its problems. An FDA undercover agent recorded a conversation with a pill-peddling physician in a small town, who complained about having excess cash he didn't know what to do with. "One of these days Uncle Sugar is going to come around and check and I'll be in trouble," he said. He had large accounts in four different banks, but was stuck, at the moment, with

$50,000 in cash over his reportable income. He guessed that he would try to explain this away as "large gambling profits," if the tax men suddenly appeared.

This inspector has investigated dozens of similar doctors, some of whom are coroners, or consultants for local companies, or have other sources of income such as pharmacies, besides their regular medical practices. Why do they continue to peddle pills illicitly on the side?

"They are pathologically greedy," the inspector said.

I wondered whether they were usually physically or mentally ill, senile, or drug addicts?

"No, you can't generalize," he told me. "One of the very worst offenders I know is in his early forties, very sharp, considered a 'good doctor' by the people in town because he makes house calls and seems concerned about his patients. From all I've heard, he really is competent medically. But he is also a major diverter of huge amounts of amphetamines to a criminal who supplies a string of truck stops. He does not peddle pills to his own patients. In fact, when I first came to town and asked for a doctor, a waitress in the cafe recommended him, saying that he was 'not like Doc-So-and-So, who just lived off the needle and pill-pushing.' "

Word gets around about these practitioners, of course. Why isn't something done about them?

Here is a case that was thoroughly investigated. (All conversations are from tape recordings.) : A teen-ager six feet tall, weighing only 136 pounds, entered the so-called "obesity clinic" staffed by half-a-dozen physicians. He asked for amphetamine "reducers," and was given a box of pills in exchange for $5, with no preliminary examination or history.

DOCTOR: Are you going to lose a little weight?

THIN TEEN-AGER: *Me* lose weight!

DOCTOR: What do you want them for?

THIN TEEN-AGER: Like, I use pills, Doc.

When asked what he did with the pills, the boy said, "I dropped 'em—took 'em—they make you feel like, you know, your body is all tightened up and you want to, like, walk, talk, drive around all night and never sleep or eat. You talk, talk, gobble, gobble, gobble, from one subject to another. You feel like you want to *do* something!"

This youngster did do something. His record shows five confinements in correctional institutions since he first began getting amphetamines from this clinic. He named about 30 other 15- to 19-year-olds who obtained drugs from this source. Eight who began with pills are now using heroin. Several others are in the state mental hospital.

A 16-year-old entered the clinic, while an undercover inspector was there.

DOCTOR: What did you do with the ones you got yesterday?

TEEN-AGER: Well, Doc, I owed some around, had to pay up, you know, to friends.

DOCTOR (*to nurse*): It's all right.

A young woman was told that she would "be taken care of at any time between 6 A.M. and midnight," when the clinic closed. When she asked, "Can I get a small amount like 20 pills at a time?" The medical director said, "No, 30 is the smallest number you can get."

Two young-looking undercover agents were asked by one of the physicians: "What do you guys do with these things, eat them like candy?" Another doctor put in, "Or do you give them to your girl-friends to make them so they won't say no?"

"Consultations" frequently began with the doctor's greeting, "How much can we get from you today?"

What did the physician-owner get, after being convicted by a Federal jury on 20 counts of illegally dispensing dangerous drugs? A $100 fine was levied for each of the 20 counts. However, the imposition of these fines was suspended, and he was not placed on probation or otherwise restricted from practicing medicine. The Court expressly stated that no moral turpitude was involved in these crimes. This operation had been investigated by Federal, state, and local law-enforcement officers, who made more than 100 dangerous drug buys over a period of several years. All this work —and the taxpayer's money—was wasted. Is it any wonder that the feeling prevails that M.D.'s are "above the law?"

The FD&C Act was never designed to regulate the practice of medicine; it was supposed to insure that only honestly labeled, unadulterated medicines are moving in interstate commerce. FDA investigates practitioners only after receiving complaints.* The situation has to be grim indeed before the government intercedes. A supervisory inspector, lecturing undercover agents, stressed: "Where physicians are concerned, you must collect a very impressive background of evidence. It is important to have a record of serious injury—death is preferable."

Frequently, the first lead on a doctor case is a letter like the following, quoted here at length because it touched off the series of investigations that culminated in FDA's first conviction of a medical doctor in good standing. The patient had contacts with a pharmacist and seven physicians, but he was hardly in the medically-supervised category as he persisted in taking a powerful male hormone with the idea of increasing his sexual prowess. The plea for help came from his wife.

Dear Sirs:

[A nurse] advised me to write you in regards to [a druggist] who has been selling my husband tablets without a prescription, bottles of 100 & on time too which my husband hasn't paid for yet . . . says on the bottle "Federal law prohibits dispensing without a prescription." If my husband continues to take these like he is & so many of them they will make him lose his mind & I think they almost did —Last year he started a small cafe, a few stools—too small for a cafe in the first place in width—& he had to squeeze behind this young waitress to get through, so you can see what happened. If he couldn't have gotten these tablets the affair would have stopped before it began. . . . I found out and put a stop to it by going to work in the cafe regardless. Now I think this druggist license should be taken away from him because him selling my husband these tablets has caused me so much mental suffering & could have caused me my life as my husband was bringing my food home to me & one or the other or both of them could have very easily poisoned me to get me out of the way. . . . I need help & I think the best help I can get right now is *to have these pills taken away from him!* At first this druggist sold these in a plain envelope so no one would know what they were, I guess, & double strength on top of it. . . . Of

*Except where investigational new drugs are involved.

course, if he couldn't have gotten them from this druggist he could always go to some cheap Dr.s like [A, B, C, and D]. I think [D] on Main Street is running some sort of house of prostutes because . . . he gives names to both men & women when they want them. Also there is Dr. [E] that my husband went to. . . . and Dr. [F]. He has a prescription from Dr. [G] in [another town] that he is saving back to get these tablets in case something happens that he can't get them from this druggist. . . . Also he was going to Dr. [H] in [large city]. . . . Well, if you want to get in touch with me don't write but get in touch through [nurse] & for heavens sake don't let my husband or this druggist find out I wrote to you or my life might not be worth 2 cents.

Respt.

Mrs.——

When "The Long-Narrow-Cafe" letter was passed on to the chief inspector in a Southern FDA district, he assigned Clemens Westerly, then completing his third year as an inspector, to the case, along with Greg James, now Deputy Director of a BDAC field office. The district was in the midst of a complicated investigation of pill-peddling among prison inmates, "B" girls in local bars, and hoodlums who had staked out territories for the distribution of Bennies to truck stops. Monitored buys established that the druggist mentioned was selling hormones and other drugs over the counter, but he was not dealing in wholesale amounts.

FDA suspected several dispensing physicians of mass diversion of stimulants and sedatives, but had never in the history of FDA been able to make a case stick against an M.D. who maintained a cover of legitimate practice. The difficulty lay in proving that the drugs were sold solely for profit.

Since about 9,000 physicians still dispense drugs in their offices, mostly in rural areas and supposedly for the convenience of patients, selling medication rather than writing a prescription for it is fairly common and not necessarily suspect. The type of medication prescribed or the amount cannot be challenged without involvement in all sorts of controversies; doctors themselves do not always agree on what constitutes "orthodox therapy" in a given case. Also, the doctor-patient relationship is commonly referred to as "sacred," and any intrusion—particularly by the government—is discouraged.

In court, however, it should be obvious to any judge that no single patient requires a bottle of 1,000 sleeping pills at a time (unless the object is euthanasia). Nonetheless, when a pillar of the community, who has delivered most of the babies in town, is accused of being a common pill-peddler, there is a tendency to look for extenuating circumstances. Other physicians stand by the doctor-defendant; grateful patients come forward to testify in his behalf; business associates and clergymen go on record as character witnesses. The Court is impressed.

One surgeon, with a 26-year history of drug violations, including narcotics charges, was sent back to his Missouri practice by a Federal judge who said he was suspending jail sentencing "for the good of the community, since he is the only doctor in town." Yet court testimony had brought out that FDA undercover inspectors purchased thousands of sleeping pills and pep-pills from this surgeon, telling him they were selling to truck drivers. His only concern was that they not peddle pills near his office "lest the Feds start investigating."

The first successful FDA doctor case could not have been made without two scientific investigative tools:

—*Tape recording*, a method of evidence-corroboration that is controversial but well-nigh indispensible where the decision to convict hangs on a few spoken words, or the absence of same—i.e., Did the physician ask the patient about his symptoms before selling him the drugs? Without recordings, it is the practitioner's word against his accuser's and doctors invariably win. (FDA never plants "bugs" on premises, so patients need have no fear that their confidences will be overheard.)

—*"Pillistic" laboratory analysis* to trace the drugs from the manufacturers to the physicians and, finally, to the consumers.

The pioneering investigative methods used by Inspectors Westerly and James are now standard.

They first checked the professional status of all the doctors mentioned in the letter. Dr. D on Main Street, for example, had received his M.D. degree from a leading university and was a member of the county medical society and the American Medical Association. He had practiced in the same office for many years with no police, narcotics, or other violations recorded. The inspectors knew they would have to proceed with caution in their fact-finding or risk being accused of damaging his professional reputation and practice. They had to be especially careful to avoid charges of entrapment—that is, inducing him to commit a crime, rather than detecting its voluntary commission.

As they were considering all these pitfalls, several coincidences brought them additional information. A vice squad detective called their attention to a prostitute who had handfuls of sleeping pills sewn into the lining of her coat. (He may have wanted to make a "Federal case" out of this because, when he arrested her, he had a painful, broken finger in a splint which she bent backward and broke again.) When questioned by the inspectors, the prostitute told a lurid story about receiving pills as payment for participating with Dr. D and a third person in sex acts in his office. This remained a matter for the vice squad. FDA did, however, have the pills analyzed and they were eventually traced back to a manufacturer who shipped enormous quantities to Dr. D.

Meanwhile, another call came from the cooperative local police. The manager of a third-rate hotel reported a "ruckus" in a room rented by one "Shorty," just released after ten years in the state penitentiary. If FDA was interested, eight bottles containing 1,000 pills each had been found in the room. Shorty was unconscious in a hospital, but his ex-convict buddy was in custody, although "high" on a combination of pills and alcohol.

After checking the drug stash, Inspector Westerly asked: "Where did Shorty get these Bennies and yellow jackets?"

"It warn't Shorty's doin'," the man replied. "It was *me* what whizzed them pills from old Doc [D]."

There was no evidence of an illegal sale. The man had learned in prison where to get drugs and how to combine them for special effects. Finding Dr. D gone, he had simply helped himself from the stockroom.

How had Shorty and his buddy managed to get pills while inside? An intercepted letter provided some clues:

Hi Partner,

Here I am in [penitentiary with 3,000 inmates]. Man, it's the closest thing to a chain gang there is. It would be as hard to beat as Leavenworth. . . . I still owe Texas nine months, but I have a good chance to get out *if* I can scrape up a few hundred. You are the only hope I have. . . . I would say that 60 percent of the guys in here use pills. *All* pills sell for 50¢ a peace. Man, that's terrific when you think they only cost about $6 a thousand. If I can score for any type such as Bennies, Turnarounds, etc., I'll sell them and split the money with you. We should be able to make about $300 a week (apeace). . . . If you can fix up a package with some Pepperonie in it, some cheese, some cookies, and maybe some Salomie, it would be perfect. You can unwrap the ends of Pepperonie and Salomie and insert pills. That is a sure way to get it to me. . . . We went through a lot together and both stuck solid. . . . If I am out and you are in, I will definitely try to get you out. . . .

Your friend, ——

Inspector Westerly sent a memo to his district director on the next phase of their investigation; it included abstracts from the recordings:

```
I entered Dr. [D's] office wearing gray cotton
slacks, a white sport shirt, and blue canvas shoes.
I carried a midget shortwave radio transmitter
wrapped in a piece of newspaper. The conversation
was recorded on a Webcor 210 tape-recorder by In-
spector [James] in Room 500 of the hotel across the
street. I wanted to see if the doctor would sell me
certain restricted drugs without first examining
me. The conversation took place as follows:
```

DOCTOR: What do you say? What have you got for me?

INSPECTOR: Well, I've got some money for you. I need some yellow jackets.

DOCTOR: What's your name? Gotta put it down . . . anyway, that's neither here nor there. If I get you in the daylight, I'll remember you next time. Now, don't take more than you need or you'll run around floating on thin air and they'll pick you up as a drunk when you're not really drunk.

INSPECTOR: Gotcha.

DOCTOR: Be careful, save money and you'll save your health.

INSPECTOR: Much obliged . . . [*Leaves office*] I have just
returned from Dr. [D's] office. He sold me 36
yellow capsules, that appear to be sodium pento-
barbital, in response to my request for "yellow
jackets." I handed him three dollars. He put the
capsules in an envelope cut in half on which was
written my name and "One at bedtime." A few
minutes after I left, Inspector [James] purchased
. . . Metandren Linguets. They were packaged
physicians' samples. Dr. [D] later told me he
thought "this man's problems are all in his head,
but he seems to know how to take the sex hormones, so I sold them." The next day, after my
order was given, we discussed the names of the
drugs, which the doctor called "Seconal" and
"Nembutal," although they were not the original
[Lilly and Abbott] trademarked products. He told
me "You know, somebody else makes 'em, then
they put names on 'em and distribute 'em."

Eventually, FDA lab sleuths traced these drugs, which included
rebottled tablets of unspecified origin, to their sources and Dr. D
was brought to trial. He entered a guilty plea, and was fined
$3,000. Judge Charles Evans Whittaker, later an Associate Justice
of the Supreme Court, gave him a real dressing down at the sentencing. He said, "Just because you have a license to practice
medicine, that doesn't mean you have a license to peddle pills."

Some years after Dr. D's death, FDA caught one of his relatives,
not a physician, peddling his remaining drug stocks to a network
of truck stops.

Shortly after completing this case, Inspector Westerly became
a member of the first FDA undercover team assigned to a truck
drivers' training school, then he began "Riding with Bennie" over
the road.

The workaday world of the nation's long-haul drivers is reflected in the songs they play on juke boxes, "Heartaches by the
number, troubles by the score. . . ." Uncertain incomes, bad coffee,
worse food, irregular hours, disrupted home life, loneliness, ex-

haustion. Many manage to keep going without relying upon stay-alert pills of caffeine and amphetamine. But, in the words of a man who has worked undercover as a government agent, union official, and truck terminal manager, "Most owner-operators, or gypsies, only survive because of Bennies."

A drug-peddler working for a Midwest syndicate told me: "Long as there's truck drivers, there'll be Bennies, and long as they need 'em, I'm gonna supply 'em!"

The ICC regulates all long-haul drivers. Some fleet trucks are equipped with a time and mileage indicator nicknamed a "Mickey Mouse." Drivers are required to keep logs divided into 15-minute units. And there are inspection points along major trucking routes. However, men who are desperate to increase their income —or who have to make up time lost playing pinball machines or wooing waitresses—find ways around regulations. They keep double and even triple logs, take back roads to avoid inspection, and they pop pills.

Physicians, all too often, are *the* major diverters to truck stops. In a half-dozen particularly notorious cases I reviewed in FDA files, these men appeared to be devoted to their small-town practices during the day, but they ran with underworld characters at night. One doctor went about heavily armed and eventually killed a man in the course of an illicit drug transaction. The physician who took over another convicted peddler's medical practice found a trap door under the office desk. Below were millions of amphetamines stored in plastic bags inside of paint cans.

These drugs are sometimes made to order for underworld use only. Their producers have no legitimate customers.

Another physician was addicted to playing pinball machines. He married a truck-stop cafe owner. Together they supplied pills to truck stops in half-a-dozen states. The madam of a 30-unit motel-brothel adjoining a truck stop wanted to know whether some kind of combination drug for her girls couldn't be devised: amphetamine so they could work all night; barbiturate so they could rest during the day; Enovid for birth control, as some of the girls were "pretty dumb"; and an antibiotic for venereal disease therapy.

But the biggest demand was—and still is—for old, reliable Bennies. An undercover FDA inspector wrote the following report about his non-FDA partner's cross-country Bennie binge:

I was hired as a student driver and sat around the drivers' room reading "Screen," "Movie Land" and other heart knockers. A drifter offered me a pill saying it would bolster my confidence so I'd be able to drive anything with wheels. The following three weeks I worked as hard, and got as dirty as any of the drivers. One day I was told I would make a trip to Maine with Jim [a 4,400-mile haul]. I drove only 200 miles, however, Jim drove all day on black coffee—he said cream was hard on the kidneys—and cokes. After coffee he took two Bennies. This performance was repeated that night and the following day. Each time, his eyes became redder and glassier. About 4 PM the next evening I had to trust Bennies' driving and crawled into the sleeper berth and dozed a couple of hours. Jim woke me up, said I had to take a pill and stay awake to talk to him. I told him black coffee was all I needed. The second night was spent talking while Bennie carried us over the road. With each Bennie, Jim's stories became more colorful . . . 90 days in jail for wrecking a bar . . . his greatest conquests, etc. Some time the next day we arrived in Maine completely broke with all our money spent for tolls. We didn't eat for a day or so. Jim took a 2-hour nap and we left early the next morning with a load of fish. The return trip to [Southwestern state] followed the pattern of the trip out. Upon arrival we were scheduled to leave the next morning for a return trip to Boston. I told the safety director that Jim had slept about 6 hours in all and I wasn't too anxious to make this next trip with him. Another driver was sent.

This investigation was instrumental in breaking up a pill-distribution ring involving doctors, truck-stop operators, hoodlums, a drug wholesaler, and several irresponsible drug firms, including a gray-marketeer who also supplied The Group with timed-release capsules.

The overlapping of drug-counterfeiting operations and the mass diversion of dangerous unbranded drugs was further illustrated when counterfeit Dexedrine Spansules were found at the scene of a turnpike accident. Twelve trucks and three passenger cars piled up; six persons were killed and seven injured. One truck driver had the spurious Dexedrine in his possession, another carried other types of amphetamine and tranquilizers. A speed exceeding 60 mph was registered at the time of the crash and records indicated several drivers had been on the road for over 20 hours. The accident occurred a few hours after midnight during a heavy fog. The speed limit on the turnpike had been lowered to 35 mph because of the hazardous driving conditions. A memo on the accident concludes: "In my conversation with state policemen I found they showed little concern about the amphetamine problem with truck drivers. They said that occasionally they do discover these drugs, but feel there is little they can do about it."

Pill-peddling is a lucrative business for some truckers. Inspector Wally Jackson infiltrated a Bennie ring and learned that one driver, after a short time in the racket, was able to pay off his mortgage, clear up his debts, purchase a brand-new $25,000 refrigerated tractor-trailer and a Cadillac for his girl friend, who was a bank teller. (When he peddled counterfeit money, she had obligingly given him authentic bills in exchange.) He added $5,000 worth of extras to his rig, including air-conditioning, chrome trim, luxury upholstering, etc. The Syndicate masterminds insisted on orders of one million pills, which they obtained through a general practitioner in a town with a population under 1,000. This physician ordered the drugs from a manufacturer in another state, but he specified on the order that they be transshipped to an address in his state, where all signs of interstate shipment were obliterated before the drugs were sent on to him.

Such renegades got around the interstate requirement of the FD&C Act for many years. So brazen was one, that at the time the Drug Abuse Control Amendments were being discussed in Congress (early 1965) he wrote on his letterhead stationery to a drug executive:

I want to stock up as this Congress will pass laws stopping dealing in them. They have no law now. Some of their Food & Drug employees try and made you think so, but there is no law and they can't make distributors tell (or show books) who they ship to, or how many they handle. Ship these in next 2, 3 weeks and I can handle some more in 2, 3 weeks again. Rec'd your last shipment and they were fine.

Resp. ——— M.D.

An isolated case? During this same period an undercover inspector in a Southeastern FDA district walked into a dozen physicians' offices in one section of one state. He asked for Bennies and yellow jackets to sell to truck drivers, and he made a point of telling the physicians that this was a money-making proposition for him. Here are some of the officially recorded comments:

DR. A: I'll write you a script tonight and you can get it filled, then you can come in tomorrow and I'll write you another script. . . .

This doctor exchanged scripts for cash. Laws, such as DACA, that put a limit on "open-ended" refills for dangerous drugs are circumvented when an unlimited number of new prescriptions are sold.

INSPECTOR: Do you have any little green speckled pills with a steak dinner in them? (*This doctor ran an obesity clinic.*)

DR. B: Diet pills? . . . They're tryin' to get a little law passed, I don't know why. They treat these things as bad as murder. If the police pick you up with a large quantity they would give you five years.

INSPECTOR: They're all right aren't they, since I got them from you?

DR. B: Oh yeah, I have your name on there and I signed my name.

INSPECTOR: Maybe I better tell you what I do. Me and a buddy have a truck stop out on Route 7—you always find this stuff around a truck stop.

Dr. B. agreed to sell at least a month's supply a time.

DR. C (*In another reducing clinic*): You don't need to lose
    weight.

INSPECTOR: No, I take them to stay awake, I run a truck stop
    . . . etc. Sue over in the Monroe Hotel, stocky
    blonde, told me to come up here. She sold me
    some orange pills she got from you.

DR. C: What did they look like? (*Opens* PDR *to colored
    illustrations. Inspector picks out pills he wants.*)

The doctor agreed to sell him two months' supply of pills
direct from his own stocks. The inspector knew that the doctor
sold many types of drugs and he said: "Me and my buddy run a
truck stop, y'know, and we have a few 'social workers.' The girls
don't think too much about getting pregnant. We have eight
girls and only two are married."

DR. C: Well, I ought to give them a cancer test, but I could
    get them refilled as many times as they want. . . . Just
    send one of your married girls in here and get a
    prescription and let the other girls use her prescrip-
    tion and take her [birth control] pills.

DR. D: Where are you from?

INSPECTOR: I work for the construction company, do you have
    $50 worth of these things? I sell them to a few of
    the guys I work with up there.

DR. D: Don't you know that's a pretty dangerous thing to
    do? Handling drugs without a license is a pretty
    serious offense. If I understand this new legislation
    it's to prevent dispensing these things at all. I
    haven't seen it yet. . . . I'm kind of stretching the
    point to sell you these. . . . You have to be careful
    peddling these.

DR. E (*office in pharmacy*): You're not with the police or
    anything? All over the state they have a big pill in-
    vestigation going on. I don't want to get mixed up in

> it. I prescribe them to people who are sick and need
> them. My wife jumped on me for [previous illicit
> sales]. This would be mighty confidential, you under-
> stand. I've gotta stick my neck out. You don't take
> many, do you? This can't be a habit—drug men and
> doctors are not supposed to let them out. No patient
> really needs this many. Take care of me, I've taken
> care of you. [After this sale of "red birds," the inspec-
> tor returned for "yellow jackets." Six separate illicit
> sales were made.]

In this random sampling of physicians in a small geographical
area, over a three-month period, the FDA man made as many as
27 buys from one doctor. It is significant that in most cases there
was a discussion of the new Federal and state dangerous drug laws.

DR. F: These things are going to be hard to get. They
             just passed a law the other day concerning these
             things. The Federal is going to pass a law too.

INSPECTOR: I read that Johnson is just putting on a show and
             they probably won't pass anything like that.

DR. F: They'll pass it. There's too much crime being
             caused by these things. You know two boys from
             Huntington, West Virginia, killed a man down in
             Georgia because they were taking these things.
             They were selling them right out of a hotel in
             Huntington in bottles of a thousand. I don't know
             where they get them. A lot of this stuff is going to
             stop when they pass the law. Right now they're
             after guys like you, but after the law goes through,
             doctors and everybody will have to keep records on
             just how much of this stuff they hand out . . . just
             like morphine.

The inspector's report went on to say that the doctor counted
out enough pills for himself and his buddy at the truck stop,
saying, "If you take too many they'll make you crazy . . . I'd better
mark 'Sleep, one at bedtime,' on here in case anyone picks you up,
you can say you bought them from a doctor—see, you can't do

that when you buy them from a peddler in the street." The inspector said that he would claim that he found them. The doctor advised him: "With this new law, they would get you anyhow." The inspector said, "What you should do, Doc, is stock up on these things before the new law comes through." The doctor replied: "Now you've got the right idea. A lot of doctors are doing just that, too." Inspector: "Yeah, and after you do that you should stock *me* up with them too!" The doctor said, "Yeah" and laughed and slapped the inspector on the back as he walked out the door.

The drugs being peddled were usually cheap, unbranded stimulants and sedatives because the doctors could buy them in bulk and the producers were frequently fly-by-night companies that didn't bother to keep records. Dr. G. had his own method for circumventing the law: For the first dozen or so buys he refused to sell the FDA inspector bottles of 1,000 pills—he insisted upon putting the pills in little white dispensing boxes, with SLEEP, ONE A NIGHT written on them. After the first buy, the doctor's parting words were, "I hope you make some money!" After the fifth buy, he said, "Here you are, I hope I can keep you in business. Just don't tell anybody where you got them." On the sixth buy, the doctor held up the little boxes of pills and said, "I'll sell you all of these you want." The inspector said, "Good grief, *I* can count them out!" as the doctor began busily filling boxes. Then he asked if he could just buy the pills in the bottles of 5,000 on the doctor's shelf. Dr. G. said: "Let's don't do that, we might both get into trouble." The physician suggested that the "pill-peddler" go out the backdoor to avoid the waiting room crowded with patients. By the twelfth buy, the doctor wearied of pouring pills into boxes and said, "I'm going to put them in a bottle. It doesn't have to be clean. . . ." He then proceeded to put "yellow jackets" into bottles that had formerly contained penicillin, according to the label, and which still had powdery traces in it. Another bottle had been filled with Renase Polythiazide tablets. When the inspector checked the amphetamines he had purchased he found three different types of tablets. All this while the doctor was explaining that people liked pills because "You can get drunk quick on them . . . and they're cheaper. . . ."

This doctor had a flourishing business going selling injectable vitamin B_{12} without ever seeing some of the purchasers. A hoodlum picked up his shipments of drugs and signed the doctor's name on the delivery receipt. It was difficult to determine who was in charge of the whole operation. But the traffic was not confined to pep pills, goof balls and other stimulants or "thrill pills." The FDA undercoverman also purchased penicillin for V.D. The observation was made: "You can charge any price you want, it's a real blind item." The Doctor consulted a price catalog and said he could get them at a lower price in weaker strengths of 250,000 units and 100,000 units, rather than the 750,000 units requested: "It doesn't make any difference as long as it's penicillin, they don't know what they're buying anyhow."

This is a most depressing situation. Is it hopeless?

President James Z. Appel of the American Medical Association has pointed out:

> Only eight of 47 State Medical Societies responding to an AMA survey have provisions for disciplinary action against a member for incompetence. Incompetent physicians, who are neither members of a hospital staff nor a medical society, are the most dangerous kind. They can be controlled only by State Medical Examining Boards. I believe we must increase the authority and activity of the State Boards beyond the area of licensing.

Dr. James L. Goddard, FDA's first physician Commissioner, has promised: "There will be no double-standard of enforcement, or special exemptions. If physicians violate the law, we intend to prosecute them."

PART FOUR

On The International Scene

To explore the international ramifications of black-market medicine, I made a number of trips abroad, interviewing and researching. What follows are glimpses of what has been and is going on in other countries in the pharmaceutical drug business, including: an account of the traffic in LSD, substandard drug production, industrial spying, smuggling of life-saving medicines, and activities of the Mafia in pharmaceuticals.

We should keep in mind that the objective of new drug research and development is to save lives and preserve health. (There is no such thing as a "bad" drug compound, per se. There are *people* who misuse or abuse drugs.) Scientific research on such substances as the lysergic acid derivative LSD should be encouraged, not suppressed. Herein lies an international dilemma.

CHAPTER THIRTEEN

Dateline: Lysergic Acid

Manhattan:

LSD interest had spread from psychiatric quarterlies to psychedelic "show biz" celebrations before I left for Europe. At an East Village lecture, a woman physician gave me a letter she had received from her LSD supplier near Stonehenge, England: "If you are interested in furthering scientific research," she said, "he will send you LSD, psilocybin and so forth. I don't know *what* we'd do without him!"

England:

Before visiting the LSD supplier, I made a stop at Eli Lilly's "works" in Basingstoke. After the usual tour of the plant, I queried the Medical Director on the status of lysergic acid compounds in England. He was not particularly eager to discuss any drugs with a member of the press because, as in America, there was a hue and cry for stricter controls.*

There was little he could say about LSD's use in England, except that it had become a prescription drug. Any general practitioner could prescribe it for anything he wished.

---

*Lilly, Sandoz and other ethical companies require the raw material lysergic acid for the production of prescription drugs used to control hemorrhaging after childbirth and to alleviate migraine headaches.

I drove on to Stonehenge, stood among the monoliths in the rain and wondered if the Druids really had used a mistletoe extract in their pagan ceremonies, and if it had an LSD-like action as a side-effect of its toxicity. I had witnessed the use of other botanicals with hallucinogenic properties by Stone Age tribesmen in the Upper Amazon and natives in remote parts of Mexico, where their use is traditional. In the United States LSD had become more tightly regulated, but more widely desired. It threatened to become part of our culture, and a boon for bootleggers, smugglers and counterfeiters.

The British LSD supplier's letterhead address proved to be a modest, semi-attached development house in a quiet village. Prams stood in the dooryards, neighbors worked in their gardens. His wife told me to come in, he would be home from London shortly. (I identified myself and the nature of my business—an inquiry into the international traffic in lysergic acid for a book to be titled *Black Market Medicine*.)

Her husband recalled my LSD chapter in an earlier book. Denouncing the "outrageous hampering of vitally important research by narrowminded bureaucrats," he said he was the biggest supplier of LSD to the United States, and that there was nothing illegal about this, so far as his own country's laws were concerned. He manufactured fine chemicals for sale to "professional people." At least six times a year, he brought LSD into the United States— using a different name and passport, which he did not reveal to me. Customs agents once checked the powder he was carrying, but since it didn't test out as heroin, he was not detained. The bulk of his sales were shipped airmail. One needs only a very minute amount of LSD, of course. His customers numbered in the many thousands throughout the world.

"If his chemists knew the value of what they were making, they'd strike for higher wages," his wife put in. I wondered where he obtained the raw material? Lysergic acid is a basic chemical compound offered for sale without restriction anywhere—Italy, Switzerland, Poland, Hungary, Czechoslovakia.*

*Since Sept., 1966, its distribution in the United States must be recorded.

Counterfeit Drug Plant

The firm reportedly made $50,000 a month for several years before being closed down by State health authorities. Non-branded generic drugs were produced here, as well as counterfeits. (Leading tranquilizers, heart drugs, hormones, stimulants, etc.) Distribution was nationwide. The company catalog stated: "Uniform tablets from batch to batch. Laboratory controlled . . . Product liability insurance carried . . . We are equipped to handle large contract accounts . . . All of our products are guaranteed to be in accordance with the Federal Food and Drug Act . . . Your inquiries are cordially invited . . ." Leading brand-name drugs were duplicated yet the catalog promised: "All formulations kept strictly confidential."

Ingredients for prescription drugs, stored in basement prior to compounding.

Production-size coating pan.

Sink used during manufacturing process, just outside toilet partition.

Gas range in mixing room.

Part of the production line.

Packing and labeling area.

LSD discoverer Dr. Albert Hofmann (left) receiving an honorary degree from Prof. Finn Sandberg of the Kungl. Farmaceutiska Institutet in Stockholm, May 1966, for outstanding achievements in phytochemistry.

Scientists Search for Cures

Dr. A. Tonolo, Italian mycologist, who discovered that *Claviceps paspali,* a fungus growing on Paspalum grass, is the best source for culturing lysergic acid.

Finn Sandberg, M.D., Stockholm

Inspector Shore waiting for LSD peddler, Washington Square. He will shortly mingle with the folk-singers around the fountain.

U.S. marshal removes LSD from bearded peddler in suburban railroad station.

Peddler's stash in apartment of university professor. Flap was cut in refrigerator door to conceal liquid LSD.

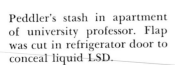

LSD counter-top packaging layout in professor's apartment.

LSD-impregnated sugar cubes, capsules of LSD and liquid amphetamine, vials of the hallucinogen, DMT, confiscated from campus peddler.

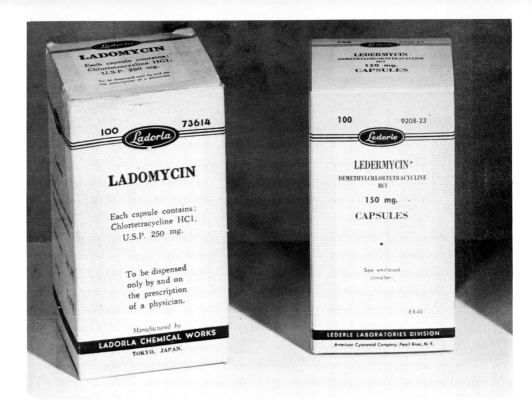

Oriental variations on the theme: Close approximations of Lederle's trademark by a different antibiotics producer.

BDAC agents qualifying as marksmen, Fort Belvoir, Va., firing range.

FDA.

Eastern Europe:

Before visiting the Slovakian Academy of Sciences in Bratislava, Czechoslovakia, I had dinner with a Cuban physician, who explained, "They let our planes land in Prague, few of the world's airports receive us." He had not talked with an American for years. As a medical school professor, he felt cut off from his colleagues. Could I possibly arrange to send him certain medical journals via a Mexican friend?

This man's isolation was somewhat unique. Having just left an international conference on alkaloids in East Germany, where I interviewed chemists from Mainland China, Russia, Nigeria, and Washington State University, among others, I was more than ever impressed with the amount of communication among the world's scientists.

Research on ergot alkaloids provides an excellent example of communication because it not only is multifaceted, scientifically speaking; it also is socially and politically a most delicate subject. The late Aldous Huxley had told me years earlier: "The nation that first succeeds in producing a really effective psychic energizer will control the world. The development of drugs that change human behavior may well prove to be far more revolutionary than achievements in nuclear physics!" It was rumored that North Koreans used LSD in brainwashing American prisoners. Many times I had heard that a small amount of LSD in public water supplies could immobilize entire populations in major cities. (Not if the water were chlorinated, however.) "It's a weapon for biological warfare—no one wants to talk about it," I was told.

But at international scientific congresses on natural products, everyone was talking about it.

What excited the scientific community was the breakthrough achieved by Italian researchers working with Nobel Laureate Ernest B. Chain, a codiscoverer of penicillin: the deep-vat fermentation of lysergic acid in a semisynthetic process similar to the mass-production methods used in manufacturing antibiotics. Scientists working in universities, drug companies, and for their governments in the United States, Japan, Canada, and elsewhere, had been engaged in a race to be the first with a practical process. Farmitalia, a firm making ethical drugs in Milan, won that race and is now producing quantities of lysergic acid in its fermentation plant in Turin.

Milan, Italy: Farmitalia Research Laboratory

Dr. Bruno Camerino, Farmitalia's Research Director, called together key members of his staff to answer my questions. A mycologist, Dr. A. Tonolo, had discovered an ergot strain, *Claviceps paspali*, which provided the highest known yield of lysergic acid. It was all the more remarkable since he found the fungus on grass native to Africa, but growing on a hillside near Rome.

Farmitalia was hard at work developing possible medicinal uses for lysergic acid, other than the well-known obstetrical and headache therapies. Of the thousand or so pharmaceutical producers in Italy, Farmitalia is one of the half-dozen companies that does basic research and that is trying to obtain patent-protection for drug discoveries. They did not market LSD.

The ticklish question was, What restrictions were placed upon the sale of the drug's starting material, lysergic acid—would they sell anyone an unlimited quantity? There was no law against selling lysergic acid, but what if it was diverted to the black market for the clandestine manufacture of LSD? That would certainly be regrettable. They sold to reputable manufacturers like Eli Lilly. What more could one say? They had not discovered LSD, that was a great scientific achievement of Sandoz, in Basle.

Switzerland:

In 1943 Dr. Albert Hofmann, a Sandoz chemist, synthesized the first natural ergot alkaloid. In the course of his work, he discovered that lysergic acid is the characteristic nucleus of all the ergot alkaloids; the derivative lysergic acid diethylamide— LSD—was prepared later that same year.* Dr. Hofmann had ex-

---

*In the United States, LSD is the oldest "new drug" in the Investigational New Drug (IND) files at FDA. Sandoz, however, withdrew this application in 1966.

plained to me earlier that he had been trying to find a restorative, or energizer, through manipulation of the molecules—his laboratory experiments resulting in LSD were not, as so many have said, serendipity, "a happy accident." At times he is not particularly happy with this discovery.

Still, he did bring to light the most potent and specific mental drug known so far—a dose of LSD is 10,000 times more powerful than the same amount of mescaline from peyote. As little as one ten-millionth of a gram provokes clinical changes. Only a fraction of the dose ever reaches the brain and after one or two hours it is excreted from the body and no longer detectable there. But the reaction may last much longer. No one really knows how long.

Several thousand studies of the drug's effects have been reported in medical and scientific journals the world over. Many specialists believe that LSD has a great potential in the treatment of alcoholism, frigidity, psychopathic personality problems, and autistic children (so withdrawn they do not even know that they are living beings).

Dr. Hofmann, as the "father" of LSD, undoubtedly hopes that his brainchild will be vindicated during his lifetime—that it will prove useful in clinical medicine. But, as Director of Natural Product Research for Sandoz, he is deeply involved with new substances derived from plants. Standing in a greenhouse, surrounded by a botanical garden, we discussed the endless variety of lysergic-acid-like compounds available in mushrooms, morning-glory seeds, mints, and many other sources. By changing a molecule here or there, who knows—one might find at last the clue to the plague of the twentieth century, mental disease, or produce, inadvertently, another drug subject to abuse.

Back in the laboratory I asked Dr. Hofmann to show me how to make LSD from the crystalline powder lysergic acid. I had studied technical descriptions in Merck *Index* and patents, both available to anyone. And I had also read newsletters circulated by college students that contain detailed recipes for preparing hallucinogenic drugs at home.

One process, Dr. Hofmann explained, would occupy less than a weekend's close supervision. It required a minimum of easily obtainable equipment, in addition to the starting material and chemical reagents. (Chemists also can work from finished drugs like Sansert.) There were four basic procedures involving chemical reactions, filtering, cooling, and isolating the LSD from impurities. This last was tricky. When I had gone out with FDA undercover agents to buy LSD, quite a bit of it was found to be contaminated or deteriorated or improperly prepared. Sometimes the color was off. LSD as made by Dr. Hofmann is colorless, odorless and tasteless. "One does need a very accurate balance for measuring," he said. "Otherwise it's dangerous."

U.S.A.:

I returned to New York where Chief Inspector Clem Westerly had assigned a new inspector the task of gathering information on adverse LSD reactions. He talked with patients at Bellevue Hospital, most of them college students, and with many doctors, and filed a report. During the next year, medical journals published similar surveys. There were an increasing number of psychotic episodes after ingestion of LSD and other hallucinogens; but most patients recovered and were discharged. A few remained under intensive therapy. Depressive states ending in suicide, sometimes months after a single LSD experience, were documented. Student users had lost interest in their studies and dropped out of school; some professional people—doctors, lawyers, engineers, psychologists and psychiatrists—deteriorated to the point where they could no longer practice. While under the influence of the drug, some users injured themselves or others because of panic or loss of touch with reality, as when a student user stepped out of a dormitory window and plunged to his death, and another ran into fast-moving traffic believing he could make it stop.

There are no production figures on LSD because the only legitimate supplier in the United States, Sandoz, has halted distribution. Only a few carefully screened researchers are currently obtaining supplies through FDA and the National Institute of Mental Health. Yet the drug is not difficult to obtain on the black market. The cost of a single dose averages $5 to $7 and it may be dispensed as a drop of liquid on a sugar cube, an animal cracker, a vitamin tablet, or blotting paper rolled up like a spit ball. LSD in capsule and tablet form indicates large scale pro-

duction in clandestine drug labs, says Boston BDAC Director
Richard A. Callahan.

New York City, American Psychiatric Association
Annual Meeting:

During a four-hour private interview with Dr. Carlo Henze,
the head of Sandoz in this country, and the late Dr. Max Rinkel,
the psychiatrist who introduced the drug clinically in the United
States, Dr. Rinkel said that he was preparing a report on LSD's
sexual effects, based upon many case studies, including those of
his colleagues. "While under the influence of LSD, the orgasm is
enhanced, especially in women. The drug releases basic inhibi-
tions—and this applies in homosexual relationships as well as
heterosexual, and in situations involving a couple or a group.
Group use is significant. The drug has been used as an implement
for seduction by persons with a professional facade . . ."

Dr. Henze expressed surprise that LSD was used for these
purposes.

Both men were highly qualified to judge clinical effects, being
medical doctors as well as pharmacologists. But they disagreed on
many points. Dr. Rinkel, whose pioneering led to wide acceptance
of the belief that there is a biochemical basis for mental diseases,
felt that LSD's specific action in the body was a still undetermined
trigger mechanism. Dr. Henze said Sandoz research indicated that
it affects a particular portion of the brain.

Dr. Henze appeared shocked at the statement by Dr. Rinkel:
"You can buy more LSD in Harvard Square than Sandoz makes
for legitimate research."

The Boston psychiatrist was more optimistic about the drug's
future in clinical medicine than Dr. Henze, who felt that its
greatest value was as an experimental tool in laboratory research.
Both men decried the black-market abuse of the drug because,
aside from the danger to the abuser, the illicit traffic was forcing
laws to be passed that would curtail truly scientific work. "We
have just about decided to stop producing LSD altogether," Dr.
Henze said.

"But they'll still be able to get it on every college campus in
the country, not to mention little hamlets—you wouldn't believe

the extent of the laity's experimentation with this drug," Dr. Rinkel pointed out. "It's a fantastic cult that cuts across all age groups and levels of society. How can you control a thing like that?"

How, indeed, when national magazines like *Playboy* are now quoting Dr. Timothy Leary, former Harvard psychologist: "LSD is the most powerful aphrodisiac ever discovered." The word is out.

In December 1966, the United Nations Narcotic Commission called for immediate international controls on the import, export, and production of LSD and substances producing similar effect because they "represent a serious danger to the individual and to society." The 21 nation commission unanimously condemned the use of LSD for anything but medical and scientific purposes.

As new pharmaceuticals are discovered and prove to be subject to abuse they will no doubt be added to the list. And their addition to national and international dangerous drug lists will certainly be challenged by some of their producers. There is wide variation in the attitude toward a specific drug's dangers from country to country. For instance, the head of Narcotics Drug Control in Sweden has told me that a certain amphetamine product was considered "more of a threat" than LSD. This drug was put on the narcotic list and is completely outlawed, as we forbid the use of heroin in medical practice in the United States. But physicians here prescribe the same brand name drug instead of other forms of amphetamine because they consider it less likely to lead to abuse.

With the rapid advances in drug development—and demand for new medications—one can only wonder where it will all end. Ten years from now there may be hundreds of "outlaw" compounds.

CHAPTER FOURTEEN

Substandard
Operating Procedure

The United States has no monopoly on the problem of substandard or potentially dangerous drugs; similar hazards exist all over the world:

Item: *The China Mail*, April 1966, reported that drug counterfeiters in Hong Kong were fined $750 for selling injectable vitamins that were nothing more than water colored with dyes.

Item: As this is written, hospitalized patients in Belgium are dying as a result of being injected with a powerful heart drug mislabeled as the hormone required for their therapy.

Item: Counterfeit, adulterated, and contaminated drugs from the Orient are being exported to Canada and other countries.

Item: A vice-president of a major United States drug company was shown ten different capsules of his firm's products which were either counterfeits or look-alikes upon his arrival in a Far Eastern country. In addition, local operatives were diverting the genuine products, separating the capsules in half, via the "dirty finger" method, and then filling half of the capsule with an inert substance.

Item: While in Latin America, I learned of other practices. A counterfeit drug plant was raided in Mexico and bogus brands of

251

Squibb, Ciba, and Hoffmann-LaRoche products were uncovered. South American doctors found patients were having bad reactions to penicillin. Counterfeiters had obtained empty Squibb vials, put in a little penicillin and a lot of peanut oil.

Item: A newspaper report from India mentioned that one newly born baby, given a laxative, was unconscious for 22 hours. Tests showed the laxative to be sweetened water and chloral hydrate, a powerful sedative. This same article reported widespread sales of counterfeit penicillin, sulfadiazine, inhalers, etc., with the criminals concerned having well-organized factories and a network of agents. An Indian doctor told me, "Half the drugs sold are fakes."

Item: A 1965 report in *American Druggist* outlined serious deficiencies in the quality of some drugs manufactured in the Soviet Union. A Soviet writer disclosed that penicillin produced in a recently built plant was found to be unsterile, and in another plant, the filling of ampules took place in a hall where "the walls and windows are dirty and there are puddles on the floor." The writer said that public health workers in one city refused to accept 160,000 "useless" ampules of calcium chloride. In another case, 70,000 ampules of strychnine nitrate and sodium arsenate had to be rejected because they contained up to 13 percent of adulterants or contaminants.

Item: In England, newspapers carried the following headlines in 1965: THE HIDDEN MENACE IN THE BABY'S DROPS, IMPORTED DRUG COULD KILL, and CHEMISTS HAND OUT KILLER DRUGS. This all started from a report written by Mr. Frank Stock, the research chemist in charge of the City of Birmingham's Analytical Laboratories. Mr. Stock's paper, "A Report on Cheap Drugs," struck at low cost broad-spectrum antibiotics, penicillin and cortisone, which had been pouring into England from Italy and Iron Curtain countries that ignore patent laws. After analyzing these preparations—found in 20 percent of the chemists' shops in Birmingham —Stock said: "Examination of samples of tetracycline pediatric drops provided the most dangerous examples of deterioration which it has been our misfortune to observe in an important pharmaceutical preparation . . . deficiencies in strength ranged from 57 percent to 73 percent below that stated on the label. The drug was utter rubbish and because of the deficiency, a child could have died."

Similar deficiencies were found in hydrocortisone and neomycin creams and ointments that contained only one-half the stated strength, with the active ingredients deposited in a sludge in the bottom of the containers. Heart drugs, asthma and rheumatism medications, and adrenalin injections also were substandard.

The fact that permission to sell manufactured drugs in England is granted virtually on demand caused Mr. Stock to object: "A solid pharmaceutical knowledge is required to safeguard quality. It makes me shudder to think that someone might be able to set up an office and sell drugs as though they were so much sugar."

Perhaps the most pertinent reaction to Stock's report came from Drs. Kalinowski and Moyes at the Worcester Royal Infirmary, who wrote a letter published in *The Lancet* in 1965:

> . . . We decided that the interests of economy in prescribing did not justify the exposure of seriously ill patients to an increased risk of reactions, and therefore insisted on supplies of British-made antibiotics. At the same time, we expressed our concern to the firm distributing the cheap antibiotics in this country, and asked for proof of their purity and safety, which they were unable to provide. We then received a warning from the Ministry that, although they could not prevent us from using British antibiotics, we might be called upon to justify our action. Despite this threat we have continued to use proven products.

Since this episode, the Ministry has not purchased certain patented drugs from unlicensed continental manufacturers. Instead, price reductions were obtained from British manufacturers.

Drug regulations in the United Kingdom and the United States have been closely studied by Dr. Joseph D. Cooper of Howard University, who concluded in a *Medical Tribune* series in 1966: "If results are to be measured in terms of human impact, no evidence was forthcoming to indicate that Britain is subject to any greater drug hazard, relatively, than the United States. If anything, it might be less."

Item: Drug quality is currently of great concern to the Canadians. Dr. H. A. Showalter, of the Department of Industry, charged that the Canadian government has been obtaining drugs "from the least competent or possibly the least scrupulous suppliers." He said that prices paid for drugs by the government were lower than those paid by the public and that "certain firms of questionable performance were obtaining a large share of the business."

McLean's Magazine reported in 1966 that the $200 million Canadian pharmaceutical market was too lucrative for unconscionable operators to ignore. "Look-alike" pills and capsules have resulted in dangerous reactions. For example, an anti-diabetic pill didn't dissolve at all in the patient. Another victim, a member of Parliament, lost consciousness while driving due to antihistamines dissolving too quickly and constricting blood vessels in his brain. A government inspector found a "kitchen table" manufacturer putting out a drug that lost its potency within two days, compared with the six-month shelf life of the same drug produced by a reputable company.

Dr. C. A. Morrell, former head of the Food and Drug Directorate, told the House of Commons: "There is nothing to prevent anybody in this room from setting up a drug company—and you wouldn't even have to tell me about it . . . New companies are a bit difficult to find. . . . Our greatest concern is raw materials from abroad where production controls are not as good as they should be."

As a result of all this, a new regulation went into effect in Canada in 1966 requiring registration of all drug producers and products. (There are over 500 drug manufacturers and distributors in Canada.) A tighter inspection program of drug manufacturing operations is now possible. Will this new regulation assure the consumer that every drug on the pharmacy shelf will be 100 percent safe and effective? The answer, according to Dr. Morrell, is no. He pointed out: ". . . it is impossible to check every batch . . . you cannot put 'government approved' on each drug. . . . If I were a doctor prescribing, I am sure that I would tend to prescribe from companies I know."

Item: Italy almost stands alone among the industrial countries in the free world in that it excludes patents for the manufacture of pharmaceuticals. This situation dates back to 1939 when the Italian Parliament during Mussolini's rule amended an 1859 statute. This constituted an open invitation for anyone to set up a drug-manufacturing plant for duplicating new processes or products developed by others. As a result, Italy has emerged as the sixth largest drug-producing nation in the world, with 1,100 manufacturing firms, of which some 950 have an average of only nine employees each. According to a recent study by the Bank of Rome, "over 90 percent of these small firms devote their entire production to the imitation of products developed by foreign or other Italian drug houses."

The larger drug producers in Italy, who have their own research programs, are clamoring for some form of patent law. According to Dr. Fulvio Bracco, president of Italy's most important drug manufacturers' association ". . . it gives the members of my association no particular pleasure to see a patent position threatened anywhere. We have been fighting for years to get some form of patent protection for our products."

But the pro-patent faction has been in a whipsaw, since the government, in effect, sets drug prices through the vehicle of the government subsidized health programs, enrolling 80 percent of the population. A drug company in Italy cannot stay in business unless its products are on the approved list of the health agency that pays for the drugs of its members. According to one industry spokesman, "The commissions never take the time to determine the real cost of the drug, whether it is an original or a copy, or whether the firm buys in bulk at little cost and merely re-packages the product."

An Italian magazine *Quattrosoldi* investigated the Italian pharmaceutical jungle in 1963. The editors invented a drug company and two "new" drugs—one based on a totally unscientific formula. Within 48 hours, the magazine claimed to have satisfied all the requirements for registering the drug, including clinical test reports. The reporters found no problem in obtaining "factual statements" from doctors, there were many offers. New drug registrations average about 1,500 per year in Italy, and it was estimated that the committee spent about ten minutes deliberating the merits of each one.

Quattrosoldi reporters revealed that an Italian pharmaceutical manufacturer can establish himself without even having a laboratory:

. . . in Milan, an inspector of the Ministry, having arrived from Rome to visit a pharmaceutical house, stated that he was satisfied that all of the necessary laboratory equipment and personnel were there. Technicians in white coats stood in front of modern machines, etc. It so happened that the inspector forgot his purse in those premises. Returning a few hours later to pick it up, he had an incredible surprise: In front of this pharmaceutical house was a moving van holding the entire equipment of the laboratory, which had been taken on loan for a few days.

The reporters went on to say "This could appear to be a joke," but they pointed out that it was not. Government publications stated that on numerous occasions, technical equipment at drug production plants has turned out not to be owned by the companies concerned, but merely borrowed for temporary window-dressing during inspections.

Quattrosoldi also unearthed outrageous drug-selling schemes. Pharmacists were offered premiums such as refrigerators, washing machines, and motorcycles, based on a point system. The larger the purchases, the more points would accrue to the pharmacist. The magazine stated:

Perhaps the trade was aware of this for a long time, but we consumers never imagined that the remedies for our diseases would be treated in the same manner as ewe's milk cheeses, to the tune of 'Carousel.' Just picture this: We enter the pharmacy, in pain or worried about someone in our home. We stop in front of those shelves filled with boxes, bottles, vials, and tubes of ointments. So many different kinds! We are waiting for that gentleman in the white coat to give us an effective remedy to restore our health. From the other side of the counter, the pharmacist cannot be insensitive to certain considerations of his own—one point means a pack of poker cards; five points, a new electric iron; 75 points, a movie camera; 9,000 points, an automobile!"

CHAPTER FIFTEEN

Pirates With Ph. D's

An Italian businessman in a silk suit stared sleepily at the talkative, overweight American chemist, while his Swiss lawyer made notes. The Italian looked at his watch. It was long past the lunch hour in the nearly deserted bar off the lobby of a luxurious Milan hotel. Soon the conference broke up. . . ."*Ciao!*" . . . Another began in the adjoining library-lounge. Scattered copies of *Mondon Economico, Finanziaria,* and *Agenzia Economica* were suitable stage props for the international industrialist guests and the people who sought them out with trade-secrets for sale.

The results of $375 million spent annually for research and development by American drug companies tempt the spies of industrial science. Formulas and manufacturing procedures have already been stolen for broad-spectrum antibiotics, hormones, and diuretics, among other drugs. The ultimate purchaser then produces the drugs—often in substandard plants here or abroad—and sells them for far less than the originator's price. "It makes sense for these crooks to pay $100,000 for a product that cost us several million dollars to develop," says an executive of a pirated firm. "For instance, it took over $20,000,000 and eight years to put cortisone into production."

The international ramifications of the theft of antibiotic and other drug secrets—worth at least $30 million—from just one

American company make the great Brink's mail-truck robbery seem a kindergarten caper by comparison. The central figure in this case was a trusted scientist who regularly had access to the newest and most important research and production developments. This man, whom I shall call Dr. Marvin (he used numerous aliases in his operations), served as an officer in the armed forces, left a spotless record in the universities he attended, and was admitted to leading professional societies. Others involved had similar academic credentials.

The key drugs stolen were and are the world's most widely prescribed antibiotics. Because of their effectiveness, FDA credits them with saving up to 1,000 lives daily in the United States alone.

Beginning in the early 1940's, hundreds of thousands of soil samples collected around the world were analyzed for micro-organisms with a broad range of activity. Finally in the late 1940's, a broad-spectrum antibiotic was found to have remarkable activity against a variety of infections. Research efforts continued to develop even more effective antibiotics. Some 500 mutants of the micro-organism's original strain were produced with x-rays, ultraviolet light and other techniques. Intricate, highly confidential processes were developed in order to find the right balance of nutritive substance to make the mold grow, to improve yields, and to extract, crystallize, dry, and analyze the product. Out of all this came superior antibiotics and, in the minds of Dr. Marvin and his associates, a plan for becoming independently wealthy by selling the secrets. Complications resulting from these thefts are alluded to in an FDA-recorded conversation between a drug purchaser and a raw materials broker.

PURCHASER: Every Tom, Dick, and Harry is selling that drug here.

BROKER: Yeah, they're getting it from Italy—that's why [the company pirated] is sore.

PURCHASER: Oh—I thought these local guys were making it from raw materials here.

BROKER: The capsules are filled here but the raw material is coming in from Italy. . . . See, here's a peculiar situation. If a company has a product that's patented here, they can protect their patent. Now the question comes up regarding government purchases. So, I say I will make the patented product, but I won't sell it to the public. I'll just sell to the government, *provided* the government will hold me free from any patents—the government can actually do that.

PURCHASER: Yeah, I heard [X company] just sold to the government.

BROKER: *Just* to the government . . . [*Long explanation of declining prices on government sales.*] So this company is now at the point where it's selling to the government at a very low price, a marginal price. And the patent holder is pissed off—with all the money he spent for clinical work and so on through the years, it's not profitable for him either. All of a sudden the government cuts down buying. [X] finds himself in a hole—he can't meet salaries, he owes money to shylocks, he has a load of the drug on his hands. So he goes ahead and sells to the regular dealers—the public. Let the patent holder sue. . . .

Dr. Marvin started taking documents and small quantities of drugs out of the laboratory a number of years before he was indicted. The insidious pirating mania spread to other employees, outside consultants, drug importers, and executives of buying firms in the United States and Italy. Numerous trans-Atlantic jet flights were made to wrap up deals in plush hotel suites in New York, London and Milan, all transactions taking place under the cover of pseudonyms. As the gang's number increased, the principals grew suspicious of each other. New alliances were formed to facilitate the peddling of secrets with an almost kaleidoscopic multiplicity of variations.

According to Dr. Marvin's later confession, the scheme had modest beginnings when small quantities of crude hormones were smuggled out of his employer's plant and sold to another drug

company. Dr. Marvin received $10 per gram and the other drug
company received $20–$25 per gram for reselling the product,
most probably to Italian companies. Another small company
became involved. They agreed to pay $15,000 for the hormones
and for the manufacturing procedures on certain antibiotics.
About this time, one of the individuals connected with the purchase of these drugs and procedures had a great deal to say to a
Congressional committee about his difficulty in securing rights to
produce these drugs from larger firms. It is a matter of record
that this "Mr. X" purchased stolen research data and drugs from
Dr. Marvin.

Part of Dr. Marvin's statement reads:

> On delivery of the procedures, [X] gave me a check as initial pay-
> ment toward their half of the $15,000 fee I was to receive. [Another
> small firm was to furnish the other half of the fee.] . . . I told [X]
> and his partner my real name and the fact that I was employed at
> [major company]. I did this because I did not think I could keep it
> secret for very long . . . since it was the only company engaged in
> the manufacture of this product. They did not act surprised and I
> am sure that they knew that the procedures and materials I turned
> over to them came from [major company].

Meanwhile, Dr. Marvin formed a new company of his own,
operating from his home with business mail directed to a post
office box. Companies Y and Z expressed interest in antibiotics.
Dr. Marvin obliged them by smuggling out procedures and cultures. One drug was of particular interest since it had not yet been
put on the market. The industry was queried, and a leading
ethical drug producer asked for more information on this product.
A hundred-gram sample was stolen and sent to them. But when
they determined that the drug was already patented, they promptly
lost interest.

By this time, Dr. Marvin had resigned from the large pharmaceutical company. Then followed: The use of equipment to micro-
film and photocopy thousands of documents, and the recruitment
of other employees to continue stealing documents and cultures.
Attempts by other companies to peddle the same secrets to a
select list of Italian firms in competition with others in the conspiracy. Accusations and violent denials that trusted associates had

"gone over" to rivals in the ring. "They stopped having anything to do with me, so they *must* be getting the cultures from someone else." "Yes—so-and-so drove an old car—now he has a new Oldsmobile!"

This advertisement appeared in a chemical magazine:

PROCESSES WANTED—Foreign manufacturer seeks information or consulting services for production of antibiotics, steroids. Products will be sold only in foreign countries where patents do not apply. All replies held in strictest confidence. Contact Dr. ——, address ——.

It had been placed by one member of the ring to trick others into showing their hands. They did. Interpol, the International Police Organization, began investigating the mystery of the stolen cultures.

Then came the inevitable welching on deals when buyers complained that they were not getting promised drug yields from the cultures. Hasty consultations and feverish work in the foreign plants to get manufacturing processes up to standard followed—but there were serious technical problems with the extraction procedures. Also, in the fermentation vats undesirable chemical analogs were forming and there was contamination. Key members of the ring crept back into the American company's antibiotic chill rooms in the middle of the night to filch specific cultures.

Personal woes mounted for the thieves as their wives complained, became ill with worry. Scientific reputations went down the drain as real identities were discovered. Coded cables crisscrossed the Atlantic with intelligence reports in frantic attempts to coordinate the operation. Members of the families were pressed into service far into the night preparing freshly-typed procedures from old stolen documents so that many prospective clients could be approached simultaneously. To assure that "the other guy has been taken care of," fake brawls were staged between members of the ring, one in the hall outside a company boardroom.

During this period, at least six Italian drug companies purchased cultures for around $400,000. None of the sellers appears to have much left of the $400,000. Dr. Marvin netted only $80,000 —despite the much bigger sums first mentioned by the Italian firms. This booty was apparently leached away by legal fees and travel expenses.

While all this was going on, the American company, of course, became suspicious. The international division had reported that their patented drugs were being produced in Italy. One Italian firm had even requested empty trademarked cartons in order to facilitate the sale of the pirate antibiotic in the United States! The patent-holder's security force noted that employees were quitting the company, only to turn up in Italian posts—it was almost a trend. Dr. Marvin later said that a technician "is living like a king in Italy—he only used to make $8,000, now he gets $18,000." The FBI was called in and dozens of employees were interviewed. After the entire scientific staff was given an explanation of the situation, an employee voluntarily admitted his role, a minor one. With this break, one after another of the members in the ring accused each other. A Federal judge sentenced a number of the drug pirates to prison terms, but they are, however, still appealing the sentencing.

More than one professor is leading a double life. Here is another type of renegade professional, this time wearing a gown and mortar board, flying the respectable flag of the one world of science—but actually he is a privateer.

These professors may have many degrees, listings in *Who's Who* and dozens of legitimate patents to their credit. They can be consultants to industry, as well as professors. They tend to travel a great deal, lecturing the world over.

Two leading drug companies, X and Y, became suspicious when one professor asked for drug samples and antibiotic cultures for "research." The resulting security check was disquieting: This man's brother was president of an obscure drug company; in addition, he was traveling all over the world buying and selling drugs as a field man for a Chameleon associate. Another relative was vice-president of the company, but he also happened to be a key employee in the laboratories of company Z. On being notified of these circumstances, company Z reacted by promptly firing the professor's relative. A mistake because it destroyed an opportunity to keep this interesting operation under close surveillance.

In his travels, one professor would ask former students employed by large pharmaceutical corporations: "What's young in the laboratory?" Rebuffs did not discourage him. After two or three meetings, a casual remark such as "there is a drug we are really excited about," was all the leverage he needed to pressure for more information. Deals with employees in different companies varied. For one person, the offer of a position as plant manager in a firm that would make the product being stolen was required. For another, a moonlighting job photostating stolen documents for less than $200 a month was sufficient. For a third, the promise of 25 percent of the products' worldwide royalties was the clincher.

The *modus operandi* of a particularly brazen type of research thief was described by a drug company official:

> He has filed patent applications here and in several countries, and has been actively selling our process information and engineering data as we have been developing it. He has customers, all well-established companies, in the United States, Great Britain, France, Switzerland, etc. They, innocent of the source, are going ahead with testing and engineering.

> The documents being peddled by the research thief contain wording and drawings identical to those in our own files—even to cost data *and mistakes*. Through some long and devoted hours of effort by a lot of top people—and a rare touch of luck—a spy in our employ was tracked down. Faced with the evidence, he confessed. But the master spy had already skipped the country. As he is indicted here and there, he skips to a third country. He files suits charging that we stole *his* inventions. He tries to weaken our fortitude by sending from the haven of his third refuge a barrage of accusations to press, government, and industry. When we finally tighten our grip on him, will he slip to a fourth country?

At this writing, one renegade professor, even though the target of millions in judgments for stealing industrial secrets, still carries on. He turned up not long ago at an international scientific meeting and blithely discussed compounds that were stolen as if they were his very own discoveries.

CHAPTER SIXTEEN

Mafia Laboratories, Unlimited

Chameleon has been described by one law officer as "The brains, the planner, and the doer all rolled up together." There are many aspects of black-market medicine that capture his interest. Smuggling is one. Chameleon and his cohorts smuggle drugs such as vitamins, sulfas, diuretics and LSD on a businesslike basis. Vitamin B_{12}, or cyanocobalamin, used to save life in pernicious anemia, is a nutritional supplement. When combined with hormones, according to one Italian manufacturer, it is an excellent treatment for impotency. Vitamin B_{12} is priced around $45 per gram by Merck and Company, the patent holder on the synthesis of crystalline B_{12}. A small bag of USP B_{12} slipped through Customs could be worth as much as $100,000.

Chameleon's associates first became involved in B_{12} years ago. A company in the Midwest produced it from sludge obtained from the municipal sewage system. This crude B_{12}, which received FDA approval for use in animal and poultry feeds, was evaluated by major drug companies for possible use in human prescription drugs but they finally refused to have any part of such material since as one employee put it, "While B_{12} from sewage is 95 percent pure, . . . one needs a four letter word for the other 5 percent."

A considerable quantity of the sewage B_{12} passed through the hands of the Chameleon group and eventually some was shipped to Italy. Checks were drawn to a fictitious person in sums of

$5,000–$10,000 per shipment. No invoices were kept. An exchange of letters with a chemist revealed that the purchasers were interested in upgrading the sewage B_{12} for human use. "It's really quite simple, just a boiling off process which can be done in any kitchen," he said. (This material is no longer produced.)

In the meantime, Italian companies were making B_{12} and a system of couriers was set up to bring the drug through New York City's airports. Avoiding duties of some 20 percent provided a distinct advantage for resale to price-conscious purchasing agents here. Another was to counterfeit Merck's labels, vials, stoppers and seals so that buyers, ordering through brokers, would think they were getting the genuine drugs at large discounts.

A major ethical drug company bought some of this material, although their quality control people should have known better —visual inspection alone would have shown that the drug was a darker red in color and its granulation was 30 percent coarser than authentic material. Merck commented: "It is obvious that this counterfeiting procedure was devised to deceive the U.S. Customs Appraiser of Merchandise by falsely representing the imported material as made in the U.S. and thereby mislead the Appraiser to treat the material as a return of American-made goods and avoid payment of applicable duties."

Another smuggling variation used by Chameleon's henchmen involved mislabeling expensive active ingredients with the names of cheaper substances to secure lower duties—a dangerous practice because a raw material passes through many stages before reaching the ultimate dosage-form and the true identity of the drug could be lost. A potent diuretic was brought in labeled as a dental anesthetic. (It may be recalled that during the raid on Mannie's counterfeit drug stash, an FDA inspector discovered an Italian label on a drum. The same labels were found on drums at Chameleon's.)

Life-saving, expensive sulfa drugs produced by American Cyanamid Company were smuggled into the United States at a duty saving of some $2 per kilo. They were invoiced and labeled as cheaper forms of sulfa. After clearing Customs, the drums were repainted and relabeled, although in most instances, the wrong drug names were put on the labels. The drums were then shipped to manufacturers, some of whom may have been aware of the mislabeling. One purchaser testified that he paid the broker $8 per pound, instead of the $1.50 that appeared on the invoice. The difference was attributed to "transportation charges." Another drug producer said that his receiving clerk made the necessary label changes—but no tests were made of the material. Where were the drugs sold? "Mostly to the U.S. Government," according to the broker.

Other variations involved importing unlicensed sulfa drugs, then disguising the foreign material by placing it in new drums affixed with labels peeled off other drums of the American patent holder. The original lot number was then cut off the label and a new lot number inserted by the broker. When investigated, this lot number was found to refer to an entirely different product.

The danger to public health from these deals is appalling. Lot numbers are put on pharmaceuticals so that quality control tests may be recorded and the material's production and distribution history determined immediately if anything goes wrong.

What happened to patients who may have become victims of this particular form of pharmaceutical roulette is anybody's guess.

Pharmaceutical pirates may be employees or outside consultants, professors—even hoodlums in search of a fast dollar. But the thief must have the right connections. A case in point is Doc, The Group's pharmacist-idea man. Since finished drugs were added to hijacked razor blades and cigars in his diversification program as a professional fence, it was only a matter of time before he became enchanted with the profit potential in pharmaceutical *research*.

This was first brought out when Chief Inspector Clem Westerly interrogated Doc on his purchase of 10 million amphetamines and barbiturates in a three-month period. Several private label firms under surveillance had shipped the drugs to him, ostensibly for distribution to other pharmacists, although he was not a licensed wholesaler. As noted earlier, they were turning up in FDA truck-stop cases throughout the country.

The Chief Inspector asked about some tranquilizers that were diverted by a city purchasing agent. This led to the revelation of a scheme involving the Mafia. A drug still in development was stolen by hoodlums with scientist collaborators inside the laboratory. Doc said, "This one drug will revolutionize a [certain] therapy. A hospital tried it on a dying man weighing almost 400 pounds with fabulous results."

"It's not a narcotic, why would the Mafia be interested?"

"They've read all about pharmaceutical profits . . . there's been so much in the papers about the money to be made. And with the government purchasing so many drugs, especially from Italy . . ."

Doc had fumbled in his initial attempts to peddle this compound on his own. Using a bogus name, he first called on an advertising executive who specialized in pharmaceutical accounts. The man said that the product and information sounded as if it came from the actual firm involved. Doc admitted this was true, he had a contact there who could deliver the entire "NDA" (New Drug Application). Doc said he would like to spend a couple of years abroad marketing the drug. The advertising man told him he'd most likely spend a couple of years in jail.

The company was immediately notified by the advertising executive of the attempted sale and the hunt to ferret out the contact began. But there were dozens of employees with easy access to research and clinical data on this drug and the security people didn't even know the true identity of Doc. Several months went by with no results. By this time, a private detective agency and Chief Inspector Westerly had come in on the case and other Federal agencies were being consulted.

The actual transaction took place in a leading Mafia overlord's nightclub. The employee-scientist brought a few ounces of the compound with him, as well as several hundred pages of test results duplicated from the company's records. Doc asked the purchasing agent to study the data and tell the mobsters what he thought about the drug's potential. The man agreed that it would be "a revolutionary breakthrough." The mobsters were prepared to make an investment of $50,000. The scientist accepted a down payment of $10,000 cash, plus a promise of more than ten times that much if the product was successful. Later, a mobster remarked that the scientist had "sold himself cheap." The first payment was the last.

Present at the meeting, but keeping their distance, were two representatives of an Italian drug company. This firm is affiliated with a company in the United States that has been in repeated trouble with FDA for producing substandard pharmaceuticals. They discussed producing the stolen product in Latin America, rather than in Italy. So far, no drug application has been registered abroad by the thieves, but drugs may be produced in Italy for export without registration with the authorities there. This is an extremely potent drug, and its uncontrolled production and distribution could be very dangerous.

No one knows how many similar compounds are going astray, now that the crime syndicates have entered the picture.

Is it an exaggeration to say that hoodlums could eventually dominate whole segments of the drug industry?

—One major manufacturer last summer sold only a few bottles of a well-known drug in one of our largest cities because black marketeers got there first.

—At least one drug company already has been driven into bankruptcy because of the counterfeiting of its most heavily advertised product.

—Countless pharmacies are forced out of business by unfair competition from unethical druggists who buy on the black market.

—East coast Mafia leaders have been holding Appalachin-type meetings which, according to authorities, focus upon ways and means to get out of narcotics and into legitimate businesses. Chemicals and pharmaceuticals have been discussed.

—FDA is analyzing counterfeits of some of Ciba, Lederle, Merck, Roche bestseller drugs produced aboard for sale in this country. According to an informant the U.S. has been divided up into a dozen drug distribution territories. The money behind this operation is said to come from a Swiss bank account. If this is, as it appears to be, a well organized underworld effort to flood the country with bogus medications, what can we do to stop it?

Debriefing

The Congress hopes, and I hope, that this Act will put a stop to such vicious business. I cannot express too strongly my determination that this good and decent and law-abiding society shall not be corrupted, undermined, or mocked by any criminal elements, whether they are organized or not. . . .

PRESIDENT JOHNSON *on signing the Drug Abuse Control Amendments (DACA), 1965.*

What difference, old laws, new laws, all the same. . . . We aren't legit, so the law don't aply to us.

TOM, THE COUNTERFEIT DRUG SALESMAN, *during a conversation with FDA Inspector Wallace Jackson, 1965.*

The subject of this book is even larger than drug counterfeiting and diversion. Ultimately *Black Market* Medicine deals with people whose lifework is the evasion and mockery of our laws.

In counterfeiting and diverting life-saving prescriptions, the lawbreakers have gone too far. Their activities place the life and health of every drug consumer in jeopardy. We must all look beyond our own pillboxes and home medicine cabinets to the basic problem of how willful violators can be driven from the drug industry.

The difficulties in prosecution, even after the most careful

269

case-making, are immediately apparent. It is now more than two years since the FDA inspections of Buggsy's butcher shop and Mannie's suburban counterfeit drug stash. Almost a year has elapsed since the dangerous drug controls became enforceable. To renegade professionals, gray marketeers, and other fringe operators, DACA has been an inconvenience. To black-market medicine-makers operating completely beyond the law, things have changed very little. Those members of The Group, associates of Chameleon, suppliers of Big Mex, and pill pushers, who were charged with violations, have had ample time to continue their nefarious trade between infrequent court appearances. Mobster moneymen have eluded the net altogether.

In crimes of this nature, one hopes for speedy trials and convictions, but one could wait forever. Tom, for instance, appeared alone at his first arraignment on drug counterfeiting. He pretended not to know what it was all about. The Federal judge said, "Don't you realize that you are entitled to counsel? I'll give you thirty days to obtain counsel and another thirty days after that to confer with him." Tom claimed he was ill and destitute. A prosecutor who had tried to send him to jail a few years earlier had told me that Tom, meanwhile, had gone through several million dollars in ill-gotten gains. As for lacking counsel, Tom had told Inspector Jackson that he had lawyers on retainer. They had, no doubt, coached him for today's performance as a bewildered citizen throwing himself on the mercy of the court. Defendants in FDA cases have even had themselves committed to mental hospitals to escape prosecution.

A major witness in one of the counterfeiting cases has reneged on an agreement to testify and is threatening to lie under oath if the subpoena is not quashed. This person, who can supply the links connecting Syndicate kingpins with pharmaceutical deals engineered by their underlings, points out that there is virtually no protection against underworld reprisals: the body of a witness in a similar case was found wrapped in heavy chains at the bottom of a well; another was blown to bits when he stepped on the starter of his car; a third was shot in a faked suicide.

It is not unusual in protracted Federal cases involving hardened criminals for potential witnesses to disappear, die, or change their stories.

Because of delays in The Group's cases, there are other losses.

Tremendous inroads are made in FDA's limited manpower and budget. For instance, a dozen or so inspectors, chemists, expert medical witnesses and government officials are repeatedly flown in from all parts of the country to stand by for days on end. Trials have been scheduled to begin at 10 A.M.—two days later, "a Civil Service" case is given as the reason for the delay. The next open date on the court calendar is weeks away, and so it goes.

Defendants have nothing to lose and everything to gain through these interminable postponements, hearings on motions, etc. There is a distinct advantage to them in the brisk turnover in young lawyers working as Assistant U.S. Attorneys and members of the General Counsel's staff. The intricacies of the FD&C Act and its many Amendments as they apply in this case, have had to be explained to these new people. All this plays directly into the hands of criminals, who happily use these time lags to continue making money, counterfeits and trouble.

An exploration of what might be done about our sluggish Federal judicial procedure is beyond the scope of this book, but I do have recommendations for speeding up convictions of counterfeiters and dangerous drug diverters, and also for detecting and discouraging these practices:

—Violations of the Federal law (DACA) and state laws patterned on it should be felonies, not misdemeanors. All states should have this law and it should be uniform. In one state where the offenses are felonies, a pill peddler warned an undercover agent, "If you're gonna get caught, make sure you sell to a Fed. The judge will let you off, it's only a misdemeanor then." Probation, not jail, is the usual outcome under the present light penalty. Federal judges and prosecutors put misdemeanor cases on the bottom of the priority pile. Juries, finding the charges difficult to comprehend, shrug them off as only misdemeanors after all. State Boards of Pharmacy and Medical Examining Boards sometimes hesitate in suspending licenses of practitioners charged with misdemeanors. Other law enforcers are not motivated to cooperate with FDA on "making piddling misdemeanor cases." Criminals like Tom think the whole thing is a big joke. But the crimes are far more serious than many felonies.

—FDA should be given the authority to subpoena records.

—FDA should be permitted to seize the vehicles used to transport contraband drugs. Other Federal agencies can confiscate cars, trucks, boats and planes employed in circumventing the law. One of the greatest deterrents to trafficking in illicit pharmaceuticals would be government seizure of tractor-trailers used in the nation-wide distribution of counterfeits, amphetamines, and hijacked drugs of all kinds. These "rigs" are valued as high as $40,000. If owner-operators were faced with losing the means of their legitimate livelihoods, they would think twice about cooperating with the underworld.

—Pharmaceutical plants should be licensed, rather than just issued an FDA registration number without any prior investigation of the professional qualifications and background of the drug producers, inspection of the facilities and equipment, etc. The actual owners should be identified, whether they are the sole proprietors, partners, or corporate investors. A BDAC Field Office Director recently received a tip that a chemist operating a drug company in his area has a "rap sheet" two pages long which includes felony convictions. Hidden owners, or "angels," in this business are loan sharks with interests in 11 related corporations. Because FDA registration is not a licensing procedure, FDA may not withhold or revoke any registrations for any reasons. Thus this firm is legally registered and in production.

—Any person or firm that alters a drug in *any* way should be closely regulated—for synthesizing, tableting, encapsulating, re-packing and relabeling all provide opportunities for changing drugs.

—There should be a central file of all known criminals engaged in drug trafficking, whether narcotic or nonnarcotic, diverted, or clandestinely manufactured. The logical place for such a file would be the BDAC headquarters in Washington. Other law-enforcement agencies, crime commissions, and public-spirited citizens should cooperate in making this the most complete central registry possible. According to investigators, reports on criminals involved with pharmaceuticals were given to Senator Kefauver but they were never made public during his hearings. These reports are said to be in the FBI archives. If so, they should be reexamined.

—Many Federal agencies are involved with the complex drug problem. Jurisdictions are fuzzy and there is duplication of effort. Eventually, all drug matters probably should be concentrated in a single Drug Administration with a Federal Drug Act designed to handle present-day problems more expeditiously than the FD&C Act. The President's Advisory Commission on Narcotics and Drug Abuse in 1963 strongly recommended a new unit in the Department of Health, Education, and Welfare, which would have authority over all legitimately produced drugs including narcotic medications. The Commission suggested that the Department of Justice take over the control of the illicit drug traffic now handled by the Bureau of Narcotics and FDA. Regulation of all drugs by a single agency is reasonable. But it is hard to separate neatly what is and is not illicit. As we have seen, there are many gray areas. This deserves further study.

—Each FDA District with a heavy criminal case load should have at least one experienced attorney on its staff to advise inspectors and BDAC agents during investigations, to maintain close liaison with the local U.S. Attorney, and to serve as the regional representative of the Department of Health, Education, and Welfare's General Counsel in Washington.

—The extremely murky legal situation surrounding the interception of telephone and other communications, the use of hidden microphones, recorders, transmitters, and all listening devices known as "bugs" must be clarified. What type of activity constitutes a threat to our national security? Is it possible to protect the right to privacy for every individual and, at the same time, provide protection against criminals who threaten our health? In his 1967 State of the Union Message to Congress, President Johnson said, "We should outlaw all wiretapping, public and private, wherever and whenever it occurs, except when the security of this nation itself is at stake—and only then with the strictest governmental safeguards. And we should exercise the full reach of our constitutional powers to outlaw electronic bugging and snooping. I hope this Congress will try to help me do more for the consumer. . . . And now we come to a question that weighs very heavily on all of our minds, on yours and mine. This nation must make an all-out effort to combat crime. . . . We appointed the National Crime Commission to study crime in America and to recommend the best way to carry that attack forward."

As an example of the confusion and controversy that exist, the majority of the President's National Crime Commission members reportedly endorse the view that electronic surveillance and wiretapping by Federal agents are crucial to the anticrime effort. But

according to *The New York Times,* November 23, 1966, Acting
Attorney General Ramsey Clark asked the Commission to avoid
the subject in its report. He reportedly said that the eavesdropping issue would act as a "red herring" to distract public attention from important but less controversial recommendations.

It is time to face the facts. Wiretapping and "bugging" are
increasingly widespread. (Senate hearings revealed that an estimated 10,000 electronic listening devices were in use in the Miami
area alone; only four were said to be employed by the Internal
Revenue Service there.) Racketeers, private detectives, nosey
neighbors, industrial spies and suspicious spouses all have free
access to this equipment. Control over the *use* of "bugs" by the
public may well be impossible. Perhaps their manufacture and
sale will have to be regulated.

FDA's electronic surveillance equipment proved extremely
valuable in determining the plans of the drug counterfeiters and
their methods of operation. Ostensibly legitimate business and
professional men revealed their criminal intentions during secretly
recorded conversations. Was this justifiable "privacy invasion?"
It seems illogical to trust the courts to issue search and arrest
warrants on the one hand, but, on the other, not to trust them
to issue *similarly restricted* orders for wire-tapping and electronic
eavesdropping by Federal law-enforcement officers investigating
serious crimes. The proposed restrictions, and they are many,
were spelled out in S. 2189 introduced during the 89th Congress,
and discussed before the Senate Subcommittee on Criminal Laws
and Procedures. This type of legislation deserves our attention.

—The Federal government should specifically budget money
and manpower for the protection of key witnesses before, during,
and after a trial for as long as necessary. Threats are often only
bluffs designed to intimidate, but they can still cause life-long
anxiety because witnesses never know when they might be carried
out. One woman who testified for the government after being
threatened had her home burned to the ground. Her child died
in the fire and her husband suffered a mental breakdown. Entire
families may have to be relocated at government expense in attempts to avoid such tragedies. A far, far greater effort should be
made to detect and punish *anyone* harassing government witnesses
in any manner. The conspiracy of silence, secured through terror,
is the underworld's first line of defense.

Not long ago, Inspector Jackson was put up in a medium-sized commercial hotel that was frequently used by FDA inspectors and government attorneys because it is close to a Federal courthouse. A former Federal Narcotic agent, now with BDAC, happened to learn of this billeting and warned that the hotel was owned by the head of a Mafia "family," and was managed through a front. By a strange coincidence, the hoodlum who made the cash down-payment on the "contract" for Wally Jackson's life belongs to this same Mafia family. As this is written, Inspector Jackson is under a two-man, 24-hour armed guard, and government lawyers and agents no longer hold pretrial strategy conferences in this hostelry's rooms, where the phones could have been tapped and the walls bugged. Because the BDAC man with investigative experience outside FDA was able to reveal the true ownership of the hotel, the case may well have been saved from ending in disaster.

Interwoven in this situation are several basic problems that must be understood and, somehow, solved before we can expect to make much progress against organized crime in general, and its infiltration of the drug industry in particular. These obstacles include the fragmentation of drug law enforcement and poor communication among the various agencies; the extensive use of legitimate fronts by ex-convicts, and the (often understandable) reluctance of law-enforcers, citizens, and criminals to divulge important information. These are closely related aspects of the over-all problem of obtaining, verifying, tabulating, and utilizing what is known as "Criminal Intelligence."

Because black-market medicine cuts across so many different business and professional levels, it undoubtedly includes a greater variety of legitimate fronts than any other illegal endeavor. These fronts serve criminals in many ways. They afford an opportunity for the investment of untaxed black money skimmed from gambling and narcotics. They increase the underworld's control of supplies and services, including transportation systems. And they lend an aura of respectability to overlords who can deal more openly with labor unions, trade associations and even legislators and government officials. While lobbying for their stated, vested interests as "ordinary businessmen," mobsters are covertly able to extend and protect their vast criminal empires. Here are some fronts used by persons involved in black-market medicine, together with crimes of record committed by one or more of the individuals:

Legitimate Fronts:

Physician
Pharmacist
Lawyer
Accountant
Hospital, clinic operator
Pharmaceutical manufacturer
Research scientist
Chemist
Chemicals producer
Drug repacker
Drug detail man
Drug wholesaler, dealer, jobber
Drug company technician
Drug purchasing agent
Raw materials broker
Exporter-Importer
Pharmaceutical machinery
  distributor
Tool and die maker
Printer
Salesman
Whole-egg mix distributor
Wholesale baker
Novelty factory owner
Bar, diner, restaurant,
  nightclub owner
Salvage operator
Hotel, motel owner
Truck-stop owner
Truck driver
Operator, moving van company
Owner, beauty shop chain
Real estate business
Construction company
Food processor
Vending machine distributor
Furrier
.... and on and on.*

Criminal Activities:

Counterfeiting: drugs, money,
  perfume, licenses, tickets, etc.
Illicit drug sales, narcotic and
  non-narcotic
Smuggling, raw materials and
  drugs as well as other items
Hijacking
Armed robbery
Burglary, other thefts
Fencing stolen goods, all kinds
Forgery
Stock frauds and other rackets
Auto and jewel theft
Lotteries, other gambling
Illicit distilleries
Loan sharking
Fraudulent bankruptcy
Bombing
Arson
Extortion
Pornography
Pimping
Pickpocket
Perjury
Threatening to maim and to kill
Assault and battery
Rape
Manslaughter
Kidnapping
Murder
... and other crimes.

*In a preliminary government investigation of underworld ownership and financing
of legitimate businesses, racketeers were found to have direct and substantial inter-

Criminals can use these fronts as excuses for obtaining continuances when their presence is required in court. I have heard them successfully plead an urgent business meeting in Europe, or professional duties that could not be neglected.

But prosecutors cannot expose the criminal backgrounds of such people during pretrial hearings or in court because this might prejudice the judge and jury. The Constitution entitles a defendant to be tried only on the specific charges made, "misbranding" or "adulteration" of Miltown, for instance. Chronic criminality can be revealed only after the verdict when the prior record of a *convicted* person is discussed with the probation officer, who then reports to the judge before the sentencing. (One exception: if the defendant elects to take the stand in his own defense on cross-examination he can be asked about his convictions.) Because of postponements this moment of truth may arrive years after an arraignment.

During investigations leading up to an arrest, all too often law-enforcers have no idea they are dealing with professional racketeers hiding behind aliases and new occupational covers. Records are scattered among various local, state and Federal agencies, are incomplete, and some have mysteriously disappeared. The prompt sharing of fundamental information, even with fellow Federal agents, seems to depend more upon, "who-knows-who-and-how-well," than any formal system.

During my first weeks with FDA undercover inspectors it was thought that we were dealing only with "petty crooks." But in recorded conversations these people mentioned names which suggested ties with remnants of a gang of executioners that predated

---

ests in: juke box routes and distributorships, cigarette vending routes, pinball machine and amusement device routes, refuse removal, dress manufacturing, garment trucking, fat rendering, linen and towel renting, fresh fruit and vegetable wholesaling, restaurant provisions, dry cleaning, laundering (including laundromats), home furnishing stores, beer and liquor distributorships, home modernization construction, aluminum awning and furniture distributorships, auto dealerships, food importing, race tracks, barber and beauty supplies, and the operation of night clubs and restaurants.

On a smaller scale: They have financial interests in insurance agencies, travel agencies, banks, factoring firms, auto-parts manufacturers, resorts, bowling alleys, record manufacturing and distribution, theatrical and nightclub booking agencies and residential building.

Murder, Incorporated and with notorious Mafia leaders in a number of states. These connections were later corroborated for me by other agencies. Why, I wondered, were they so reluctant to work directly with FDA? Some FBI and Narcotics Bureau agents and organized crime experts in metropolitan police departments told me that they had no idea FDA was "really involved" with any hardened criminals. Because inspectors at that time lacked police powers, it was assumed that their work was the type that could be done by a scientifically-oriented certified public accountant and was just about as hazardous. My otherwise knowledgeable interviewees were genuinely shocked to learn that FDA was dealing with lieutenants of Mafia bosses whose names appear on the "family" charts.

There was another unfortunate aspect to this lack of communication. Detectives on local narcotic squads seldom realized or remembered that FDA has jurisdiction over LSD and the pep pills and goof balls that turn up in narcotic cases with increasing frequency. Valuable leads to nonnarcotic drug sources and evidence were discarded instead of being shared with FDA.

However, when information from outside agencies was volunteered, it proved extremely valuable. For instance, this memo on a key member of The Group engaged in a business not related to drugs:

> . . . has a history of labor union racketeering and
> Communist activiites . . . is trying to take over
> the [X] industry in this area . . . supposedly has
> machinery for large volume production . . . alleg-
> edly doing this as a cooperative venture with [Mafia
> members] who provide the muscle.

The report went on to say that the former employment records of this man's legitimate business partners included pharmaceutical manufacturing and pharmacy. This was all news to FDA.

About half of BDAC's 200 trained undercover agents were formerly FDA inspectors. The rest were picked from thousands of applicants with backgrounds in the FBI, IRS, Federal Bureau of Narcotics, Customs, Labor Department, State Department, Crime Commissions, Immigration, Alcohol and Tobacco Tax

Division, and police departments in many parts of the country. The BDAC force now includes pharmacists, chemists, lawyers, CPA's, and men with 20 years' experience as detectives, as well as recent college graduates. They have all received six to eight weeks' intensive training in the use of firearms, karate, and the latest investigational techniques. The chances are very good that from now on there will be much greater inter-agency cooperation because BDAC is made up of men from varied backgrounds with extensive personal contacts.

The Bureau of Drug Abuse Control is a fledgling agency—necessarily preoccupied with organizing, recruiting and training. Their first six months' enforcement record is heartening: over 1,000 criminal investigations were initiated, of which 230 involved LSD or other hallucinogens. Three million, five hundred thousand dollars in drugs, at the going illicit price, were seized. One seizure involved 2,000,000 amphetamines; another consisted of 153 grams of LSD, equivalent to 1,500,000 doses. More than 100 arrests were made. Many of the persons arrested were armed and had criminal records. In 98 instances, defendants entered guilty pleas to charges filed in Federal courts. Eight elected to stand trial and all were convicted. A number were primary diverters responsible for supplying dozens of peddlers. BDAC is basically concerned with shutting off illicit drug supplies at the source, not with compiling impressive arrest records. As men who have chased Bennie peddlers from truck stops and drug pushers from street corners know only too well, if two petty crooks are removed, two or more can be expected to replace them, sometimes within hours. "Running where the heat is, putting out brush fires" puts the name of the agency in the newspapers and gives taxpayers the feeling that something is being done, but it is no way to wage successful war against powerful racketeers.

Painstaking intelligence gathering is the only professional method for combating organized crime. It is agonizingly slow, dangerous, and often disheartening work. Infinite care is needed in working out the details of the cover stories and strategy for infiltrating agents into organized gangs and for developing informants. There should be no other distractions or duties for either the planners or the doers. Months of labor and much money may be expended with very little to show for it. Investments need to go far beyond simply making large sums of cash available for "buys." For instance, the agent's cover should be consistent. He cannot drive a painted-over "fuzz" car and wear his own moderately-priced clothing and be expected to pass himself off as an affluent wholesaler or flashy mobster. This is no 9 to 5 job to be attended to during the normal government office working day. As Supervisory Agent Sam Wolfe of the Atlanta BDAC Office put it, "The big possums walk at night."

After studying BDAC operations in Washington, attending classes for undercover agents, and interviewing men in the field, I was dismayed that although BDAC was designed to combat criminals masterminding the dangerous drug traffic, much of its time is devoted to non-criminal matters. Former Chief Inspector Clemens Westerly, who helped to organize BDAC, is little better off, so far as trained personnel and even office help are concerned, than he was when I copied the daily crises from his record of telephone calls in the New York District. Eliminated now are foods, cosmetics, and hazardous substances, but he is very much preoccupied with legitimate drug producers who contest the listing of their products as "drugs subject to abuse" under DACA.* Within a period of two months, some 50 inspector man *years* were devoted to preparing for hearings on tranquilizers. (In 1964, FDA devoted only 56 man years to its entire investigation of illegal drug cases in this country.) Although he is a division director, Mr. Westerly has only two assistants and one secretary to help him monitor *all* of the Federal criminal cases involving dangerous drugs in the U.S.A., draw up new regulations, arrange the hearings that are permitted by law, and handle other duties. It is necessary to call upon FDA inspectors and BDAC agents in the field to get these largely non-criminally oriented chores accomplished. Cases involving hardened criminals are meanwhile neglected.

BDAC agents are supposed to spend about 40 percent of their time auditing the records of manufacturers, wholesalers, etc. An audit, or accountability survey, of a company like Merck requires two to three weeks of an agent's time. Accountability surveys cannot be delegated to a man who simply has a good head for figures. They require the pharmaceutical know-how of an Inspec-

*This is their legal right under DACA.

tor Oscar Cohen, combined with insights into the criminal mind that come from long association, as in the undercover assignments of a Wally Jackson.

Accountability surveys have disclosed criminal diversion. They are also a means for delineating, for the first time, amphetamine and barbiturate synthesis, dosage form production, and distribution. That is why it is necessary to include all companies in the program, rather than concentrating only on suspected law-breakers. But for men who have just received intensive training as undercover agents, the business of compiling these records is often tiresome. It can be frustrating, as when Kerry Shore, now with BDAC, spent a month working undercover developing an LSD case involving a major distributor in Greenwich Village, but missed a crucial "buy" because that day he had to check records in a legitimate drug company.

In the old days, FDA inspectors were put in jeopardy by doing double-duty—inspecting a grain elevator in a little hamlet in the morning, then putting on old clothes to buy Bennies at night. Things haven't changed much.

When Abe and Bert were about to be audited, they sent their company records to lawyers and BDAC had to fight for several weeks to obtain them. Some alibis for drug shortages sound as if they were dictated by an attorney. When a BDAC agent arrived early one Monday morning to survey the stock of a Big Mex supplier, he was told, "It sure is a funny coincidence, but I was burglarized over the weekend and they took an undetermined amount of unspecified drugs." So-called accidents during manufacturing and packaging are offered as reasons for discrepancies. It is becoming common practice among the gray-marketeers to destroy punches after large runs of illicit drugs are produced to prevent their being traced to the source.

These are the old, old problems. But BDAC is trying to move out of the business of fighting "brush fires" in *schlock* shops, truck stops, and drugstores run by renegades. They do hope, eventually, to have the means to cope with well-organized Syndicates. Already there are experts on the staff and in the field. New recruits are receiving the benefit of their experience.

For instance, Director Jack Bologna of BDAC's Baltimore Field Office, one of the originators of the Mafia "family" chart idea while on a detail with Senator John L. McClellan's Labor Rackets Subcommittee, told agents-in-training:

> A new image is being created for organized crime. The change is as dramatic as that of the 1940's, when white fedoras and pin-striped suits gave way to charcoal hues of conservative cut. Today, the hierarchy of organized crime are becoming the financial pillars of civil libertarian groups, but *not* because the groups went looking for them. . . . The public relations advisors to gangdom have convinced the vice lords of the need to support the cause of individual liberty, through handsome donations through favored lawyers. Any appreciable increase in national sentiment hostile to law enforcement enhances the gang leader's chances for hung juries or acquittals.

Mr. Bologna went on to name Mafia members who have attended national political conventions, and whose "mouthpieces" have consorted with judges even at the Federal level. He pointed out that the Mafia has an organizational structure somewhat parallel to that of the United States—it has three branches, executive, legislative and judicial. Elders with great power may operate behind comparatively humble fronts, while some of their underlings, running more conspicuously lucrative businesses, live as one might expect a millionaire to live.

There is a need to distinguish between the one-time or occasional criminal offender and the members of a disciplined criminal band, who persistently, systematically and daily violate the law. One of the bills introduced in the 89th Congress would have made it a crime to belong to the Mafia. A police chief testified, "If enacted, this would be the most devastating blow ever dealt to the hierarchy of organized crime." While the Mafia is close to the core of the problem, there are many non-Mafia members in the total picture, which includes representatives of every ethnic group. The difficulty of proving membership in a professional criminal organization would doubtless be insurmountable.

A more practical approach would be an investigation of underworld ownership and financing of legitimate businesses, with preliminary concentration on those having to do with our drug supply. Mr. Bologna has suggested sampling the tax returns of 100 leading racketeers who have *convictions* for crimes involving murder, narcotics, gambling, labor racketeering, moonshining, antitrust violations, extortion, aggravated assault, bribery, tax evasion, securities law violations, and defrauding the public, creditors, or the government.

From the 100 individual returns, the total adjusted gross income reported could be broken down between income from legitimate sources and income from apparently illicit sources. Also, the industrial and business categories from which these racketeers reported dividends, interest, and profits could be tabulated by company names and geographical areas. After this, a field investigation could include interviewing the major nonracketeer firms in the industry, and attempts to determine:

—The methods by which racketeers made their initial investments.

—The competitive techniques used by racketeers after they became established, particularly predatory or terroristic tactics.

—Whether the number of firms increased or decreased after racketeer involvement.

—Whether racketeers infiltrated or got control of trade associations and/or labor organizations.

—Whether racketeers have engaged in mergers or further acquisitions in the industry during the past five years.

In addition, consideration should be given to such measures as S. 2731 introduced in the last Congress by Senator Harrison A. Williams, Jr., of New Jersey, which would amend the securities laws to require disclosure of the identity of any person or group acquiring as much as 5 percent of the voting stock of any registered company. Senator Williams, who is chairman of the Senate Securities subcommittee, said the provisions were designed primarily to expose underworld figures who might be attempting to take over legitimate businesses. The bill required ". . . full disclosure for the protection of investors of: (i) the background and identity of all persons by whom or on whose behalf the [stock] purchases have been or are to be made; (ii) the source of the funds used or to be used in making the purchases . . . and, if any part of the purchase price is represented . . . by funds borrowed or otherwise obtained for the purpose of acquiring, holding, or trading such security, a description of the transaction and the names of the parties thereto . . ." etc.

Investigation and legislation designed to pinpoint actual company ownership also would be useful in dealing with fly-by-nights, who may or may not have any connection with crime syndicates. President John F. Kennedy called attention to FDA's problems when he said, "An uncooperative small minority of [pharmaceutical] manufacturers can engage in a game of hide-and-seek with the Government in order to avoid adequate inspection. But protection of the public health is not a game. It is of vital importance to each and every citizen." The "game," as we have seen in the cases of Abe and Bert, includes setting up new companies in other geographical areas to escape detection, and using relatives, pharmacists, and other fronts as corporate owners. This lessens the chance of being charged with violation of Federal probation and receiving heavier penalties on subsequent offenses.

There must be thousands of relatively "innocent" persons with no criminal records being used as fronts for gray and black marketeers. Countless others are unwitting collaborationists in such illegal activities as the production of counterfeit drugs, when they supply machinery, raw materials or packaging not under controls. One of the best sources of information in criminal activities in the drug field are citizens who don't like what they see, as when one wrote to Chairman Walter A. Munns of Smith Kline & French: "I think there are bogus labels for drugs being printed in this city by the thousands," and he passed this on to Chief Inspector Westerly.

During the 1966 Senate hearings on legislation to combat organized crime, an International Brotherhood of Teamsters' legislative counsel attacked bills to protect witnesses on the grounds that "We do not want a nation of informers. . . . The use of informers is contrary to principles of fairplay, decency, and our Anglo-Saxon tradition."

I am not suggesting that we become a "nation of informers." But in the face of an insidious health threat, and lacking adequate controls, we must, *for our own protection*, remain alert to the fact that illicit pharmaceuticals are being produced and distributed under a wide variety of legal covers. FDA cannot protect us by stopping these practices unless they are first brought to its attention. (Appendix E. BDAC Field Offices)

Ethical people in the drug industry, physicians, pharmacists, and especially, drug detail men, could help FDA a great deal more than they do. County medical societies and chapters of pharmaceutical associations should set up committees to work closely with FDA on this problem. There is some hesitation about volunteering information lest the motive be misunderstood. A security man working for a drug company told me, "If I were to pass along certain information I have, it might be looked upon as an attempt on the part of the regulated to curry favor with the local regulators." This should not be the case. Cooperation is in the public interest.

As an example of how vigilant citizens have helped, not long ago a salesman of drug manufacturing equipment became suspicious after making a sale to a man who asked that the machines be left in his garage at home, rather than installed in his drug plant. There are no legal restrictions on such sales or deliveries, but the salesman alerted FDA. When they followed up, they found the customer turning out counterfeits on the new equipment in his garage.

Why should FDA need help, now that BDAC is established?

Statistic: the Baltimore Field Office, to cite a specific case, has fewer than a dozen agents to cover five states. One might say that the public receives BDAC protection in this area at the rate of one-half agent per state per year. One non-BDAC authority on dangerous drug controls told me that "hundreds of agents are needed to clean up the New York-New Jersey mess."

Legislators should take pride in the passage of the 1965 Drug Abuse Control Amendments. But protection that exists mostly on paper is, in some ways, worse than no law at all. It gives us a false sense of security, and it frustrates the men who are trying to enforce it.

President Johnson, in signing Drug Abuse Control Amendments, created the first new Federal law enforcement bureau in 30 years. Yet before it could even reach its *minimum* complement of manpower, it was severely restricted. If the President and Congress really hope that "this Act will put a stop to such vicious business," they should give FDA's Bureau of Drug Abuse Control the men, money, equipment, and additional authority it needs to do the job.

APPENDICES

DIVERSION AND COUNTERFEITING

OF PRESCRIPTION DRUGS

LEGAL DISTRIBUTION CHANNELS

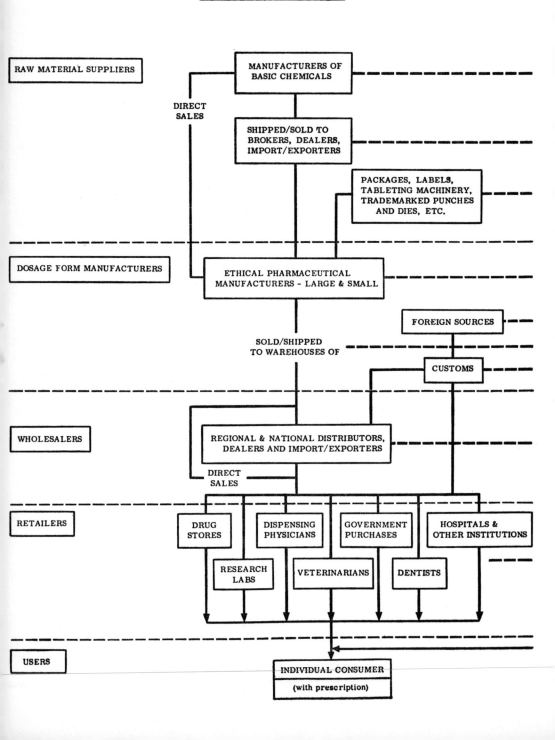

BLACK MARKET OPERATIONS

Pharmaceutical Diversion may occur at any point in the complex chain of legitimate drug distribution. from the manufacturer of the basic chemicals to the point at which the finished dosage form reaches the consumer.

Raw materials may be natural or synthesized products - many have industrial uses other than in pharmaceuticals. Chemicals may be synthesized in clandestine laboratories - or, illegally smuggled from abroad.

Fictitious names may be used to order dangerous drugs such as LSD, DMT, mescaline sulfate, amphetamine. etc.

Counterfeited labels and packages. stolen tableting or encapsulating machinery. illegally manufactured trademarked punches and dies may be employed.

Imitations and counterfeits are manufactured in garages, homes and other non-registered establishments. Also: patent infringement; sales to unauthorized persons; thefts of product and trade secrets of ethical manufacturing firms. Generic firms that counterfeit trademarks as a sideline. "Moonlighting" scientists engaged in illegal activities.

Patent infringement in certain countries.

Hi-jacking of shipments; diversion of legal drugs (in transit) to illegal channels.

Illegal identification to secure low duties; illegal re-entry of U. S. produced drugs; thefts at docks; smuggling.

Shady distributors, dealers, etc. who:
- Contract repackagers of "Tailings", Findings and Leftovers
- Handle counterfeits and imitations
- Fence stolen genuine drugs
- Invoice drugs to fictitious physicians and druggists and then intercept shipments .
- Sell illegally to retail outlets without records

Dealers/Salesmen who purchase samples from physicians and repackage.
Dealers who divert veterinary products to human consumption.
Employees who, unknown to management, steal and sell products to unauthorized persons.
Abuses on "returned" drugs (outdated, etc.)

Peddlers, street pushers, who sell to users without prescription.
Employee diversion in drugstores, hospitals, etc.
Druggists who buy cut-rate, suspect merchandise and intermix and substitute.
Physicians who dispense to unauthorized persons for profit.
Retailers who buy large quantities and resell to dealers, thus confusing normal trade pattern.
Drug abusers who share or sell drug illicitly.

DRUG ABUSERS - THRILL SEEKERS
(no prescription)

APPENDIX B

Drug Identification by Pillistics

The Food and Drug Administration's procedure to establish the source of drugs is similar to the ballistics method of firearm identification by examining a recovered bullet. Just as the impressions left on a bullet by the rifling of a gun barrel are unique, microscopic marks left on a tablet by a punch in a compressor are distinguishable from those left by any other punch.

Even though dozens of punches bear the same company monogram, it is still possible to positively identify which punch produced which tablet *if* there is an authentic tablet from each punch available for comparison. FDA inspectors obtain samples of drugs directly from the machines in use during plant inspections. These authentics are filed in "drug libraries" which are kept as up-to-date as possible.

According to Director William V. Eisenberg of FDA's Division of Microbiology, legitimate companies are usually cooperative about supplying tablets and capsules from each of their machines. "They'll even hand us the work sheet, which includes the drug's formulation and the technique for processing it," he told me. This is a great help in the identification of drug constituents, because New Drug Applications on file do not necessarily contain all the information needed by pillistics experts.

The problem lies, of course, with gray- and black-market producers of substandard and counterfeit drugs, who seek anonymity. It is relatively easy for FDA's chemical sleuths to detect a counterfeit through laboratory analysis and comparison with reference samples of the best-seller drug copied. Proving who made it, when, and where is something else again. Not long ago a consumer became ill after taking a Diuril tablet. She submitted all the tablets remaining in her prescription to FDA and they were traced to a machine belonging to a notorious counterfeiter who had been shut down several years earlier. Were these old tablets, or was someone else using his machinery? The matter was referred to BDAC for undercover investigation.

Not all drugs analyzed are counterfeits. Some have been legitimately produced and diverted; pillistics has been helpful in determining not only the source, but also the point where diversion took place. Since the passage of the Drug Abuse Control Amendments of 1965, it is no longer necessary to prove that dangerous drugs seized have moved in interstate commerce. But it still is necessary to determine the source of the drugs when cases come to trial, and FDA's drug identification work is largely confined to samples used as evidence.

Establishing the source of generics also has become increasingly important. More than a thousand companies in the United States manufacture plain white tablets that have a wide variety of therapeutic uses—yet they bear no distinguishing marks. In cases of drug mix-ups it is vitally important that the drug be identified.

There are no instant tests for the identification of most prescription drugs, although more and more major ethical companies are putting tracers into ingredients and are using distinctive tablet and capsule shapes, special inks, and, in one case, identification codes on the individual dosage forms.

FDA has fewer than a dozen pillistics experts. Dr. Albert H. Tillson heads the main drug identification laboratory in the Microanalytical Branch of the Division of Microbiology in Washington, D.C. Four FDA Districts—New York, Atlanta, Kansas City, and Los Angeles—are also doing some of this work. The microscopic and microchemical steps needed to analyze a single drug sample require from one to three hours, but the total processing, including writing the report, may take one specially trained chemist the better part of a day. It would be impractical to expect FDA to analyze prescriptions for consumers as a public service.

Although the work is highly technical, the equipment required is not extensive. It consists of a wide-field (10X to 60X) microscope and a polarizing microscope, plus the all-important drug library of authentics. The procedure begins with a visual examination of the drugs of unknown origin. (If they are part of the evidence in a case, they have been given a number, then sealed, dated, and initialed by each FDA employee handling them in order to maintain an unbroken chain of evidence.) The shape, color, monogram, weight, and size of the individual tablets and capsules are noted, as are any gross punch marks, machine scratches, monogramming ink blurs, lumps, pits, or other imperfections visible to the naked eye. Next they are examined under the wide-field microscope at its lowest power. The width, depth, and angles of the score marks or center grooves on tablets are measured with an ocular micrometer in the lens of the microscope. Variations in the groove are usually more significant than those in the monogram. Other signs noted for comparison are ridges formed at the tablet's edge.

The final step requires a polarizing microscope to identify the active ingredients and the fillers in the drugs. Early in 1967, the New York District's pillistics expert, Mr. George Troublefield, an analytical chemist, explained to a jury how counterfeit amphetamines were detected by the optical-crystallographic method:

"Fillers are identified by the polarizing microscope. Each crystalline compound has its own optical properties that serve to differentiate it from others. As polarized light of a single wavelength passes through crystalline material, it travels at different rates of speed. The difference in the velocity of light is characterized as the refractive index of the material. A portion of a crushed tablet [or a crushed "seed" from inside a hard-gelatin capsule] was placed in an oil with a suitable refractive index. The compounds were identified by referring to the determinative file of optical-crystallographic data, and by comparison with authentic samples of the compounds.

"The active ingredient, dextro-amphetamine sulfate, was identified by a microchemical test. It was placed in a basic medium of approximately five percent sodium hydroxide in a microscopic cavity slide. Then a cover slip with a drop of gold chloride on it was inverted over the solution. Amphetamine is volatile, so it was caught in the drop of gold chloride. This, examined under the polarizing microscope, had a long, thin, highly-colored needle formation." [When I looked through Mr. Troublefield's microscope at dextro-amphetamine it reminded me of skyrockets.]

The samples of tablets in this trial proved to be underpotent counterfeits, with one ingredient missing, made on machinery that had changed hands several times. Fortunately, Mr. Troublefield had authentic tablet and capsule samples in his drug library for comparison purposes. The capsules, also counterfeit, contained an excessive amount of the active ingredient. While they looked like the authentics to the naked eye, under the microscope there were a number of differences:

instead of four types and colors of seeds, there were eight; there were white seeds, while the authentic product had lightly tinted seeds, but no white ones; and the active ingredient was not properly distributed.

Two physicians were called to the stand to testify for the government on the dangers of such drugs. Both agreed that patients could be seriously harmed by such medications.

APPENDIX C

The Bureau of Drug Abuse Control

By John Finlator, Director.

During the past several years an alarming increase in the abuse of stimulant, depressant and hallucinogenic drugs has become apparent.

At hearings held by the House of Representatives Committee on Interstate and Foreign Commerce, statements were made that over 9 billion barbiturate and amphetamine tablets and capsules are produced annually in the U.S.A. of which a substantial percentage reaches illicit channels. No accurate figures are available on the abuse of tranquilizers, but the production figures exceed those for the sleeping pills, pep pills, and narcotics combined.

The "mind changing drugs," the so-called hallucinogens or psychedelics, and LSD in particular, are taking the newspaper play from the hard narcotics and other abusable drugs. There has been a great deal of talk and much written about LSD's supposed power to expand the mind and to make it function in creative and inventive new ways, but Dr. James L. Goddard, Commissioner of Food and Drugs, while testifying before the Senate in May, 1966, stated "This is just not so. The records of many hospitals show the admission of patients who have taken this drug and have literally lost their minds. They have lost the power to think and to reason and to create—lost all power to use what is so fundamental to a life of achievement. . . . The Food and Drug Administration has embarked on a strong program to curb the illegal and illicit practices associated with LSD. We have the laws and regulations to do this . . . and we are pursuing it with all our energies."

As early as 1951, Congressional hearings on proposed legislation to place barbiturates under controls similar to those for narcotics were held. Hearings were conducted again in 1956 on both barbiturates and amphetamines, followed by other hearings in 1957 and in 1962. In January 1963, the President's Advisory Commission on Narcotic and Drug Abuse urged that all non-narcotic drugs capable of producing serious psychotoxic effects when abused be brought under strict control by Federal statute. Hearings resumed in 1964 and a bill, S 2628, passed the Senate unanimously August 15, 1964, but was not acted on by the House before it adjourned. H.R. 2 was introduced January 4, 1965, and after extensive hearings, was passed by the House March 10, 1965. The Bill was amended by the Senate and passed June 23, 1965. After the House agreed to the Senate version the Bill was signed into law July 15, 1965, by President Johnson to become effective February 1, 1966.

This new law, known as the Drug Abuse Control Amendments (DACA):

(1)   Provides for control over the manufacture and handling of three groups of depressant or stimulant drugs: barbituric acid, its salts and derivatives; amphetamine, its salts, and optical isomers; and any drug which contains a substance found by the Secretary of Health, Education, and Welfare to have a *potential for abuse* because of its depressant or stimulant effect or because of its hallucinogenic effect.

(2)   Eliminates the necessity for the Government to prove interstate shipment of a depressant or stimulant drug.

(3)   Requires wholesalers and jobbers of these drugs to register with FDA annually, and requires registered drug manufacturers to indicate whether or not they are producing depressant or stimulant drugs.

(4)   Provides for officers of the Department of Health, Education and Welfare, who are designated by the Secretary, to conduct examinations or inspections with authority to:

(a)   Execute seizures with or without libels of information,

(b)   Execute and serve arrest and search warrants,

(c)   Make arrests without warrants in certain cases,

(d)   Carry firearms.

The Amendments also prohibit:

the unauthorized manufacture, processing or compounding of controlled drugs;

distribution of the drugs to unauthorized persons;

possession of the drugs except for personal use, use by members of the family, or use for family pets;

refilling prescriptions for the controlled drugs more than five times or more than six months after they are initially prescribed; failing to prepare, obtain, or keep certain required records of manufacture, receipt and distribution; and failure to permit inspection and copying of these records;

making, selling, keeping, or concealing counterfeit drugs.

Drug abuse cannot be eliminated through the application of law enforcement techniques alone. Consequently, the Food and Drug Administration established a new Bureau—the Bureau of Drug Abuse Control [BDAC]—to handle all aspects of the drug abuse problem.

Some of the objectives of BDAC for the next five years are to:

1. Eliminate to irreducible quantities the stimulant, depressant, hallucinogenic and counterfeit drugs in illicit traffic.

2. Provide an integrated national and international scientific data storage and retrieval system giving the most up-to-date and accurate medical, scientific and operational intelligence on controlled drugs.

3. Obtain extensive base line data on the scope of the drug abuse problem.

4. Enhance State and local capabilities to control selected drug commodities through cooperative compliance and educational programs.

5. Enhance consumer self-protection through an informational program that will provide education on the dangers associated with drug abuse.

6. Foster voluntary compliance of the law by the regulated industry to reduce diversions of abuse drugs from legal channels.

7. Build an in-house training facility to train the Bureau's Agents, as well as other enforcement officials in drug abuse law problems and controls.

The Washington staff of BDAC is divided into three Divisions:

A Division of Investigations to develop policies and procedures for the inventory audit of manufacturers, wholesalers, pharmacies, hospitals, etc.; and for coordinating field investigations of illicit traffic.

A Division of Case Assistance to develop and maintain guidelines for the preparation of cases; monitor cases on which legal action is recommended; provide guidelines for interpretation of statutes and regulations; and develop policies and procedures.

A Division of Drug Studies and Statistics to develop and provide scientific information for field investigators, specialized groups, such as physicians, pharmacists, and manufacturers, as well as the general public. It has responsibility for statistical studies of the drugs under BDAC's control and monitors them from production through ultimate distribution. In addition, through cooperation with other units in FDA and the National Institute of Mental Health (NIMH) it initiates studies to determine the potential for abuse of drugs which affect the central nervous system.

In addition to overt and covert criminal investigations, Agents will undertake a record accountability program of production and distribution records for controlled drugs to achieve four main objectives: 1) to detect diversion of controlled drugs from legal channels of distribution; 2) to develop reliable data regarding the flow of controlled drugs in legitimate channels; 3) to determine the adequacy of records and security measures being maintained by manufacturers, processors and distributors of those drugs; and 4) to produce a deterrent effect on those who might otherwise, either deliberately or carelessly, become party to the illegal diversion of drugs.

A vast educational program has been initiated through speeches, papers, and conferences. Letters have been sent to the country's 55,000 licensed pharmacies, explaining their responsibilities under the law. Pharmacy leadership conferences have been held and more are scheduled. Two special bulletins have been distributed to law enforcement officers at Federal, State and local levels and to Security Officers at colleges. A series of Fact Sheets concerning the Amendments and the drugs subject to control have been made available to colleges, high schools, military installations and to service organizations.

In cooperation with the International Association of Chiefs of Police BDAC has initiated a series of training institutes to acquaint police officers with the dangers of drug abuse, to show them how drug abuse can be detected, and to indicate the sources of illegal suppliers.

A movie "Bennies and Goofballs" has been produced and is available without charge for showing through the BDAC Field Offices.

A contract has been signed with the National Association of Student Personnel Administrators to start an educational program, on drug and narcotic abuse, for college students and student personnel administrators. The Federal Bureau of Narcotics and the National Institute of Mental Health are also participating in the activities of the contract.

Studies are planned to determine the abuse potential of many existing drugs on the basis that abusers may resort to drugs, other than those under control, as illicit sources of controlled drugs are eliminated. Sociological as well as psychological analyses are planned to determine methods of introduction, the relation of "the source" to the abusing group, the significance of the lack of information, or presence of misinformation, on health hazards among drug users, and the economies of drug supply and stimulated demand.

The FDA will not undertake studies of the personality traits of drug users, or the therapeutic effect of drugs in relation to their use in psychiatric practice, nor will it engage in basic or methodology research. It will use, to the greatest extent possible, research instruments already available or under development by the NIMH, in attempting to gauge attitudes toward drug abuse in relation to social class and economic groupings.

To foster cooperation with State organizations, BDAC has launched a "State Pilot Drug Store Program." Currently, agreements have been reached with six states—Florida, Texas, Indiana, Georgia, Washington and New York—to monitor the practices of pharmacists with regard to controlled drugs and their record-keeping practices.

A Model State Drug Abuse Control Act has been prepared and forwarded to appropriate officials of State Governments for their consideration. This Act is patterned after the Federal statute and provides the means for uniform law enforcement at the Federal and State levels.

A great deal of misconception exists on LSD, its legitimate use in research and the controls maintained over this hallucinogen by the Government.

Under the provisions of the Federal Food, Drug, and Cosmetic Act, the FDA has been directly concerned with LSD for a number of years.

Sandoz Pharmaceuticals of Switzerland, the firm manufacturing LSD, made its first contact on the drug with FDA in 1953 to discuss clinical investigations it was planning to pursue in the U.S.A. The drug was regarded as a "new drug" as defined by the Law and FDA agreed to its distribution only to research psychiatrists, properly qualified to investigate the drug and use it solely as an investigational drug.

For ten years, from 1953 to 1963, experimental investigations with LSD took place in this country.

In 1962, the Kefauver-Harris Drug Amendments were enacted by the Congress. This new law modified the definition of a new drug and required that a drug be effective as well as safe before it could be marketed commercially. The investigational studies of LSD, which had been completed up to that time, in Europe as well as in the U.S.A., did not establish the safety or the efficacy of LSD. The drug, even today, is regarded as a new drug and it has not been approved for marketing.

In June of 1963, FDA issued new regulations requiring that the sponsor of an investigational new drug prepare and file with FDA an acceptable, rational program of experimentation including adequate pre-clinical testing. In short, the program had to be reasonably safe and responsibly conducted.

Sandoz Pharmaceuticals drew up and filed a basic investigational plan for testing LSD under the new regulations. Eventually about 70 researchers received LSD samples from Sandoz under the investigational exemption.

During the period from about 1960 to the present, illegal production, distribution and use of LSD began to mushroom. Public reaction, too, began to build to major proportions and in April 1966 Sandoz decided to withdraw its sponsorship of investigations with LSD, and psilocybin, another hallucinogen.

If Sandoz, as the only legal sponsor, were to leave the field, all LSD research would have to stop and the drug would have to be recalled from sponsored investigators. The FDA discussed the problem with the NIMH and the Veterans Administration and agreed to allow a small group of a dozen investigators to continue their studies. After termination of the Sandoz investigational sponsorship of LSD, the firm transferred its remaining stock [of LSD] to the NIMH. Therefore, the only legal supply of LSD in the U.S.A. for clinical research on humans is either in the vaults of the NIMH, or held by the handful of investigators approved to continue studies.

BDAC is currently supplying crime laboratories, health laboratories, and similar facilities with small quantities of LSD to be used as a "standard" in their chemical analysis.

Some persons obtained LSD for investigational use before 1963. Appropriate action has been taken to round up any of these remaining supplies in the hands of unauthorized investigators.

An advisory committee of the NIMH assists FDA in reviewing all investigational exemptions. This cooperative arrangement allows legal experimentation on a pre-clearance basis, under conditions that limit use to qualified physicians in carefully controlled clinical environments.

More than twenty years have passed since LSD was first explored for its effects upon the mind. Over a decade of experimentation has taken place in this country. An estimated 2,000 papers have been published on the material, nevertheless it still has no place in medical practice. LSD is still an investigational agent and still regarded as far too dangerous to handle, except under the most carefully controlled conditions.

This paper began with the statement that over 9 billion tablets and capsules of dangerous drugs are manufactured and traded in the U.S. each year, and that a substantial percentage ends up in the hands of drug abusers. This is a problem of great and sobering impact. Proper research and education, coupled with scientific law enforcement at the Federal, State and local levels should enable us to lick the problem of drug abuse, widespread as it may be, and thus rid our communities of one of the most destructive evils in modern society.

The job won't be easy, but it can and will be done.

FOOTNOTE: After the author's discussions with BDAC officials, they indicated that they would undertake a counterfeit-drug survey.

FDA CASE-MAKING FLOW SHEET

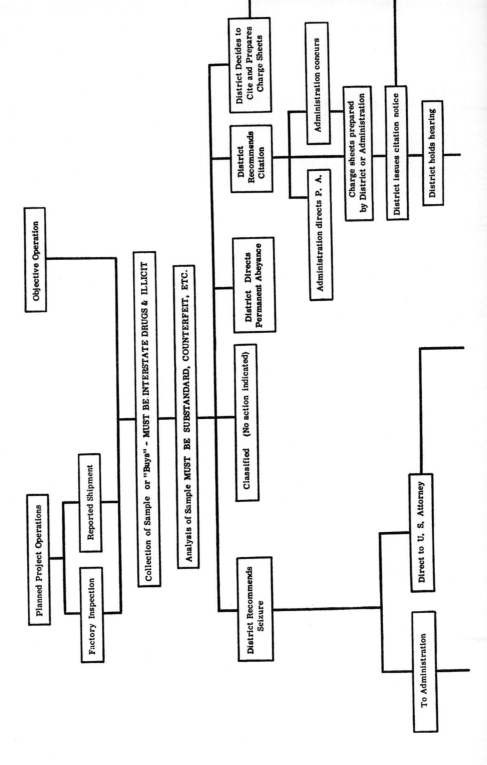

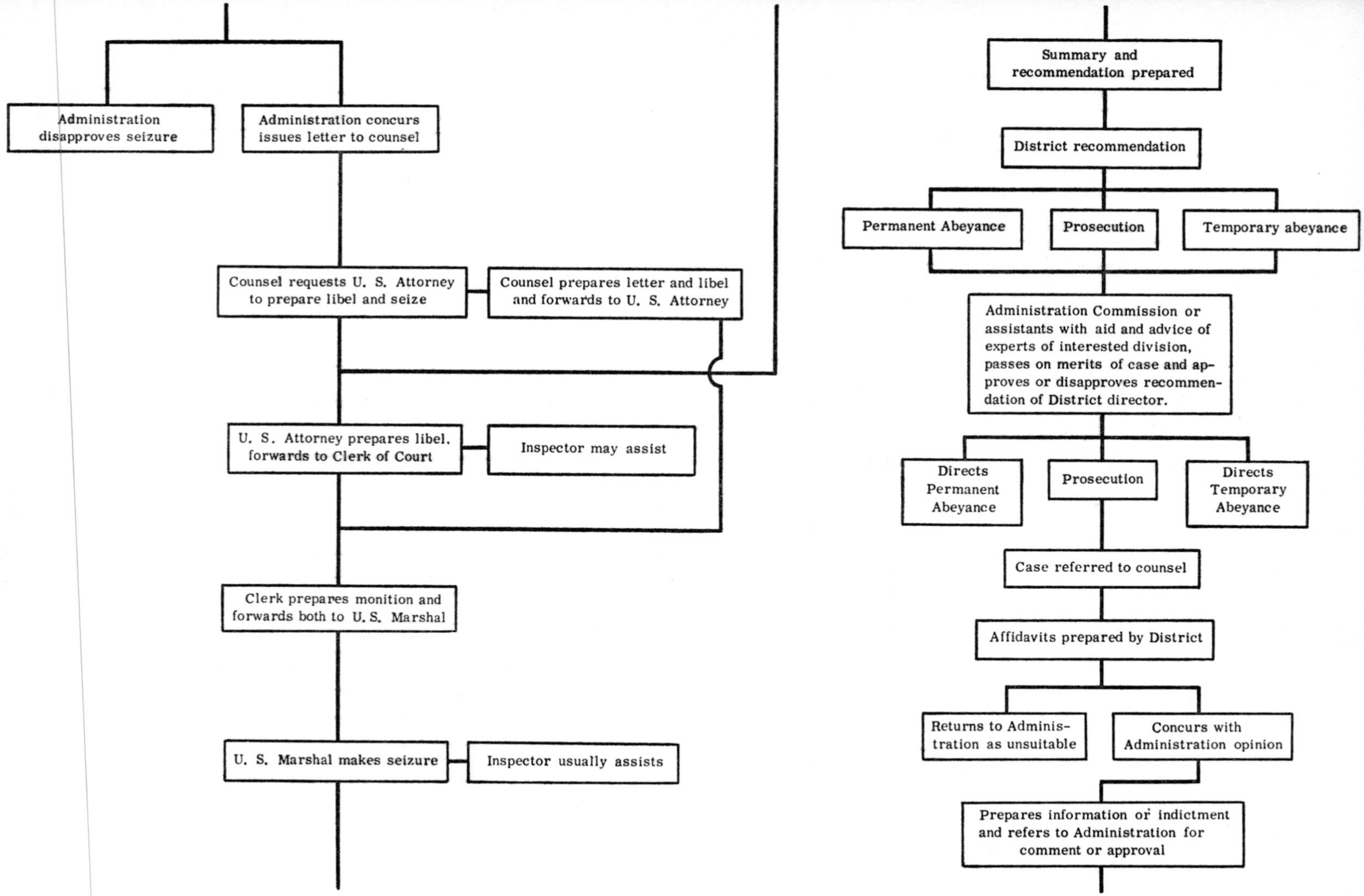

Administration disapproves seizure
Administration concurs issues letter to counsel
Counsel requests U. S. Attorney to prepare libel and seize
Counsel prepares letter and libel and forwards to U. S. Attorney
U. S. Attorney prepares libel. forwards to Clerk of Court
Inspector may assist
Clerk prepares monition and forwards both to U. S. Marshal
U. S. Marshal makes seizure
Inspector usually assists
Summary and recommendation prepared
District recommendation
Permanent Abeyance
Prosecution
Temporary abeyance
Administration Commission or assistants with aid and advice of experts of interested division, passes on merits of case and approves or disapproves recommendation of District director.
Directs Permanent Abeyance
Prosecution
Directs Temporary Abeyance
Case referred to counsel
Affidavits prepared by District
Returns to Administration as unsuitable
Concurs with Administration opinion
Prepares information or indictment and refers to Administration for comment or approval

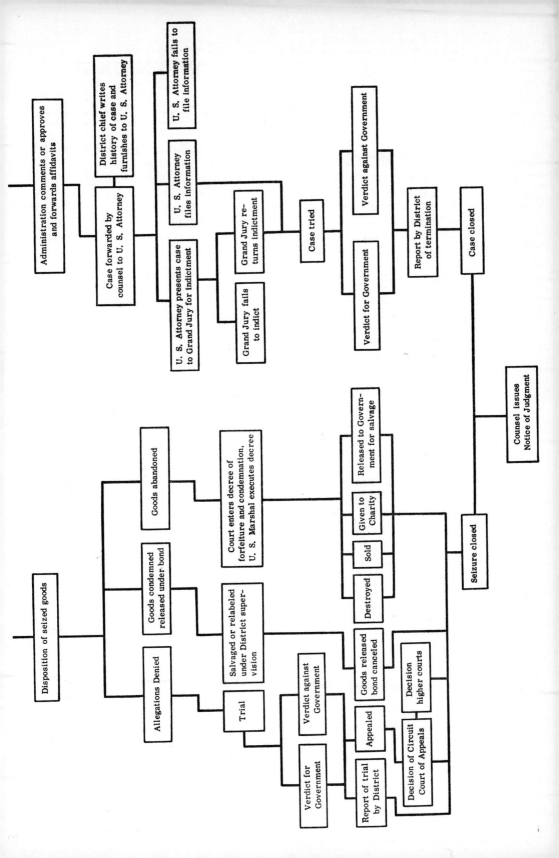

APPENDIX E

BDAC Field Offices

Atlanta Field Office
William B. Logan, Director
1831 Peachtree Rd. N.E.
Atlanta, Georgia 30309
404-526-5930
Alabama, Florida, Georgia, Mississippi, South Carolina, Tennessee

Baltimore Field Office
Jack Bologna, Director
401 Water Street
Baltimore, Maryland 21202
301-752-8460
District of Columbia, Kentucky, Maryland, North Carolina, Virginia, West Virginia

Boston Field Office
Richard A. Callahan, Director
Room E-311, JFK Building
Boston, Massachusetts 02203
617-223-6632
Connecticut, Maine, Massachusetts, New Hampshire, Rhode Island, Vermont

Chicago Field Office
Otto Heinecke, Director
205 W. Wacker Drive
Room 1700 Engineering Bldg.
Chicago, Illinois 60606
312-828-5850/51/52
Illinois, Indiana, Michigan, Ohio, Wisconsin

New York Field Office
Edward Kelly, Director
346 Broadway, 12th Floor
New York, New York 10013
212-264-8457/58
Delaware, New Jersey, New York, Pennsylvania, Puerto Rico, Virgin Islands

Dallas Field Office
Robert N. Hinds, Director
1114 Commerce Street
Dallas, Texas 75207
214-749-3917
Arkansas, Louisiana, Oklahoma, New Mexico, Texas

Denver Field Office
John S. Healey, Director
1814 California Street
Denver, Colorado 80202
303-297-4291
Colorado, Idaho, Montana, Utah, Wyoming

Kansas City Field Office
Evert L. Atkinson, Director
U. S. Courthouse, Room 803
811 Grand Avenue
Kansas City, Missouri 64106
816-374-5604
Iowa, Kansas, Minnesota, Missouri, Nebraska, North Dakota, South Dakota

Los Angeles Field Office
Patrick W. Fuller, Director
714 W. Olympic Boulevard,
  Room 1010
Los Angeles, California 90015
213-688-2650
Alaska, Arizona, California, Hawaii, Nevada, Oregon, Washington

Resident offices have been opened at Miami, San Francisco, Seattle, Indianapolis, Greensboro, N.C., San Diego, Detroit, and St. Louis. Twelve additional offices are scheduled for operation in FY 1968.